ADDING SOLAR HEAT TO YOUR HOME

No. 1196
$12.95

ADDING SOLAR HEAT TO YOUR HOME

BY ROBERT W. ADAMS

TAB BOOKS Inc.

BLUE RIDGE SUMMIT, PA. 17214

FIRST EDITION

FIRST PRINTING—SEPTEMBER 1979
SECOND PRINTING—JANUARY 1980
THIRD PRINTING—JULY 1980
FOURTH PRINTING—MARCH 1981

Library of Congress Cataloging in Publication Data

Adams, Robert Wynne, 1939-
    Adding solar heat to your home.

    Includes index.
    1. Solar heating. I. Title.
TH413-A3   697'.78   79-17178
ISBN 0-8306-9768-3
ISBN 0-8306-1196-7 pbk.

Cover courtesy of the U.S. Department
of Energy and The Aluminum Association, Inc.

Contents

Introduction

By the end of this decade, the use of solar-powered systems to provide heating, cooling, and hot-water services for homes and public buildings will be a necessity. These systems will eventually be competitive economically with fossil fuels and electrical systems throughout the United States. By 1985, solar heating and cooling systems could supply about 10 percent of the total United States energy consumption now being used for residential and commercial space heating and cooling. By the year 2000, solar energy could provide 20 percent of the energy needs of the United States.

Until recently, proposals for using the sun's energy on a significant scale were likely to be received with skepticism. During the past 10 years, however, the increasing cost of conventional fuels and the political uncertainties related to the supply of petroleum, and the problems associated with electrical energy generation from nuclear sources have modified this skepticism dramatically.

Although solar energy is the most abundant form of energy available, it is also one of the most dilute and intermittent forms, and therefore, requires sophistication methods of collection and utilization.

Unlike nuclear power, the use of solar energy produces no dangerous radiation or radioactive wastes. Nor are skies blackened by death carrying pollution. Nor does it lend itself to foreign boycott and corporate intrigue.

Solar heating and cooling are feasible today. All it takes to harness this abundant energy source is the combination of ingenuity, economy, and husbandry.

There are no systems in this guide that the average homeowner cannot install if he has the time, patience, desire to work, and follows this simple guide. Just be sure to read this book from cover to cover to get a clear understanding of what is being explained. By doing that, you should have no problems in designing and building a solar heat system for your home.

Robert W. Adams

Chapter 1
Understanding Energy

The sun is a huge nuclear furnace that is continuously producing a large amount of energy. The sun will eventually run out of fuel, but don't worry. Most estimates indicate that by using only one percent of its mass, the sun will shine for another one billion years. The temperature at the center of the sun is estimated to be 20,000,000°C. This falls to a temperature of about 6,000 °C, or 18,800 °F at the surface and then rises again until, at the outer edge of the corona, the temperature reaches 1,500,000°C. The total amount of energy radiated is about 42,000 kilowatts per square meter. This amount of energy is so large that it is hard to comprehend.

The earth receives only a small fraction of the sun's energy. About two calories per minute per sq. cm. or 1.41 kW/sq. meter reaches the upper limits of the atmosphere. This measurement is called *solar constant*. Of the two calories, only about 45 percent reaches the earth, 37 percent is reflected by the atmosphere, and about 20 percent is absorbed by the atmosphere. The remaining portion (43 percent) equals about 7×10^{17} kWh/years or 30,000 times what man now uses. Plants use only 2 percent of this energy.

What happens to all the rest? A large part of it is reflected to the atmosphere. The rest goes to heating the earth's surface and is used in part to evaporate water from the oceans, seas, lakes, rivers, streams, etc.

This water, which falls as rain and snow, is the source of all fresh water, and subsequently all hydroelectric power. Through the differential heating of land and water, huge convection currents are created. These currents, modified by the rotation of the earth (Coriolis forces) create the earth's winds and ocean currents. Of all the power sources known to man, only geothermal, nuclear, and tidal generated power cannot be attributed directly to the sun.

HISTORY AND UTILIZATION

Man has developed three basic methods for collecting solar energy directly:

- the flat collector method, using unfocused or diluted solar radiation.
- the concentrating collector which uses concentrated or focused solar radiation.
- the photovoltaic or photogalvanic cells which uses dilute solar radiation.

The first two methods convert sunlight directly to heat; the third converts it directly to electricity. Concentrators, convex lenses, or concave mirrors, (parabolic), are the oldest known types of solar collectors. Evidence of both convex and concave mirrors have been found in ancient civilizations. It is assumed that they were used to start fires.

In 212 B.C., Archimedes used a large battery of mirrors to set the sails of invading ships on fire.

Serious studies of the sun and its potential began in the 17th century. By then, diamonds had been cut and melted. Galileo and Lavoisier utilized the sun in their researches. In 1774, Lavoisier used a 52-inch lens to heat materials in his scientific studies. The heat produced was theroretically purer than other forms because it contained no contaminants, such as ashes or soot.

By the early 1800's, heat engines were operating with energy supplied by the sun. Small solar furnaces have been used to power steam generators since 1870. In 1878, ice was produced using solar energy.

In early 20th century, solar energy was used to power water distillation plants in Chile and irrigation pumps in Egypt. In 1929, Robert Goddard applied for patents on five different solar devices to be used on his projects of sending a rocket to the moon. Most of the projects were considered ridiculous because they were so far ahead of their time.

By the end of 1930, many Californians were making practical use of solar energy. "California hot water heaters," as they were known, produced hot water in many homes. Other devices similar to present day collectors were used to heat homes. Many passive systems were located throughout California, as many architects began to design buildings that incorporated solar design to some extent.

Frank Lloyd Wright, was one of the first great architects to recommend that solar energy design be employed in the construction of new buildings. Mr. Wright lived long enough to see some of his ideas and recommendations become reality.

The first building to be heated by solar energy-generated hot water (through a circulating process) was built at the Massachusetts Institute of Technology in 1938. Some 18 other experimental buildings employing solar design were built between 1938 and 1960. These experimental projects employed solar energy as their *total* heating energy source. Performance data recorded on those projects is used as engineering design data today.

10

In 1970, a 1000-kW solar-furnace was built in Odeillo, France. The system utilizes a 2,000 sq. m parabolic mirror system. Light is reflected into the mirror by 63 reflectors, measuring 45 sq. m. The transformed energy is then transferred to a heat absorber. Temperatures up to 4,000°C have been reached.

One of the earliest flat-plate collectors was built in 1874, in northern Chile. The energy was utilized in an application to distill salt water. The still produced 6,000 gallons of fresh water per year for 40 years.

Photovoltaic cells were first brought to international attention when their use was utilized on the early satellites. Several auto manufacturers are now experimenting with solar powered automobiles that will be able to travel at 25 mph, utilizing solar energy in the form of photovoltaic cells, as the energy source.

Twentieth-century space-age technology gave solar energy its mightiest boost. NASA Engineers took a small amount of knowledge and developed enough energy to enable spacecraft to be self-sufficient, once they reached outer space. Much of this achievement was directly related to solar energy utilization via photovoltaic solar collectors.

WHAT IS ENERGY?

Energy is defined in thermodynamics as the capacity to do work. From a practical point of view it is the basic ingredient for all industrialized societies. In the United States, energy is currently derived from four primary sources: petroleum, natural gas and natural gas liquids, coal and wood. The supplies of these common energy sources, except for wood, are *finite* or limited). Their lifetime is estimated to range from 15 years for natural gas to 300 years for coal. As current energy sources become exhausted an energy gap will develop, exacerbated by the synergistic effects of population growth and increased dependence on energy. After nonrenewable energy sources are consumed in what some authors call this "fossil fuel age," mankind must turn to longer term permanent energy sources. The two most significant of these are nuclear and solar energy. Nuclear energy requires highly technical and costly means for its safe and reliable utilization and may have undesirable side effects. Solar energy, on the other hand, shows promise of becoming a dependable energy source without new requirements of a highly technical and specialized nature for its widespread utilization.

Don't be alarmed at the technical aspects of solar energy. As I promised you earlier, you will build your solar system from the information set down in this guide. Just hang in there!

Of the total national energy consumption, roughly 20 percent is used in residential buildings, 14 percent in commercial buildings, 41 percent in industrial processes, and 25 percent in transportation. The major uses of energy employed in buildings are for space heating, air conditioning, and service hot water supply.

Space heating of residences accounts for 11 percent of the total national energy consumption, while space heating for commercial occupancy repre-

Table 1-1. Percentage heat losses from typical houses.

HEAT LOSS THROUGH	TYPE OF HOUSE		
	UNINSULATED	MODERATELY INSULATED	WELL INSULATED
ROOF	25	13	4
WINDOWS AND DOORS	25	27	15
WALLS	25	15	24
FLOOR	5	5	2
INFILTRATION	20	40	55
Total	100	100	100

sents an additional 7 percent. Air conditioning represents 2.5 percent of the total national energy consumption but has a growth (annual) potential of about 16 percent in residences. The energy losses are caused by inadequate insulation, excessive ventilation, high rates of air infiltration from outside, and excessive fenestration (the arrangement of doors and windows in a building).

Building heat losses have recently been recognized by the federal government as a major cause of fuel-resource waste. In the Minimum Property Standards (1965), the Department of Housing and Urban Development (HUD) permitted heat losses of 2000 BTU/(1000 cu ft ^{3}) ($^\circ$F). Let's look at that formula again. What we have is 2000 BTU divided by 1000 cubic feet times Fahrenheit per day. The reduction in energy consumption required by the standards is to be achieved primarily by improved thermal insulation and reduction of air infiltration. Approximately 40 percent of space heating fuel can be saved through more effective insulation and improved draft control in commercial buildings. It may appear at the present time technologically and economically feasible to reduce heat losses in buildings to approximately 700 BTU's (1,000 cu. ft) per day through the use of proper design, increased insulation, and reduction of unnecessary ventilation and infiltration.

Table 1-1 illustrates the reduction in building heat loss that can be realized by adding storm windows and increased ceiling and wall insulation. This guide contains an extensive list of the energy conservation methods for buildings, and presents the relative efficiency of each in several climatic zones of the United States.

Solar energy is the world's most abundant permanent source of energy. The amount of solar power intercepted by our planet is 170 trillon kW, an amount 5,000 times greater than the sum total of all other inputs (terrestial, nuclear, geothermal, and gravitational energies and lunar gravitational energy). Of this amount, 30 percent is reflected to space, 47 percent is converted to low-temperature heat and reradiated to space, and 23 percent powers the evaporation-precipitation cycle of the biosphere; less than one-half percent is represented in the kinetic energy of the wind and waves and in photosynthetic storage in plants. The amount of the sun's energy intercepted by the earth is only a tiny fraction—one thousandth of one millionth—of the total released by the conversion of 4 million tons of hydrogen per-second to helium in the sun.

Although it is abundant, solar energy impinging on the earth's atmosphere is relative dilute, (approximately 430 BTU's divided by the product of hours and square feet). Traversing the earth's atmosphere dilutes it further by attenuation, local weather phenomena, and air pollution. Moreover, solar energy is received intermittently at any point on earth. The solar energy that arrives on earth is of two forms: direct radiation and diffuse radiation. Direct radiation is collimated and capable of casting a shadow; diffuse radiation is dispersed or reflected, by the atmosphere, and then collimated.

In considering how solar energy can best be used, the ratio of direct to diffuse becomes important. The direct to diffuse ratio or the ratio of direct to diffuse radiation is on the order of 5, but for a large city the ratio of direct to diffuse radiation may be on the order of 2. The amount of direct radiation diminishes as air pollution increases.

On the average the radiation striking 1 square foot of the earth's surface is on the order of 100 to 200 BTU divided by the product of hours and square feet. See Fig. 1-1.

The intensity of solar radiation that actually reaches the earth's surface at a given location depends on several factors.

- The earth takes an elliptical orbit around the sun, so the solar intensity increases as the earth gets closer to the sun and is reduced

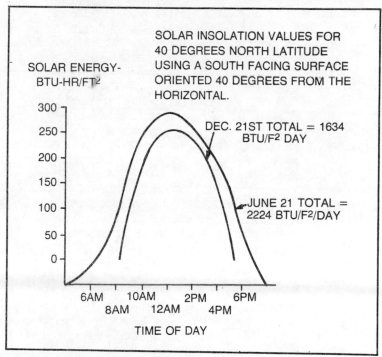

Fig. 1-1. This graph shows the insolation values for a fixed collector during both a summer and a winter day.

as the earth to the sun distance increases. The total change in intensity is small (28.4 BTUh/ft^2 or 8.2mW/cm), but still important.

- The tilt of the earth's axis with respect to the ecliptic plane causes the changing seasons and variation in hours of sunlight. This causes the major variations in solar availability, which changes for any given season and different latitudes.
- Solar radiation is also lost due to scattering and absorption as it passes through the earth's atmosphere. Clouds, dust, and even moisture in the air can cut down on the sunlight that reaches the ground.

Chapter 2
Solar Retrofit and You

Let us look at a few basic questions:
  • What are your energy needs?
  • What is the cost of present available energy in your area?
  • What does the future offer in available energy potential?

Once these questions have been answered, you are better prepared to move on to the planning stage.

REQUIREMENTS

The average homeowner requires approximately 500 kilowatt hours per month. Nationwide, the average price consumers paid for electrical energy rose 80 percent between 1970 and 1977, according to the Federal Energy Adminstration (FEA). The average use level for 500 kilowatt hours—a use level close to average monthly residential consumption, rose about 7.4 percent in 1975 to $19.26, according to the Federal Power Commission (FPC). The average 1974 bill had been $17.93. In 1977, the average homeowner paid $28.14 for 500 kilowatts.

Statistics vary from agency to agency, but the numbers all support the same conclusion. Electricity is no longer cheap, and it is growing more expensive all the time.

Why, we ask? The price is rising because the cost of production is rising dramatically. Electric power systems are frightfully expensive to build and maintain. The cliche is that the power industry is "the most capital intensive" industry there is. What that means, according to the FEA, is that $3.63 must be invested to produce every annual dollar that the sale of electric power generates. By contrast, the nation's automobile industry invests only 67 cents per dollar of annual sales.

Building and plant maintenance is high, but according to the FEA, "fuel expenses for utilities are the single largest production expense for utilities... Between 1970 and 1977 the price of oil, gas, and coal used by utilities increased 540 percent, 251 percent, and 249 percent respectively."

Utilities burn these fuels to generate electricity. "Electric utilities burned 34 percent of all the energy consumed in the United States in 1977," the FEA said.

Most state regulatory authorities permit utilities to pass their ever increasing fuel costs directly to the consumers through devices called "fuel adjustment clauses." In 19.5, all but six states had such clauses in effect.

According to a Library of Congress study, electric utilities raked in $9.2 billion in new 1975 rates (1976 and 1977 figures aren't available yet) and fully $5.9 billion of that was gained under fuel adjustment clauses. After studying these facts it is easy to determine why the cost increase in fossil fuels has escalated so rapidly.

KEYS TO WISE ENERGY USE

There is increasing interest in solar energy and many people would like to utilize solar energy in buildings. With or without the application of solar energy systems, the following keys to wise energy use will help you to save energy and money by managing the way that you use energy for space heating and cooling and water heating.

(SPACE HEATING)

1. Turn thermostat down.
2. Open drapes on south side and where sun will enter building. Close drapes at night and during dark cloudy days.
3. Shut off heat in unused rooms.

(SPACE COOLING)

1. Turn thermostat up.
2. Close drapes to block out sun during the day. Open drapes and windows at night.
3. Shut off air conditioning in unused rooms.

(WATER HEATING)

1. Turn thermostat down.
2. Use less water.

THE ECONOMICAL ASPECTS OF SOLAR ENERGY

Solar recovered heat can be used for numerous residential, commercial, industrial, and agricultural processes that require a fairly low grade of heat. Solar recovered heat can heat homes and other buildings, dry laundry, heat water, cool buildings, produce low-temperature steam, dry grain, desalinate seawater, heat swimming pools, etc.

Nearly all solar applications are economical in that conventional fuels are saved by using solar energy. However, the initial cost of solar equipment is high in relation to conventionally fueled equipment. Thus, the economic attractiveness of using solar energy is generally viewed in terms of how many years are required to pay back the extra cost of the solar equipment with fuel savings. The primary purpose of this guide is to acquaint the reader with enough information and solar facts as to enable him to cut the initial cost by doing a great part of the retrofit preparation and installation himself. I have always believed that to understand is one step away from doing.

SOLAR PAYBACK

The solar payback period depends upon the solar application. If solar can be used year round, such as for domestic hot water service, then the payback time is much shorter than if it were used only during the winter months, such as for space heating. In fact, domestic hot water heating is probably the most attractive solar application, because of the short payback period, and requires such a small amount of collector area. In most areas of the United States only 40 to 60 square feet of collector is required to meet 70 percent of the annual hot water demand in the average home.

300 to 500 square feet of collector is needed to space heat and furnish 50 to 75 percent of the annual space heating and hot water demands of most homes. If fuel costs continue to rise, and they will, the payback periods will be even shorter.

COST

The initial cost of a solar heating system (one that will provide from 50 to 75 percent of the total annual demand for the average home) is presently 2.9 times that of an oil-fired hot water (circulating) system, and approximately 5 times more than an electric heating system. However, the do-it-yourselfer can cut this cost considerably, especially in retrofit. Labor is a large segment of initial solar installation, the back-up system is already there, and most homes have a fair amount of insulation already. Again, I cannot overstress the importance of adequate insulation.

Generally speaking, when compared with electric heating, the savings of a solar heating system will pay back the original cost of the solar equipment and installation in 3 to 5 years. These figures can be cut considerably by the do-it-yourselfer, who doesn't have the labor factor, and who shops on a wholesale basis for his equipment. The above figures are based on $0.42/kWh for electricity.

There are several reasons why solar equipment is more expensive than conventional systems:

- The cost of the collectors, the heat storage system (container), and the piping and controls that must be added. Add these items to the backup system and the labor factor and it is easy to see why the *solar heating* system is expensive.

- The solar-energy industry is in its infancy; production volumes are low. Therefore, the cost of the solar equipment is higher now than it will be as production increases. However, the cost is still relatively fast payback. In considering retrofit, the backup system cost can virtually be eliminated. If the homeowner is handy with tools, most of the labor can be done by him.

SELECTION OF A SYSTEM

Before you can sit down and design a system that will incorporate all of the previously mentioned factors, you must first take a close look at what you have. Make a list of things to check in predesign.

- Home or building location for the collector— east, west, north, or south.
- Present insulation quality. Doors, windows, attic, and basement. If there is no basement, you may need to check building skirt in relation to ground level and wind resistance.
- Type of roof. Pitch, valleys, and height. Check to make sure that there is an unblocked path for sunlight to travel. A clear, unblocked southern exposure is needed if possible.
- Present heating system: Gas, electric, fuel oil, coal, wood, etc.

Here, you begin to put your system together. In order to hold down costs, it is important to utilize any existing parts of the present system that you can: duct, pipe, boiler, plenums, fans, controls, coils, etc.

Hey, it's beginning to come together. Go back and check that predesign list very closely and correct any and all inadequacies that you may have found. Double check insulation. You need to make sure that the insulation in your home is adequate, especially in the attic, basement, and underneath the house.

THINGS TO CHECK

What type of heating system is currently being used? Where can we save money? If you have forced air, you should be able to modify without much difficulty, using all duct and most controls. If you have a hot water or steam system, you should be able to modify with ease, utilizing most components and thereby saving money in our retrofit. Remember that everything we reuse saves money. Make a list of all reuseable components. You can do this quite easily, utilizing an old method of organization.

Take a pad and pencil and make a thorough checklist of all the items that need to be checked in the predesign list. Devote adequate time to these items. Don't be haphazard—be thorough. Put on some old clothes, take a good explosion-proof flashlight, get into the attic, basement, and underneath the house. Check out everything in detail. This is a very important part of the project—the money saved will be yours! As an example, are the doors and windows sealed properly? Storm windows and doors will pay for themselves in just a few short winters. Heat is too expensive to lose through inadequate fitting or weatherstripping. Get the home tight!

Check your roof. You are going to need an area large enough to place the solar collectors without obstructions and preferably facing south. If you have a basement, begin to calculate the feasibility of a storage-facility location. If you don't have a basement, begin a selection process and start planning. As you progress in your predesign study, begin to shop for prices and availability of materials and solar components that you may need in your retrofit. GOOD PLANNING is essential.

SELECTING A DESIGN

You have completed your predesign checklist. Now you need to begin to choose a design. Designing your system depends on many variables. Read and study carefully all chapters of this guide before making any final decisions on system design.

Don't forget that building your own solar system can be a real family project. Everyone can get involved by participating in the task and enjoying the experience. Come on, let's get to work!

HOME OR BUILDING LOCATION

In checking our predesign list, we find that we have "home or building location for the collector" listed. Why, we ask, is solar collector location so important? One of two major factors influencing the energy used on any site is the sun. The other is the wind. The sun delivers wanted energy during

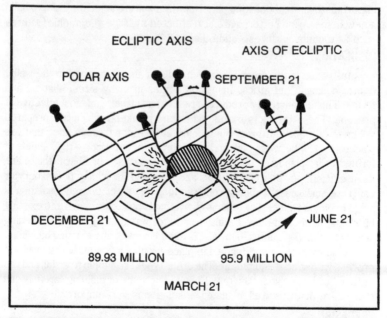

Fig. 2-1 The tilt of the earth's axis with respect to the ecliptic plane causes the changing seasons and the annual variations in the number of hours of daylight and darkness.

cool periods, but it also at times provides excess heat which may be removed at great expense in energy.

Let's look at the simple things first. The sun always rises, reaches its zenith, and sets in the same points of the compass. It varies geographically, being higher in the sky in southern than in northern latitudes. Season variation also occurs, of course, because of precession of the earth's axis, and the sun is higher in the sky during the summer and lower in the winter. To better understand what has been said here, let's take a look at Figs. 2-1 and 2-2. Notice that a surface most nearly to a right angle to the sun's rays will absorb the most energy from the sun. So given something less than a sun directly overhead, a sloped ground surface will absorb more than a flat one. When the sun is at it's highest peak or point, it will be most nearly at a right angle to the ground. Therefore a slope facing south (in the northern hemisphere) absorbs most of all. Slopes that face east and west will get less heat from the sun, and one facing north will get the least. Flat surfaces make little difference. After reading this you should realize why your solar collector will be more efficient when installed with a tilted angle. The angle of tilt will be explained in detail in a later chapter.

The second major factor is wind. Wind deprives you of heat during cool periods but is most helpful in removing unwanted heat in times of excess warmth. In our hemisphere the prevailing winds generally blow from west to east. But seasonal and nonregional variations may find warm and often moist winds blowing from the south and cold dry winds from the north. It is important to know about wind patterns when you are selecting a site to build a new home. Wind patterns are also effected by large geographic features such as mountains, forest, and other buildings.

INSULATION

Insulation is the means by which cells of air are trapped in the walls, floors, ceilings, and attics. Insulation comes in many sizes, shapes, and forms. Those industrially produced are most available, and most effective at present. These products include batts and blankets, which are prepared volumes of expanded glass fiber, mineral fiber, or organic fiber that are placed in walls, between ceilings, and flooring; fiber boards—rigid sheets of formed cellar plastic or cemented (pressed) particles or fibers (these are most efficient per-unit of thickness and are good for adding to masonry or concrete surfaces of existing construction); blown or poured insulation is loose expanded mineral or organic fibers that is placed or blown into existing buildings; foamed in-place cellular plastic foam that is injected into framing spaces and then solidifies. This also is useful in insulating existing buildings. Of the above, blown and foamed in-place require a commercially available process with special equipment. The other types are simple to install and can be installed by just about anyone. Check your home or building carefully and make sure that it is well insulated. Insulation is very important.

PREDESIGN

In considering how solar energy can work for you, some very basic rules MUST be considered. The following is a list of points to consider in the evaluation of predesign.

20

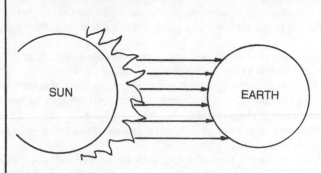

A FLAT-PLATE COLLECTOR WORKS BEST
WHEN PERPENDICULAR TO THE SUN'S RAYS. THIS
IS BECAUSE IT MINIMIZES REFLECTION FROM THE
INSULATING COVER AND ALLOWS THE GREATEST
AMOUNT OF SUNLIGHT TO HIT EACH UNIT OF SURFACE
AREA OF THE COLLECTOR. THEREFORE THERE ARE
CERTAIN ANGLES AND DIRECTIONS WHICH ARE BEST
FOR THE COLLECTOR. ALSO, BECAUSE OF THE OBLIQUENESS
AND INCREASED ATMOSPHERIC ABSORPTION OF THE SUN'S
RAYS, SOLAR HEATERS ARE NOT CONSIDERED PRACTICAL IN
THE EXTREME HIGH LATITUDES (ABOVE 45° NORTH AND
45° SOUTH). IN THE NORTHERN HEMISPHERE THE COLLECTOR
SHOULD FACE SOUTH. THIS IS BECAUSE THE SUN RISES IN
THE SOUTHEAST AND SETS IN THE SOUTHWEST. IN
NORTHERN HEMISPHERE IT SHOULD FACE NORTH FOR THE
CORRESPONDING REASONS.

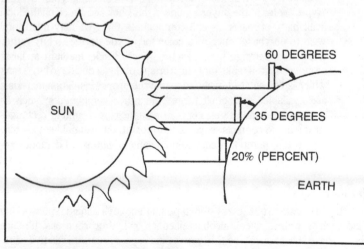

Fig. 2-2. A typical sun to earth angle.

- Potential gross square-footage (home or building size). It isn't feasible to retrofit a home or building that has less than 900 square feet.
- Availability of collector units mounting space. Roof, wall, or ground location, such as the backyard.
- Condition of home in respect to air infiltration. Cost of insulating, weatherstripping, and tightening-up the home enough to meet solar-heating requirements.
- Availability of space requirements for a properly sized solar-storage facility using water, liquid, or air.
- Relative ease and cost of solving the potential freezing problems if water is selected as the heat transfer medium. In this consideration the following criteria must be considered.

  —Susceptibility to corrosion and leakage.
  —Susceptibility to overheating.
  —Number of plumbing connections required.
  —Need for rapid drainage of system.
  —Need for testing of collector working fluid. (Heat transfer medium.)
  —Need for periodic replacement of collector working fluid. (Refer to chapter on collector working-fluids, corrosion, and maintenance.)

- Compatibility with domestic hot water heating. Remember, the overall payback of your system will be greatly increased by utilizing solar heated domestic hot water.
- Ease of construction in your retrofit.
- Availability of materials needed. After selecting your system "type," refer to the buyer's guide in this book and check on the local availability of materials and components that you may need, and wish to purchase, such as a collector, if you decide to buy rather than build; storage mass, such as rock, brick, medium or large stone; insulated tanks for heat storage, or if you decide to buy a tank which isn't insulated, make sure that the proper insulation materials are available. And don't forget the other components, such as pumps, fans, and valves; copper or plastic pipe; round or rectangular duct; and controls, such as thermostat, differential heat switch, fan switch, pump switch, solenoid valves, motorized damper controls, etc.

Working Fluids

If you decide to utilize a system type that employs a liquid type working fluid such as water, glycol, alcohol, silicones or hydrocarbon oils, be sure that you are able to purchase the type of fluid in your area with relative ease, as these fluids will have to be changed from time to time.

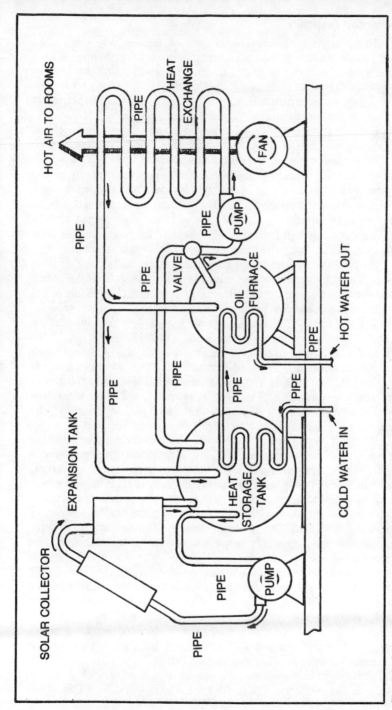

Fig. 2-3. A typical solar heating system showing an oil furnace as the backup.

23

Overall Cost Feasibility

This is probably the most important consideration to be made when solar retrofitting your home. Solar hardware isn't cheap. Neither are the other energy sources. Electricity prices are steadily rising, as noted in Chapter 2. The prices of oil are right behind electricity. In many areas, new natural gas hookups are banned. With future OPEC price hikes on petroleum and new federal energy taxes, these trends are certain to continue.

Heat from the sun costs nothing; moreover, manufacturing competition and mass production of solar components should hold the price of solar hardware below the pace of present day inflation. The real clincher for homeowners like yourself is the government's new solar incentive. The incentive is a generous tax credit of $2,000 or more that can add up to a very solid discount on the purchase of a solar heating system. It is reckoned by the federal government, and many state and local governments, that by bringing down the high front-end investment, the incentive makes solar energy more than competitive with conventional heating energies.

Solar energy is here. The federal government predicts that 2.8 million homes (half of them new) will be solar equipped by 1985. Solar equipment manufacturers are far more optimistic; they predict that by 1985 there will be 11 million homes solar equipped with two-thirds of those retrofitted.

The average contractual cost of new home solar-equipped installations is $8,500. Retrofit is running on the average of $5,000 per home. These averages were based on a solar contractors' cost analysis, sponsored by the Department of Energy. The study concluded that the low-high went from $5,000 to $12,000: retrofit from $3,000 to $8,500. This study was based on the contractor furnishing all equipment, materials, and labor. Labor was found to be approximately 60 percent of the total cost, with material and equipment accounting for 15 percent and 25 percent, respectively.

The ideal retrofit prospect is a house that is electrically heated with a forced air system. The present heat distribution system of the home is very important when considering solar retrofit. If you have a forced air stream, you're in good shape because you can use the same ducts to distribute heat from your solar storage facility. If you have hot water radiator or baseboard heat, you have a choice of installing a pre-heat (solar heated) system, as shown in see Fig. 2-3. Or you can install a new forced air system because solar heated water generally is not hot enough for baseboard units or radiators.

There are other critical factors to consider. Ideally, the solar retrofit candidate should have a southern roof exposure, the reason being that roof top collectors should be exposed to the sun for at least *six* hours per day during winter months. As mentioned at the beginning of this chapter, the roof should be large enough to accommodate the needed number of collectors. The collectors can be placed on the ground, but this is slightly more expensive and in a lot of instances isn't practical.

Throughout this book you will read about the importance of proper insulation and weatherstripping. GET THE HOME TIGHT! This is the primary prerequisite in solar retrofit. Without it the retrofit is certain to be a failure. Take advantage of tax credits that might be offered to homeowners for adding "winterizing" improvements. The average home can be adequately improved at low cost, and yet you can kill two birds with one stone by getting a tax credit along with a savings in energy.

Retrofitting is fairly complex because of the wide range of variables. This guide is intended to help the homeowner who wishes to retrofit his home and solve the problems of retrofit by informing him of the variables and assisting in their solution. If, however, there is a problem that you can't seem to find the answer to, don't hesitate to get professional help. Most of the equipment manufacturers listed in the Buyer's Guide of this book will help you with design problems. Included in Chapter 4 is a sample heat-loss calculation sheet. If you have a question about design requirements, send a copy of the completed calculation sheet to the equipment manufacturer. A majority has said that they will be glad to answer any questions and assist in the design by making suggestions.

Chapter 3
Solar Collectors

What is a solar collector? It is a device for intercepting the sun's rays and converting them directly to some conveniently transportable form of energy. A solar *heat collector* absorbs the sun's energy and converts it to heat. A photovoltaic collector converts the sun's rays directly to electricity. A brief discussion will be given to photovoltaics in Chapter 7.

How does a flat-plate collector work? A fluid, known as a *working fluid*, such as water or air, passes through the collector, picks up the sun's heat from the hot absorber surface and transports that heat away from the collector. The heated fluid can be used directly or it can give up its heat to a storage container. Heat is then removed from the storage facility as needed. The following is a general synopsis of the flat-plate collector and storage systems.

LIQUID-TYPE FLAT-PLATE COLLECTORS

The chief component of an indirect solar system is the solar collector. This component converts the sun's radiant energy into heat energy that is transported into the house by a working-fluid.

The flat-plate collector may be mounted in the roof, on the roof, directly to the roof, on or in the walls of the house, or mounted on its own support structure at the proper tilt angle in the backyard, side yard, etc.

How It Works

The sun's energy is absorbed on a flat-plate surface. The plate is usually constructed of copper, aluminum, or steel. There are two categories of flat-plate collectors: air-types and liquid types. They are utilized according to the type of working-fluid that is circulated through them to affect and transport the captured solar heat.

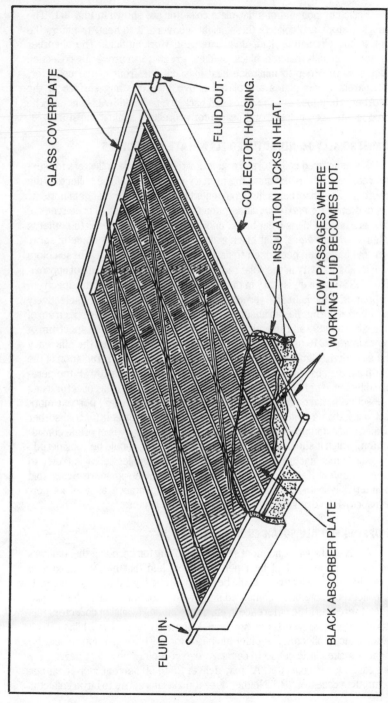

GLASS COVERPLATE

FLUID OUT.

COLLECTOR HOUSING.

INSULATION LOCKS IN HEAT.

FLOW PASSAGES WHERE
WORKING FLUID BECOMES HOT.

BLACK ABSORBER PLATE

FLUID IN.

Fig. 3-1. Flat-plate collector.

Basic components of a flat-plate collector are shown in Fig. 3-1. The absorber stops and collects the sunlight, converts it to heat, transfers the heat to the circulating fluid, designated the working-fluid. The absorber surface is usually painted black or dark green to improve its collection efficiency. In order to minimize heat loss out the front of the collector, transparent cover plates are placed above the collecting surface of the absorber. Heat loss out the sides and back are reduced by insulation. The components are enclosed and sealed for protection against moisture.

COMMERCIALLY MANUFACTURED FLAT-PLATE COLLECTORS

Manufactured collectors are superior to homemade collectors for several reasons. Let us examine the primary component of the collector: the absorber. The absorber is that component of the collector that gets hottest. It is darkened for *maximum* absorption of the sun's energy. Three types of color are used: One is a flat black; another is a flat dark green; the other is called a *selective black*. Flat black and flat dark green paints come in spray cans and have long been used to darken collector absorbers. These colors have an absorptivity in the solar radiation region of the spectrum of approximately .95 and an emissivity in the thermal radiation region of the spectrum of about .95; that is, it also reradiates heat at a significant rate. A selectively darkened absorber has an absorptivity in the solar region of the spectrum of approximately .90 and an emissivity in the thermal region of the spectrum of approximately .10 or less. Thus, a selective surface improves the efficiency of the collector significantly because it greatly reduces the reradiation of the heat from the absorber. For example, when operating at a 100° F temperature difference between collector absorber and outside air, a collector using a selective surface and single glass cover delivers 25 to 50 percent more heat daily than a collector using a flat black or dark green (flat) absorber surface and a double glass cover. Therefore, if efficiency is of prime consideration, which it should be, a manufactured collector should be considered.

Many manufacturers sell to the public on a wholesale basis (refer to buyer's guide). Keep in mind that many different designs are being sold commercially with considerable variation in appearance as well as performance. Be very selective in shopping for collectors.

SHOPPING FOR ALL SOLAR EQUIPMENT

A buyer of solar equipment should be looking for a product that delivers the maximum amount of heat per unit area, and that has the maximum durability. Both objectives should be sought at the lowest cost. Traditionally, collectors have been compared simply on a cost per square foot basis. When there was little difference in efficiency among available collectors this was an acceptable basis for comparison. But now, with the availability of high performance collectors, a different basis for cost comparison should be used. It makes little sense to compare two collectors on a cost per square foot basis, when collector "A" may deliver 25 to 50 percent more heat per month than collector "B." Neither does it make any sense to buy a collector that has a short life expenctancy, as the collector may fail before it can pay for itself in fuel savings.

EFFICIENCY

The amount of heat delivered per month by a given collector depends upon the temperature level of the heat needed for a particular application, the efficiency of the collector at the required temperature level, and local climatic conditions.

Different applications require different temperature levels of heat. Pool heating, for example, requires a fairly low temperature level of heat, somewhere on the order of 10° F below ambient to 20° F above ambient temperatures. Space heating and domestic water heating require a moderate temperature level, on the order of 60°F to 120°F above ambient. Power generation requires a much higher temperature level, on the order of 350°F to 700°F above ambient.

The hotter a collector is expected to operate above its surroundings (ambient) the more time that must go into design of the collector to reduce heat loss from the collector to its surroundings. Thus, the type of collector should be matched with the temperature level of heat required for that application.

The efficiency of a collector is also dependent upon the incident solar radiation. The more intense the solar radiation, the more efficiently a given collector will operate.

The performance of a given manufacturer's collector should be determined by performance tests made by an independent testing laboratory. Test procedures should be those as established by the National Bureau of Standards.

If a manufacturer cannot or will not furnish you, the consumer, with a copy of the test results relative to the equipment in question, and a warranty clearly establishing your guarantee, take your business elsewhere.

The firms listed in the Buyer's Guide of this book were chosen with select care. As the author of this book, I took great care and exercised extreme caution in the selection; however, the final decision is left to you, the buyer.

Several additional cautions should be kept in mind when shopping for solar components. Manufacturer's price sheets vary widely in costs per square foot of collector, and in what one receives for the money, aside from differences in efficiency. Some manufacturers base their price on cost per square foot of gross collector area, while others base their price on cost per square foot of net absorber area. The gross collector area can be as little as 10 and as much as 50 percent more than net collector area. Some manufacturers include no provisions for mounting the collectors; thus such provisions must be provided by the installer, (you). Some make no provision for attaching flashing to their collectors. Often this is desirable to hide the pipes of ducts at the top and bottom of the collector. These are fairly insignificant items, but some manufacturers sell a kit that can be installed easily. This is very handy for the do-it-yourselfer, and it can save money.

Some manufacturers give the efficiency of their collector based upon net collector area, while others give their efficiency on the basis of gross area covered. Where a limited area is available for mounting collectors, the criteria for choosing a collector should be the one that produces the greatest amount of heat from the total area available for mounting.

Most prices are quoted F.O.B. the factory or some distribution point, so shipping and sometimes packing charges must be added. Be sure to clarify these "costs," and try to establish a definite receiving date. It doesn't make sense to pay packing and shipping costs from the other side of the globe, or to buy equipment that won't arrive until the thirteenth month of next year. The only true basis for comparison between one given piece of equipment and another is the total installed price per unit of heat delivered per unit of time.

COLLECTOR SIZING

Proven accurate performance predictions are the simplest means of sizing collectors in your area. Most local utility companies will provide you with as much information as they have. I might add that this information gathering is intense in most areas of the country. With the information you acquire from the utility company, coupled with your ability to determine your required heating needs (this can be accomplished by completing the sample calculation sheet on pages 66-69, you have a good start. Another idea is to look around your neighborhood. Find a house that is comparable to your own. Talk to the owner. He may be able to update you on the efficiency of his system, thereby supplying you with very valuable information.

When sizing a collector it is important to determine if 35-percent or 40-percent collector efficiencies can be expected every month. With this helpful knowledge you will be able to make some good starting decisions. For instance, you will be able to predict how much solar heat to expect form each square foot of collector. The size then follows from the average monthly heat demands.

The performance of your collector is difficult to predict when it is tied into a heating system. Some of the variables that decide the final results are:

- Site conditions.
- Heating demands of your house.
- Design criteria such as the operating temperature, collector tilt, and storage facility.

All of these factors directly affect your collector's efficiency. However, if you have followed the rules set forth in this guide, success should be right around the corner.

A well designed collector should be able to collect 1300 BTU per square foot of NET collector (absorber) on a sunny winter day. Remember, though, that not all of the BTU collected will reach the rooms. You can expect heat losses from piping, the storage facility, and air infiltration.

All piping, liquid or air, should be well insulated. Your storage facility should be large enough to contain an adequate amount of heat storage. Some solar energy will be rejected in any event during extended periods of sunny weather, even though the outside will be lost through construction infiltration. Only when the proper sequence of sunny and cloudy days occur can all the available energy be used.

This is being realistic. Another realism is you can utilize, through your solar system, a large percentage of your heating needs, thus saving you money.

Consider a 100-square foot house with a heating demand of 12,000 BTU per degree day, or approximately 84 million BTU in a 7000-degree day climate. This demand is distributed over the heating season (late September through early May). Little heat is needed in October or April. The bulk of the heat demand is needed December through February, just when sunlight is *best*. Such a house needs approximately 600,000 BTU on a day when the outside temperature averages about 15°F. On such a day, provided it is sunny, this much solar heat can easily be supplied by 500 square feet of good collector. With a 35°F temperature rise (from 85°F to 120°F, for example), 2000 gallons of water will absorb all of the solar heat. Under average operating conditions, one square foot of this same collector gains only 350 BTU of useable heat per day, or 84,000 BTU for the entire seven-month heating season. The 500 square feet of collector will supply about half of the needed 84 million BTU.

Knowing this, it is perfectly reasonable to assume that by doubling the collector size from 500 to 1000 square feet, you will automatically meet the entire heating demand; all 100 percent. That assumption is wrong. By doubling the collector size, you will provide approximately 75 percent, because the larger collector will not work at full capacity as often as the smaller one. In this example, the usable heat per square foot of collector drops from 84,000 BTU to 69,000 BTU because the house cannot use the added heat in the fall and early spring. Therefore, the system must reject more heat during successive sunny days in January. What if we were to increase the size of the storage facility? Even if the storage size were doubled, the system would have to reject excess heat during the fall and early spring. Here is the rule governing such action: As collector size increases for a fixed heat demand, the amount of solar energy provided by each square foot drops because of the decreased load factor on each additional square foot.

ABSORBER DESIGN

There are three common categories of absorber designs. Each design is based on the method in which the absorber is used to bring the working fluid in contact with the absorber plate.

The first category is the tube-in-plate absorber. It is referred to as the tube-in-plate because tubes are inside the plate. These tubes allow the working fluid to circulate inside the plate. The tubes, or working fluid

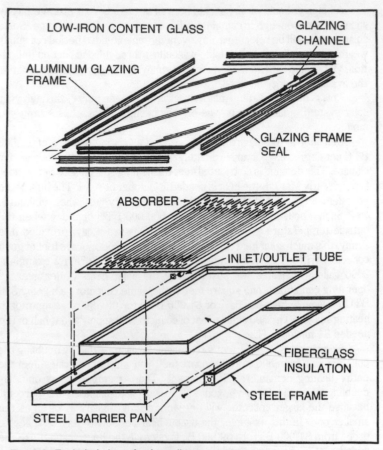

LOW-IRON CONTENT GLASS

GLAZING CHANNEL

ALUMINUM GLAZING FRAME

GLAZING FRAME SEAL

ABSORBER

INLET/OUTLET TUBE

FIBERGLASS INSULATION

STEEL FRAME

STEEL BARRIER PAN

Fig. 3-2. Exploded view of solar collector.

passages, are built into the plate itself during the manufacturing process. This type of plate enjoys a very efficient heat transfer to the working fluid, as shown in Fig. 3-2.

The second category includes all open-faced absorbers that allow the working fluid to flow across and/or over the front surface, as shown in Fig. 3-3.

The third category of absorber design includes all flat-plate absorbers that have tubing attached to either side. See Fig. 3-4. This is one of the absorber designs that you will be encouraged to build in this guide. Another is the open-faced type that allows the cool working fluid to be pumped from the storage facility to a header pipe at the top of the collector. The header pipe has 1/32-inch holes drilled across its face. The working fluid (a liquid) flows out of the small holes and onto a corrugated metal sheet that is the absorber (see Fig. 3-5). The working fluid then flows down the valleys of the corrugated sheet. A gutter at the base of the sheet gathers the warm water,

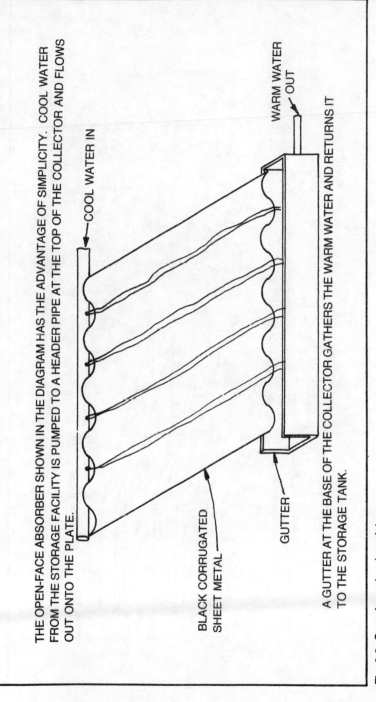

THE OPEN-FACE ABSORBER SHOWN IN THE DIAGRAM HAS THE ADVANTAGE OF SIMPLICITY. COOL WATER FROM THE STORAGE FACILITY IS PUMPED TO A HEADER PIPE AT THE TOP OF THE COLLECTOR AND FLOWS OUT ONTO THE PLATE.

COOL WATER IN

WARM WATER OUT

BLACK CORRUGATED SHEET METAL

GUTTER

A GUTTER AT THE BASE OF THE COLLECTOR GATHERS THE WARM WATER AND RETURNS IT TO THE STORAGE TANK.

Fig. 3-3. Open-face absorber plate.

33

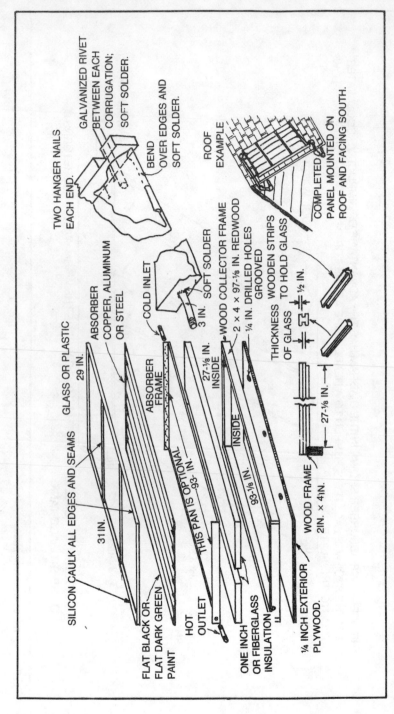

TWO HANGER NAILS EACH END.

GALVANIZED RIVET BETWEEN EACH CORRUGATION; SOFT SOLDER.

BEND OVER EDGES AND SOFT SOLDER.

ROOF EXAMPLE

COMPLETED PANEL MOUNTED ON ROOF AND FACING SOUTH.

GLASS OR PLASTIC 29 IN.

ABSORBER COPPER, ALUMINUM OR STEEL

COLD INLET

SOFT SOLDER

3 IN.

WOOD COLLECTOR FRAME 2 × 4 × 97-⅛ IN. REDWOOD ¼ IN. DRILLED HOLES GROOVED

THICKNESS WOODEN STRIPS TO HOLD GLASS

THICKNESS OF GLASS

½ IN.

SILICON CAULK ALL EDGES AND SEAMS

ABSORBER FRAME

27-⅛ IN. INSIDE

31 IN.

THIS PAN IS OPTIONAL

93-⅛ IN.

INSIDE

93-⅛ IN.

27-⅛ IN.

FLAT BLACK OR FLAT DARK GREEN PAINT

HOT OUTLET

ONE INCH OR FIBERGLASS INSULATION

INSIDE

WOOD FRAME 2IN. × 4IN.

¼ INCH EXTERIOR PLYWOOD.

Fig. 3-4. A typical flat-plate collector.

34

which then flows into a pipe and is returned to the storage facility where the process begins again. I should mention here that the corrugated sheet is painted a flat black or a dark green because without this heat gathering surface, our absorber plate would not be as efficient.

THERMAL BONDING

In the early years of solar flat-plate collector experimentation, the absorber plates were made of flat metal sheets with copper tubing soldered, wired, glued, epoxied, welded, or clamped to the surface of the sheet. After thousands of trial and error techniques, the experimenters learned that the most important aspect of absorber construction was good thermal bonding. They found that the conduction of heat into a single foot of tubing could be as high as 1100 BTU/hr/°F for a securely bonded tube (usually soldered), or as low as 10 BTU/hr/°F for a poorly wired, clamped, soldered, glued, or welded tube.

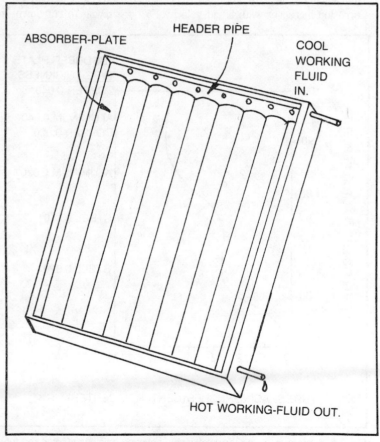

Fig. 3-5. A typical open-face flat-plate collector.

The primary design requisites for tube-type absorbers are the type of metal, its thickness, and the size and spacing of the tubes. The absorber with tubes spaced approximately 6 inches apart and that has good thermal contact with a flat-black or dark-green painted copper sheet 0.010 inches thick is 95 percent as good as a completely covered working-fluid absorber. For the do-it-yourself homeowner who wishes to build his collectors, we advocate the following: ABSORBER SHEET to be 0.010-inch copper sheeting; COPPER TUBING to be type M; SIZE of the RISERS (the tubing soldered directly to the absorber plate) to be ⅜ to ⅝ inches, outside diameter; SIZE of the HEADERS (that tubing running along the top and bottom of the plate) to be ¾ to 1 inch, outside diameter; and SPACING of the RISERS to be 4 to 6 inches, center to center. See Fig. 3-6 for a detailed plan.

Tubing size to and from the collector is important because the smaller a tube, the faster a liquid must travel through it to carry off, or transfer, the same amount of heat. Another bad aspect of increased velocity is corrosion. Corrosion increases with liquid velocity. We are trying to cut down on

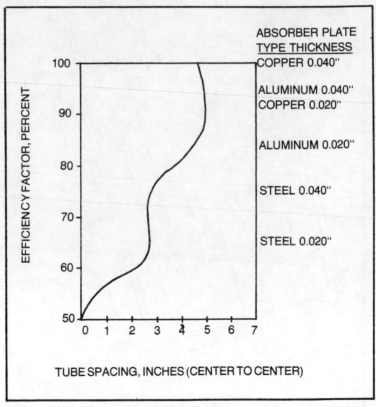

Fig. 3-6. A graph showing the relationship between efficiency factor and tube spacing.

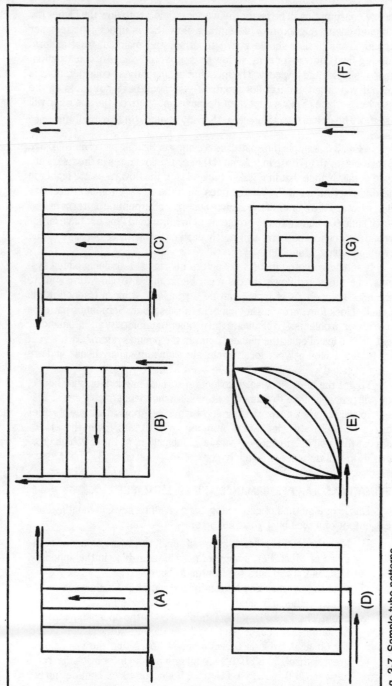

Fig. 3-7. Sample tube patterns.

energy consumption. The faster the working-fluid has to flow the higher the pumping costs. A good flow design is a flow that is under four feet per second. Your design should strive to attain and maintain total uniform working-fluid flow, no- or at most; low pressure drops; ease of construction, (keep it simple) and low cost. The most important of these considerations is flow. If you attain uniform flow control, you won't have hot spots on the absorber surface. This is important because hot spots on the absorber will lose more heat than the other areas, thereby resulting in an overall efficiency loss.

In Fig. 3-7, sample tube patterns are shown. Sample patterns in (A) and (B) are better than those in (C) and (D) because flow rates in the risers are more equal. Notice that in Fig. 3-7 (C) and (D), the flow rates are higher in the end risers than in the middle ones, and the surface temperatures are higher toward the center of the sample absorber. Serpentine patterns in Fig. 3-7 (F) and (G) eliminate the problems of uniform fluid flow but have larger pressure drops. They are also much easier to construct because of the fewer plumbing connections.

It should be noted that for collectors utilizing self-draining piping systems, the tubes and flow patterns must be arranged to allow for complete draining. Trapped air in piping can be a problem. If air is trapped it will partially block flow, creating hot spots in the absorber. Serpentine patterns have fewer problems. To eliminate the problem completely, an automatic air vent can be installed at the highest point in the piping system. Such a vent can be purchased at your local wholesale plumbing supply house and are easily installed.

To get the necessary solar collection surface needed for your house, you will probably have to connect a number of independent collectors. This hookup will require a network of piping. Figure 3-8 shows a sample of series and/or parallel networks. For a number of collectors (over three), we suggest that you use the series-parallel combination, as the low/high pressure drop will be more effectively controlled.

ESTIMATING SOLAR PERFORMANCE AND COLLECTOR SIZE

This is one method of estimating average efficiency and monthly solar heat output of a well built solar collector.

1. Find the total number of hours of sunshine for the month from the maps of Mean Percentage of possible sunshine in the appendix. Example: 148 hours for Boston in January.
2. Find the average day length for the month from almanacs or the local weather bureau; 10 hours for Boston in January.
3. From The Clear Day Insolation tables in the appendix, calculate the number of "collection hours" per day. For the selected collector tilt angle, this is the number of hours that the insolation is greater than 150 BTU/ft^2. Count one-half hour for insolation rates between 100 and 150 BTU/ft^2; 7 hours for 40°N. latitude and 60° tilt.

4. Determine the total collection hours per month by multiplying the sunshine hours per month (from step 1) by the collection hours per day (from step 3) and dividing by the average day length (from step 2); 148 hours × 7 hours ÷ 10 hours = 104 hours.
5. Determine the total daily useful insolation, defined as the total insolation during collection hours, by adding the hourly insolaton rates (from the Clear Day Insolation tables) for those collection

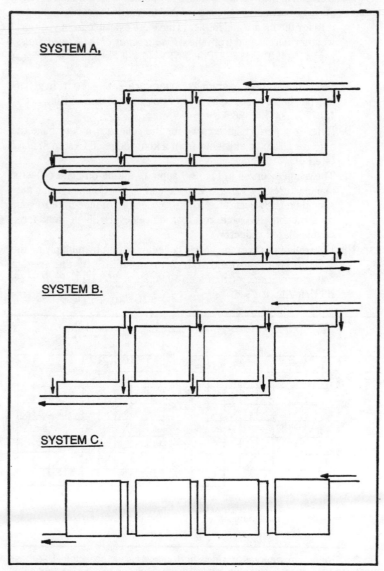

SYSTEM A.

SYSTEM B.

SYSTEM C.

Fig. 3-8. Sample series and/or parallel networks.

39

hours described above; $187 + 254 + 293 + 306 + 293 + 254 + 187$ = 1774 BTU/ft^2/day.

6. Determine the average hourly insolation rate I during the collection period by dividing the total daily useful insolation (from step 5) by the number of collection hours per day (from step 3); 1774 BTU/ft^2/hr.

7. Determine the average outdoor temperature during the collection period from one-half the sum of the normal daily average temperature for the month and locale. (These are available from your local weather bureau and from the *Climatic Atlas of the United States*, pages 2-24; T = ½ (38°F + 30°F) = 34°F ^{OUT} (38°F + 30°F) = 34°F.

8. Select the average operating temperature T$_{ABS}$ − T$_{OUT}$. In general, you should examine a range of possible values for T$_{ABS}$; ΔT = 120°F − 34°F = 86°F.

9. Refer to a performance curve for the collector to determine the average collector efficiency from a knowledge of T (step 8) and I (step 6).

   The sample curves in Fig. 3-9 apply to a tube-on-plate collector manufactured by Revere Copper and Brass Company, but they should be fairly accurate for most collectors of moderate to good construction. Average collector efficiency is 38 percent for a double-glazed collector.

10. Determine the average hourly collector output by multiplying the average hourly insolation rate I (from step 6) by the average collector efficiency (from step 9); 0.38 × 253 BTU/ft^2/ft = 95 BTU/ft^2/hr.

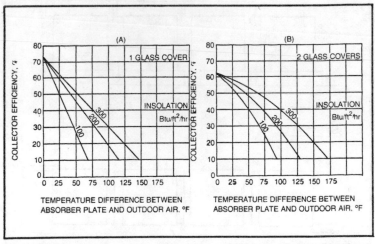

Fig. 3-9. Performance curves for single and double-glazed collectors. Use these graphs to estimate collector efficiency from the insolation rate and temperatures of the absorber and outdoor air.

40

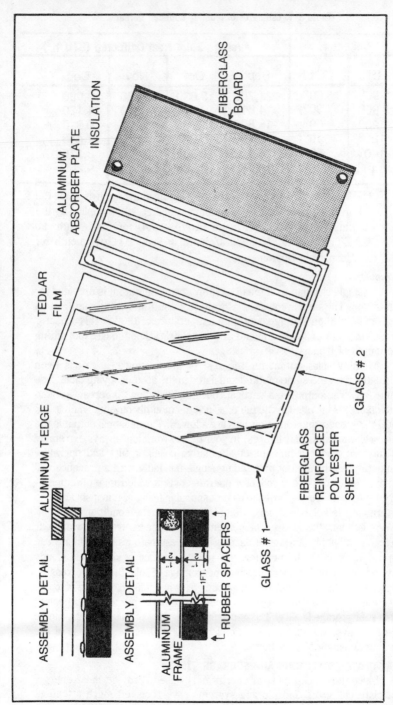

Fig. 3-10. Garden-Way flat-plate collector components.

Table 3-1. Estimates of monthly collector output.

Collector:		Average Solar Heat Collected (BTU/ft^2)			
Temp. (°F)	Tilt	Sept	Oct	Nov	Dec
90°	60°	21,700	19,630	13,780	13,080
90°	90°†	14,615	19,781	14,310	14,170
120°	60°	18,600	15,855	11,130	9,810
120°	90°†	12,700	16,006	11,660	11,445
140°	60°	16,275	12,835	9,010	8,175
140°	90°†	10,160	12,986	9,540	9,265

11. The useful solar heat collected during the month is then the average hourly collector output (from step 10) multiplied by the number of collection hours (from step 4) for that month: 95 BTU/ft^2/hr × 104 hours/month = 9880 BTU/ft^2 month for January in Boston.

Example:

A sample calculation of mean monthly solar heat output is provided for illustration. The sample collector is located in Boston and facing south at a tilt angle of 60°. At an average operating temperature of 120° F, this collector has an efficiency of 38 percent and gathers 9880 BTU per square foot during the month of January.

Monthly solar output for the rest of the heating season has been calculated with the same method and listed in the accompanying table. See Table 3-1. The output of a vertical collector (including 20 percent ground reflectance) is included in the table, as are the monthly outputs when 90° F and 140° F operating temperatures are allowed. The seasonal output is the sum of all these monthly figures. In your design work it is always extremely useful to consider a number of alternative collector tilts and operating temperatures, instead of proceeding single-mindedly with a preconceived design. As almost every collector operates over a wide range of temperatures and its efficiency varies in a corresponding fashion, it is instructive to determine the solar heat collection for a few of these conditions.

In general, the greater the percentage of house heating you want your collector to supply. the more difficult it is to estimate its size using these simplified methods. Remember, the actual sequence of sunny and cloudy days becomes more important as the percentage of solar heating increases. For example, if a full week of cold, cloudy days happens to occur in January, your collector would have to be enormous to insure 90 percent solar heating (also your storage facility), but good approximations of collector size can be made for systems that are designed to supply 70 percent or less of the heating demands of your home.

FLAT-PLATE COLLECTORS AND STORAGE SYSTEMS

Since the concept of solar energy and its use to provide cheap energy, flat-plate collectors and storage systems have received much attention.

Jan	Feb	Mar	Apr	May	TOTALS
12,480	14,640	18,000	14,720	15,225	143,255
13,000	15,250	10,925	5,040	2,520	109,611
9,880	11,590	14,250	12,160	12,325	115,600
10,400	12,200	8,625	3,240	1,800	88,076
7,800	9,150	11,250	10,240	9,425	94,160
8,320	9,760	5,750	2,160	1,080	69,021

†With 20% ground reflection.

Much research and development has been done and continues, as these items are primary requisites in the recovery of useable solar energy.

Commercial collectors are available from suppliers throughout the United States. Refer to the Buyer's Guide in this book.

A general type collector is diagrammed in this chapter. See Fig. 3-4.

The collector is a plate. It is usually constructed of sheet metal (steel, copper, aluminum). Its purpose is to promote heat transfer. The plate surface is painted or glazed dark green or black, because these colors have a high absorption (low reflectivity) of solar radiation. The duller (flatter) and darker the colors, the better the absorption. For example, have you ever noticed how much hotter a dark colored automobile is that sits out in the sun, compared to a light colored automobile, sitting directly next to it?

Plastic or Glass?

The insulating panel should be plastic or glass. Glass is preferable because it is cheaper and wears better. Plastic tends to cloud with age. There can be one or more layers with insulating air spaces trapped between. As a rule, the higher the desired temperature, the more layers required. See Fig. 3-10.

The glass cover(s) enables the collector, or heater, as many refer to collectors, to accomplish what is known as the "greenhouse effect." When dark surfaces are heated, they emit long-wave (infrared) radiation. Glass, which is transparent to short-wave visible light, is almost opaque to long-wave radiation. When the long-wave rays are trapped by the collector plate, a concentrated amount of heat is retained.

The next step in utilizing the concentrated "trapped" heat is to get it from the collector to where you want to use it. This step is accomplished by utilizing a working fluid, which is either liquid or air. See the chapter on working fluids.

Many techniques are used to transfer the collector heat to the working fluid. If air is the working fluid, the transfer can be accomplished by blowing or circulating the air through an enclosed insulated space behind or over the collector, or if a multiple pass system is used, both. See Fig. 3-11.

If water, or a liquid working fluid is used, the liquid is usually forced through s-shaped tubes that are welded, or in the case of our sample design, soldered to the collector plate which is constructed of sheet copper. See Fig. 3-1.

Another transfer method is to allow the liquid to trickle down on top of the plate, as shown in Fig. 3-5. Once the collector heat has been transferred to the working fluid it may be taken directly to where it is needed and/or a storage system. Because of the inconsistency of the incoming sunlight (nighttime, clouds, rain, snow), the storage facility is an extremely important segment of the system.

The simplest and most commericially available storage system is an INSULATED tank filled with water or rocks, as in Fig. 7-20. Here we see the heat taken directly to the storage facility, passed through the rock bed, through the house, and returned to the collector, where the process begins again. This is only one of many storage applications. This particular application requires motorized dampers. The damper is controlled by a control sensor that is mounted on the collector, as shown in Fig. 7-22. The sensor detects the heat temperature inside the collector and closes off the outlet side of the collector when the sensor senses that the collector heat is too cool to circulate. When this occurs, the motorized damper diverts the working fluid through the storage facility. Should the working fluid be liquid, the sensor would activate a solenoid valve, thus closing off the flow of liquid and allowing what liquid was in the piping to drain back into the storage tank, thus eliminating the possibility of a freeze-up.

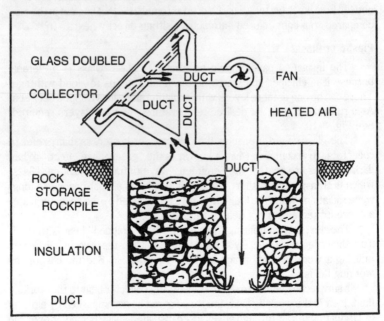

Fig. 3-11. Typical multiple pass warm air solar collector.

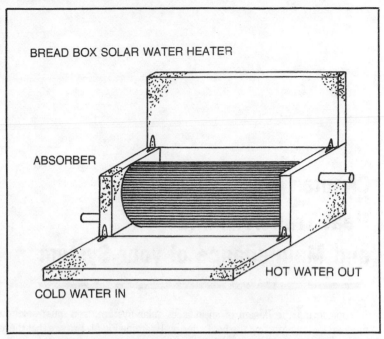

BREAD BOX SOLAR WATER HEATER

ABSORBER

HOT WATER OUT

COLD WATER IN

Fig. 3-12. A simple solar water heater can be built from an old water tank. To make it into a solar water heater, paint it black, connect it to the hot water system, fill it with water, and expose it to the sun. To increase efficiency, put the black tank in a box with glazing for heat retention, add reflectors around the tank, and enclose the tank with insulation during the night or cloudy days.

Heat can be stored in rocks, broken bricks, pebbles, water, water-glycol solutions, and brine. Efficiency varies with different systems and the type of use intended for the stored heat, the working fluids used, and the general overall design of your particular system.

By now you should have a good working knowledge of what your requirements are. Incorporate those requirements with one of the systems discussed throughout this guide, with the primary criterion being efficiency.

DO-IT-YOURSELF SOLAR WATER HEATER

In Japan, there are thousands of solar water heaters in use, many of which are no more than a black box on a roof filled with about 30 gallons of water. In the morning, the box is filled with tap water and by late afternoon the water is heated to over 100°F.

A simple solar water heater can be built from an old water tank. To make it into a solar water heater, paint it black, connect it to the hot water system, fill it with water, and expose it to the sun. To step up the efficiency, put the black tank in a box with glazing (for heat retention), add reflectors around the tank, and enclose the tank with insulation during the night or cloudy days. See Fig. 3-12.

Chapter 4
Heat Transfer Fluids
and Maintenance of your System

In considering the design of an indirect solar system, you must select a medium for transporting the heat energy. Examine Fig. 4-1 to see that there are two primary heat loops: one links the solar collector to the heat storage container, and the other delivers the heat from the storage container to the house. Liquids or gases may be used as the heat transport medium in either loop. Presently, water, oil, and various solutions of ethylene glycol are the most popular liquids. Air is the only gas type that is being used effectively, and is the only type of gas that will be covered in detail in this guide. The following criteria should be considered carefully in selecting a heat transporting medium.

- Relative cost, including initial, operating, and long-term maintenance.
- Compatibility with the present building design.
- Compatibility with the back-up system considered.
- Compatibility with other mechanical apparatus that can be utilized.
- Relative complexity.
- Long term reliability.
- Climate (notably freezing).

In instances where personal comfort requires only simple space heating, air-type transport systems are recommended because of their simplicity and longevity. When domestic hot water is desired, however, the choice between liquid and air systems becomes more difficult.

WHEN FREEZING IS NO PROBLEM

In these applications, the commonly used fluid is water. In many cases, it is desirable to use potable water as the fluid. An example is a solar water

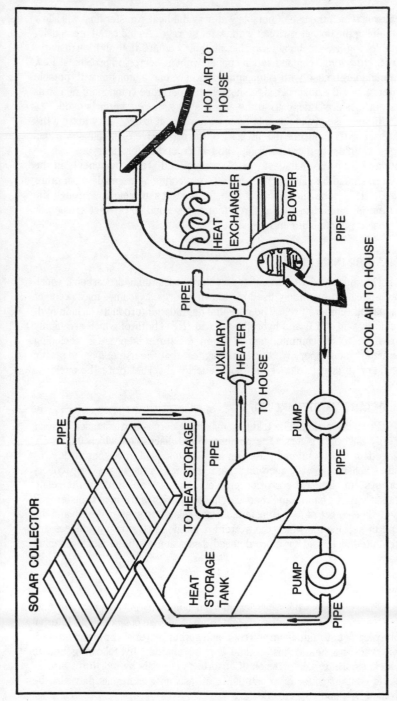

Fig. 4-1. Typical indirect or active system for solar heating.

47

heater in which the use of potable water as the heat transfer fluid will allow combining the collector circuit with water storage. As indicated previously, potable waters are highly variable in their composition and corrosivity. Most, *but not all*, can be used in copper without corrosion problems. Few are suitable for use with aluminum, so do not use aluminum with potable water. Since the absorber is the highest temperature component of a solar system, scale will deposit on the absorber if a *scaling* water is used.

In the case of aluminum or steel with water, it is necessary to treat the water in order to insure the integrity of the protective oxide films. Various types of inhibitors are available, and instructions for their use can be obtained from the manufacturer. Aluminum and steel components in the system should be galvanically isolated from components made from other metals. It is desirable that heat transfer fluid design velocity through the system be limited to two to three feet per second to prevent erosion or corrosion of aluminum and copper.

COLLECTOR INSULATION

Degradation of the chlorinated and/or fluorinated hydrocarbons, which may appear to be widely used in "blowing" organic foams, may occur at stagnation temperatures. The potential degradation products include hydrochloric acid (HCl) and hydrofluoric acid (HF), both of which are highly corrosive to all common metals when moisture is present, including aluminum and copper. We therefore suggest that the use of foamed plastic insulation in direct contact with solar energy absorber plates be avoided.

IMPORTANT MAINTENANCE TIPS

Precaution should be taken to maximize corrosion resistance of solar energy absorber plates. The guidelines and discussion which follow are offered for consideration by the user as he develops his own specific designs and establishes specific operating characteristics for his solar energy collection system. Internal corrosion problems in solar absorber plates relate primarily to the nature and chemical characteristics of the heat transfer fluid used. The choice of heat transfer fluid also relates to system design and the type of service for which the system is intended. General guidelines are presented, followed by more detailed discussion of the reasoning behind them.

GUIDELINES

Flat-plate absorbers, fabricated from aluminum and copper, offer high heat transfer, high strength to weight ratios, and ease of fabrication. Internal corrosion of both aluminum and copper absorber materials by direct interaction with the heat transfer fluid can be avoided by following known guidelines. External corrosion of absorber materials by moisture, atmospheric contaminants, or constituents of insulating materials may also be avoided by good collector design.

These general guidelines must be tailored to apply to specific designs and the operating characteristics of specific solar energy collection systems.

Solar collector working fluids are classified as follows:

- **Nonaqueous**
  - —Silicone Fluids
  - —Hydrocarbon Oils
- **Aqueous**
  - —Untreated potable (tap) water.
  - —Inhibited water-deionized or distilled only.
  - —Inhibited glycol/water mixtures-(deionized or distilled only).

Nonaqueous Guidelines

When considering a nonaqueous fluid, always choose a stable, noncorrosive, anhydrous fluid.

Aqueous Guidelines

Always use distilled or deionized water when diluting glycols. The glycol will last longer and corrosive elements will be removed. *Do not* use potable (tap) water.

Water and water-glycol mixtures must *always* be *inhibited*. The corrosion inhibitor(s) must be compatible with the fluid and the metals in the system.

For inhibited water or inhibited water-glycol recirculating systems, check pH (acidity) periodically to ascertain changes in fluid characteristics. When the pH is outside of the manufacturer's recommended range, the system *must* be immediately drained, flushed, and the fluid replaced.

Always flush the system to remove metal chips, flux, and dirt before filling with a heat transfer fluid. *Always* dry out the system after flushing and before adding the heat transfer fluid.

Maintain fluid velocities lower than two to three feet per second to avoid erosion or corrosion.

Do not permit hard (scaling) water or salt water to flow through solar absorbers. Heat transfer can be severely reduced by the scale which may form on the fluid passages.

Avoid dissimilar metal contact (galvanic effects). This can be achieved by providing a one-metal system (all aluminum, all copper, etc.) or by electrically isolating the collector panels from the rest of the system by using transition joints or plastic couplings.

Avoid the use of foam plastic insulation in contact with solar absorbers. Degradation products of organic foam and the presence of moisture may cause external corrosion of solar absorbers.

Special Guidelines for Copper

In nonfreezing climates or in freezing climates where reliable drain down systems are installed, water-gylcol or inhibited water are *generally* not required. Most often, ordinary potable (tap) water can be used. Exceptions are scaling waters and waters of unusual corrosivity to copper. Generally, where copper plumbing tube has provided excellent service, one can expect excellent service from copper absorbers.

Special Guidelines for Aluminum

Aqueous fluids (water or water-glycol) *must* be inhibited. *Always* use distilled or deionized water as the base fluid in aqueous systems.

A "getter column" is recommended in bimetallic systems to remove copper and iron from the fluid. See Fig. 4-2.

Discussion

Two general types of collector service exist. One application has the heat transfer fluid remaining in the absorber even when the temperature drops below 32°F (0°C). Normally, some sort of freeze protection is required. The other application either has the fluid drained from the absorber or the temperatures do not drop below the freezing point so no freeze protection is required.

APPLICATIONS REQUIRING FREEZE PROTECTION

Fluids generally used are either nonaqueous fluids, such as silicones or hydrocarbon oils, or are aqueous solutions of water and inhibited glycols. These two types of fluids will be discussed separately.

In principle, *water-glycol* mixtures are not of themselves corrosive to either aluminum or copper. Corrosion problems may develop with such systems either because of water chemistry (impurities in the water) or

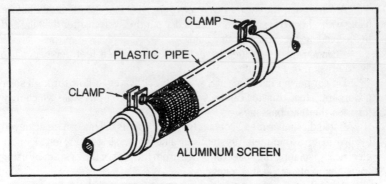

Fig. 4-2. Typical "getter column." The purpose of the getter column is to prevent corrosion in the solar collector panels. A piece of aluminum screen is used to attract the corrosive elements from the water before it reaches the aluminum panels. Getter columns can be made from plastic (PVC) pipe or from radiator hose. If you elect to use radiator hose, the ¾ CPVC feed line must be increased to 1½ inches with the proper adapters. Insert a piece of rolled up aluminum screen in as you make the column. Get as much screen inside without completely blocking the flow of water. Allow the getter column to act as a splice in the line. Clamp and tighten securely.

because of degradation of the glycol. Glycol problems may adversely affect both copper and aluminum. Glycol breaks down gradually in use. The end products of glycol degradation include organic acids which will progressively and substantially lower the pH of water-glycol mixtures to levels at which the resulting acid solution will become seriously corrosive to aluminum and copper, as well as to steel. Commercial automotive antifreeze formulations contain various "buffers" and "inhibitors." The buffers are intended to prevent the pH from dropping. Their effect is not permanent and if glycol degradation is allowed to continue indefinitely, the buffers will be used up and the solution will become acid. This in part accounts for the usual recommendation that, in automotive service, the water-antifreeze mixture be drained and replaced at safe intervals, usually one or two years.

It is important to note that one of the major factors determining the rate at which glycol degrades is the temperature to which it is exposed. The higher the temperature, the more rapid the degradation. Although "normal" maximum operating temperatures for most solar collector systems are below maximum automobile radiator temperatures, solar collectors will reach higher temperatures under stagnation conditions. When the heat exchanger fluid is *not* circulating through the absorber, as when heat storage is full, the temperatures for well designed double-glazed collectors with a nonselective black absorber surface are in the range of 375°F to 400°F. (The use of selective surfaces will raise stagnation temperatures.) At such a temperature, glycol degradation will be substantially accelerated.

It has been reported that copper in contact with glycol catalytically accelerates degradation at elevated temperature. It follows that the condition of the water-glycol solution solar service must be monitored and that the water-glycol mixture *must* be replaced when degradation has progressed to the point that the solution will become acid. System maintenance is critical. Operating conditions, including temperature profiles of solar systems, are quite variable from system to system. Therefore, it is not possible to generally prescribe specific intervals for replacing the heat transfer fluid as is done in automotive service. It also follows that system monitoring is critical.

Logically, this leads to the conclusion that water-glycol antifreeze mixtures should be used only in applications in which reasonable monitoring and maintenance is assured, or in systems which do not reach high temperatures. This statement applies whether the absorber is aluminum, copper, or steel. The comments and suggestions which follow and which relate to system operation with water-glycol antifreeze heat transfer fluids must be regarded as only applicable to adequately monitored and maintained systems.

Multimetal solar systems may be compared to automotive cooling systems. In the case of aluminum, particulary those cars in which an aluminum radiator is used or in which an aluminum block or aluminum head is used, these systems do operate successfully and may be presumed to offer satisfactory corrosion performance. They are, indeed, multimetal systems in that the heat transfer fluid (water-antifreeze mixture) circulates not only through aluminum (the aluminum radiator or the aluminum block) but generally also circulates through steel, copper, and brass components and comes in contact with soft solder used in the joining of copper and brass components. This type of multimetal system appears to be comparable to a "typical" solar energy collector circuit. The coolant used in this type of automobile system is a water-ethylene glycol mixture and the ethylene glycol contains various inhibitors and buffers which are intended to make it compatible with the multimetal cooling system. In the case of General Motors vehicles, it is our understanding that the coolant is made to their Specification GM-1899-M, Antifreeze Concentrate-Ethylene Glycol Type. This specification calls for corrosion performance by the coolant intended to make it compatible with multimetal sytems containing aluminum. Coolant produced to other specifications may or may not perform equally.

The usual automotive coolant mixture uses ordinary tap water. Of course, the composition and corrosivity of tap water varies widely and certain geographical areas use quite corrosive tap water. There is some indication that, under some circumstances, the corrosivity of the tap water used is a factor in the eventual corrosion performance of the automobile multimetal system. Since a solar collector system is a stationary system, it is reasonable to suggest that the variable of possibly unsuitable tap water be avoided through the use of distilled and/or deionized water in the mixture with the commercial ethylene glycol antifreeze. This appears to be a worthwhile and not too costly precaution.

Galvanic corrosion problems may occur because of the presence of dissimilar metals in a multimetal system. Less "noble" metals will corrode preferentially in contact with more "noble" metals: copper will galvanically corrode aluminum or steel, steel will galvanically corrode aluminum, etc. One source of galvanic corrosion is direct electrical connection between two dissimilar metals. Dissimilar metals should be electrically isolated from one another.

Another source of galvanic corrosion is the presence of ions of the more noble metals in solution which galvanically deposit on the surface of the less noble metal. In most circumstances, this type of corrosion of copper components is not a factor. In the case of aluminum, it can be. The inhibitors in commercial automotive antifreeze formulations are designed to minimize this problem by suppressing corrosion of all metals in the system and thereby reducing the extent to which metal ions go into solution.

The use of a getter column, through which the heat exchange fluid circulates before entry into the aluminum portion of the system, is also suggested. Such a getter column would consist of a plastic cylinder containing a series of aluminum sheets. The water circulates over this surface and the function of the surface is to pick up "heavy metal" ions which may have gotten into the system as the result of "tramp" material within the system.

Fluids are available which are nonionic and which, therefore, will not support galvanic corrosion. The manufacturer of the fluid should be consulted for his recommendations concerning conditions for which it is suited. Characteristically, nonaqueous heat transfer fluids have lower thermal capacity and inferior heat transfer characteristics as compared to water-glycol mixtures. This means that for equal heat transfer efficiency, the wetted area of heat transfer surface and the total cross section of the heat transfer passages in a solar absorber panel will have to be greater when such fluids are used than when water-glycol mixtures are used.

Chapter 5
Insulation

This chapter offers some tips on energy conservation in your home. It stresses cheap and effective methods of minimizing infiltration and conduction heat losses. As mentioned previously, this is the first step of retrofit for solar space heating. These same tips will help in reducing your summer cooling requirements. Refer to Table 1-1.

Air infiltration usually accounts for 25 to 60 percent of the total heat loss in existing homes. In homes with inadequate insulation, the heat loss from air infiltration exceeds conduction losses through the walls, ceilings, and floors by up to 35 percent. Therefore, proper insulation is a *must*!

Proper insulating often requires a major insulation overhaul, but you can save money by doing the labor yourself. In selecting your insulation, keep several things in mind. First, determine your needs. This can easily be accomplished by drawing a rough sketch of your home and discussing your projected requirements with an insulation retailer. Next, shop for price. Don't get over-anxious. Look for high quality. Last, can you install the product yourself?

Measures for reducing infiltration include a general "tightening-up" of the structure and possibly the foundation, caulking and weatherstripping the doors and windows, cleaning and possibly redesigning fireplace air flows. Also, install a vapor barrier in or on all outside walls, also if it is a pier-house, Visqueen or other similar sheathing should be tacked to the floor joists. The same applies to a home that has a basement. You can also create wind breaks for the entrances and the entire house if possible.

To tighten up your home, begin with the obvious. Repair and close up cracks and holes in the foundation (patching materials can be bought at local hardware stores, building centers, and lumber yards). Repair missing or broken shingles and siding. Check the caulking. Any hardened, cracked, or

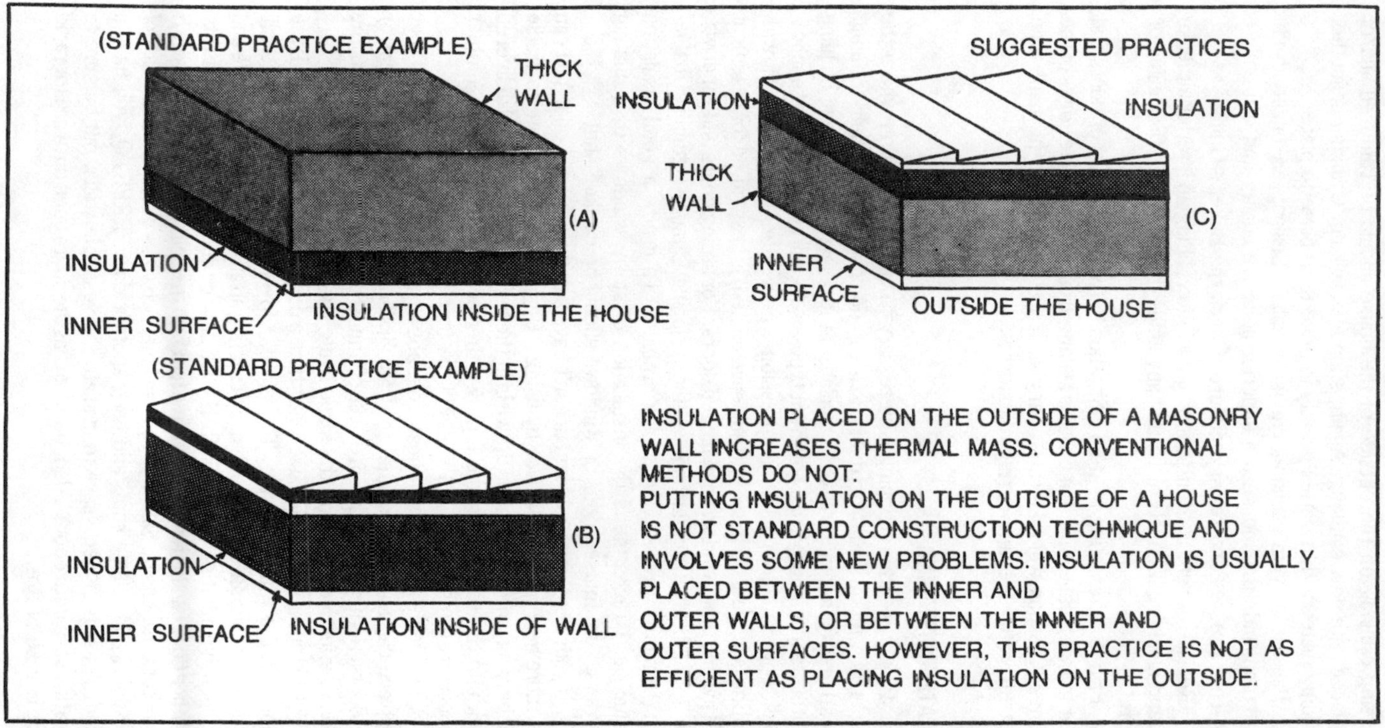
(STANDARD PRACTICE EXAMPLE)
THICK WALL
(A)
INSULATION
INNER SURFACE
INSULATION INSIDE THE HOUSE
SUGGESTED PRACTICES
INSULATION
INSULATION
THICK WALL
(C)
INNER SURFACE
OUTSIDE THE HOUSE
(STANDARD PRACTICE EXAMPLE)
(B)
INSULATION
INNER SURFACE
INSULATION INSIDE OF WALL
INSULATION PLACED ON THE OUTSIDE OF A MASONRY WALL INCREASES THERMAL MASS. CONVENTIONAL METHODS DO NOT.
PUTTING INSULATION ON THE OUTSIDE OF A HOUSE IS NOT STANDARD CONSTRUCTION TECHNIQUE AND INVOLVES SOME NEW PROBLEMS. INSULATION IS USUALLY PLACED BETWEEN THE INNER AND OUTER WALLS, OR BETWEEN THE INNER AND OUTER SURFACES. HOWEVER, THIS PRACTICE IS NOT AS EFFICIENT AS PLACING INSULATION ON THE OUTSIDE.

Fig. 5-1. Standard insulation practices. Insulation inside the house at (A), insulation inside the wall at (B), and insulation outside the house at (C).

missing caulking on the outside of the house should be removed and/or replaced with new caulking. Again, shop for caulking. Caulking is another building material that varies greatly in price from place to place.

In selecting your caulking, choose a sealant. Sealants are quality caulking compounds that possess a superior adhesive quality and can endure hot-cold stresses and resist moisture. Check the Buyer's Guide.

Replace or refit ill-fitting doors and windows. Plug up interior air leaks around mouldings, baseboards, and any holes that may be in the ceiling or floor.

Prior to attempting to stem infiltration between windows or doors and their frames, make sure that no air is leaking around the outside edges of the frames. Caulking will take care of any such problems and at the same time prevent water seepage during rainstorms.

WEATHERSTRIPPING

Proper weatherstripping is necessary to check infiltration where the edges of windows and/or doors join (or don't join) with their framing. Weatherstripping materials are available at local hardware stores, building centers, and lumber yards. Different types are required for different applications. For example, gasket compression-type weatherstripping (black with a fabric face, peel off back, and adhesive coated) is best suited for casement and awning type windows and hinged doors. For sliding doors and windows, the spring-bronze or felt-hair weatherstripping is more suitable. Double-hung windows present more of a problem. To insure a good insulation technique, I recommend the installation of storm windows or insulating barriers. Any unused door or windows should be caulked shut.

If your fireplace is old and doesn't have a damper, install one. You can get more heat from a fireplace by using a C-shaped tubular grate to cradle the burning wood. Cold air is drawn in at the bottom, warmed, and delivered back into the room from the top by a thermosiphoning process. Another popular method is to install vents in the flue.

The vents will reclaim heat from hot air rising up the chimney. Your fireplace can also be modified to draw air directly from the basement or outdoors. Otherwise, the fire will continue to draw warm air from the rooms, effectively cooling the same living space you want to heat.

Cold air flows into a house everytime a door is opened, especially if the door is on the windward side. Therefore, a foyer or vestibule entrance will effectively eliminate this problem by creating an air-lock effect. A simple and inexpensive addition can be built. If your door or doors open into a hallway, another door can be hung four or five feet into the hallway to make a foyer. If your entrance has no hallway, you can build two walls out from either side of the door, add a little roof, and hang another door. PRESTO, you have a vestibule. It isn't necessary to insulate the vestibule walls, but be sure to weatherstrip both doors. Also, be sure that the doors open outward for rapid exit in case of fire.

Did you know that air can actually infiltrate the walls themselves? Wind pressure forces air through tiny cracks in the wall material, especially through wood siding. A good vapor barrier, however, will solve this problem. It will also add to maintaining a comfortable indoor humidity. If your home is an old home that doesn't have a vapor barrier, it is not practical to add a barrier, unless the inside surface of the walls are being removed for remodeling. If, however, that is the case, foil-backed fiberglass insulation, or polystyrene can be installed as an effective vapor barrier. A cheaper method of substituting for a vapor barrier is by painting your home with a high quality low-permeability paint. Check this out with your local paint dealer.

WALLS, CEILINGS, AND FLOORS

The best investment that you can make in your home is insulation. Thermal performance standards of buildings are determined by matching the insulation costs against fuel costs until the purchase price of the insulation and the projected cost of fuel bills reach a minimum. In the past, the amount of insulation yielding this minimum cost gave the walls a total thermal

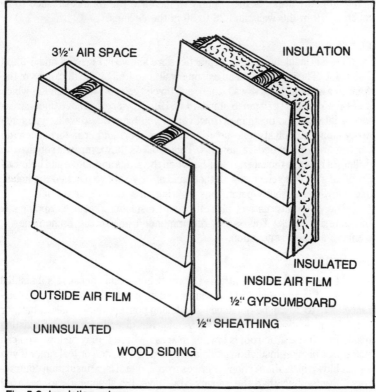

Fig. 5-2. Insulation values.

Table 5-1. Sample calculations of U-values.

Wall Construction Components	R-values	
	Uninsulated	Insulated
Outside air film, 15 mph wind	0.17	0.17
Wood bevel siding, lapped	0.81	0.81
½″ Sheathing, regular density	1.32	1.32
3½″ Air space	1.01	—
3½″ Mineral wool batt	—	10.90
½″ Gypsumboard	0.45	0.45
Inside air film	0.68	0.68
TOTALS (Rt)	4.44	14.33
U-values (U = 1/Rt)	0.23	0.069

resistance, or R-value, of about 11, but with rising fuel costs it makes more sense in many areas of the country to increase the total resistance to as much as 19 in the walls and 25 to 30 in the ceilings.

Walls

Typical insulation standard practices are shown in Figs. 5-1 and 5-2 and Table 5-1. The insulation of an existing wall is limited by the thickness of the wall. In a standard 2 × 4 wall, there are three types of wall insulation which meet the desired resistance standard of 19. They are cellulose fiber, urea-formaldehyde, and urethane. However, if you have 2 × 6 walls, you have many choices. Polystyrene-beads, cellulose-fiber, and urea-formaldehyde can be blown into wood frame walls. This process, however, will require the drilling of holes in the interior wall between the studs and above and below all firebreaks. If you select this method, and after you have patched the holes, use a low-permeability paint, thus insuring an added vapor barrier.

The other alternative, blanket or batt insulation, requires ripping out the exterior walls. This is not recommended unless the homeowner is planning a major renovation.

THE ATTIC

The insulation of the attic is the most important, because substantial amounts of heat are lost in the winter and gained in the summer. A resistance of 25 to 30 can be obtained by installing poured, thick blanket, batt, or loose-fill insulation on the ceiling framing or directly on top of existing insulation. If the attic roof is low, or in areas where it may be low, you can maneuver blanket insulation into place by using a garden or leaf rake. If you select blown insulation, shop for prices from several local insulation contractors. Remember that the money you save by shopping can be used elsewhere in the retrofit.

Table 5-2 shows that mineral and fiberglass insulation will *not* provide the desired resistance of 19 in a 2 × 4 stud wall. If you attempt to compress these insulators to increase their specific resistance you will get the opposite effect, as compression reduces the air spaces needed to slow the flow of heat.

MASONRY WALLS

One method of insulating masonry walls is to blow loose-fill or foam insulation into existing air spaces. This method is possible if the plate for the ceiling rafters doesn't cover the concrete block cores and/or the cavity wall construction. Rigid board insulation can also be placed on the outside of a masonry wall and replastered or covered with siding.

FLOORS, BASEMENTS, AND FOUNDATIONS

Tacking foil-backed insulation supported by wire mesh to the underside of the floor, (leaving at least a one-half-inch air space) will provide a high resistance. If there isn't enough room to get under the house, seal the foundation but leave adequate air vents (one on each side will be appropriate). If the basement is being utilized as living space, insulate the foundation walls all the way to the base of the foundation.

WINDOW INSULATION

Windows are difficult to insulate, as you can see by examining Fig. 5-7. Even with all the aforementioned improvements, a lot of heat can still be lost by conduction through the windows. A single pane window loses heat about 25 times faster than a well-insulated wall of the same total area. Many methods can be used to cut those losses. Storm windows are the most practical and least expensive. Other methods are insulating curtains and insulating shutters.

Insulating curtains can be made of tightly woven material lined with "fiber-fill," a loose stuffing or blanket-type insulating material, or other heavy material. The curtain can be suspended from a curtain rod or hanger or attached directly to the top of the window frame.

Another method is to insulate the windows with removable insulating shutters. With ingenuity and modern building materials, small miracles are possible. Practical, inexpensive shutters can be made of wood, hinged on one side and covered with styrofoam insulation. Shutters should be weatherstripped to obtain maximum effect. A latch should be installed in order to draw up and fasten tightly.

If entrances and windows are exposed to prevailing winds, you may need to install wall or fence extensions, overhangs, baffles, and plantings to deflect the wind. Windbreaks lower the wind velocity and reduce air infiltration. The distance from the house to the windbreak, measured from the leeward side, should not exceed four times the buildings height. Check with your local agricultural extension service center. They can suggest the trees and shrubs best suited for your area.

Table 5-2. R-values of common insulators.

INSULATION MATERIAL	R-VALUES		
	FOR ONE-INCH	INSIDE 2 × 4 stud wall*	INSIDE 2 × 6 stud wall
MINERAL WOOL	3.0	13.7	19.7
FIBERGLASS	3.5	15.5	22.4
POLYSTYRENE	4.0	17.2	25.2
URETHANE	6.5	25.9	38.9
VERMICULITE	2.5	11.9	16.9
CELLULOSE FIBER	4.5	18.9	27.9
UREA-FORMALDEHYDE	5.5	22.5	33.4

*Includes insulating value of siding, sheathing, and air films.

DOORS AND WINDOWS

The loss of heat through existing doors and windows can be reduced by adding an additional layer of glass (storm sash or panel). This is a good idea if only a single layer of glass is provided. Securely seal cracks around glass, sash, and window frames to prevent air infiltration. If your home doesn't have storm doors or windows, install them. The money that you save will be your own. Do not, I repeat, do not try to save money at the expense of insulation. Refer to Fig. 5-7.

THE ROOF

The roof of your house is more important than you might think. It is more than just a cap or cover. It is a shelter. It is a shelter from rain in all

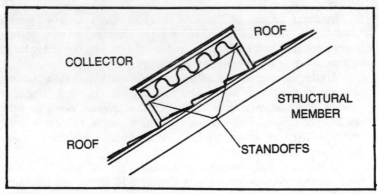

Fig. 5-3. Stand-off mounting. Elements that separate the collector from the finished roof surface are known as stand-offs. They allow air and rain water to pass under the collector which minimizes problems of mildew and leakage. The stand-offs must also have adequate structural properties. Stand-offs are often used to support collectors at an angle other than that of the roof to optimize collector tilt.

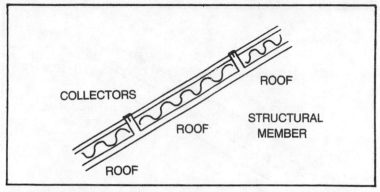

Fig. 5-4. Direct mounting. Collectors can be mounted directly on the roof surface. Generally, the collectors are placed on a waterproof membrane on top of the roof sheathing. The finished roof surface, together with the necessary collector structural attachments and flashing, are then built up around the collector. A weatherproof seal between the collector and the roof must be maintained, or leakage, mildew, and rotting might occur.

climates, snow in colder ones, and sun in warmer ones. It is also a shelter from the wind and windblown particles. The exterior surfaces and over all shape determine how effective it is as a shelter and will largely determine what your house looks like. I mention that because more than likely that's where the solar collector is going to be installed. Roofs are either flat or pitched. A low-pitched roof between 1:12 and 6:12 will shed water, and the lower pitches will retain snow for insulation. Valleys, where two roof angles come together and join, are the only areas to worry about on your roof.

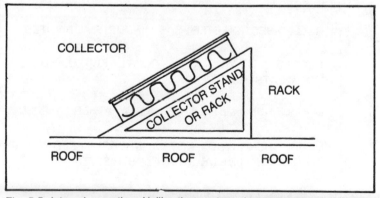

Fig. 5-5. Integral mounting. Unlike the previous three component collectors which can be applied or mounted separately, integral mounting places the collector within the roof construction itself. Thus, the collector is attached to and supported by the structural framing members. In addition, the top of the collector serves as the finished roof surface. Weather tightness is again crucial to avoid problems of water damage and mildew. This method of mounting is frequently used for the site built collectors.

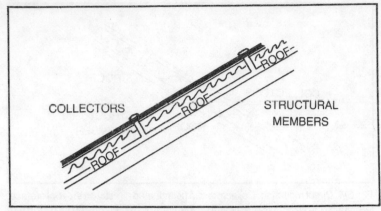

Fig. 5-6. Rack mounting. Collectors can be mounted at the prescribed angle on a structural frame located on the ground or attached to the building. The structural connection between the collector and the frame and the building or site must be adequate to resist any impact loads such as wind.

Sometimes it is very hard to set and position a large solar collector or series of collectors across roof valleys. However, it can usually be accomplished, if it is absolutely necessary. We must be very careful when anchoring the solar collector to the roof, because we don't want to damage the roof. Collector mountings for roofs are shown in Figs. 5-3 through 5-6.

Remember to select a good location with a southern exposure. I would like to clarify one thing here. It is not necessary to set and position your

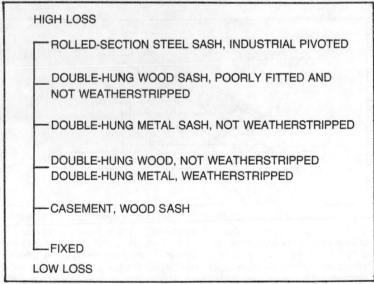

Fig. 5-7. Air infiltration heat losses for various windows.

collector on your roof, but there are many practical reasons for doing so. For instance, a roof-mounted solar collector is usually free of any obstructions that might hinder direct sunlight to your collector. It's free available space. It's not in the way of people, barbecues, and grills. I might remind the reader that children are fascinated by easily accessible, ground-mounted collectors, as are dogs and cats that find their warmth enticing. Vandalism is another point to be considered. Collector glass covers are easily broken. Plastic, while not easily broken, is easily scratched and mutilated. I recommend that collector location be given careful consideration.

Chapter 6
Design

Heating requirements are determined by two factors: the local climate and the insluation value of the house and/or its heat loss potential. Heat is lost faster in cold climates; therefore, heat loss is related directly to climate. There are many methods used to estimate heat loss. For simplicity and accuracy, I have chosen the sample design and calculation sheets shown on pages 66-69. Use the sheets to calculate the heat loss of your home. For this example we will use an average home located in Dayton, Ohio.

Step 1: The first step in determining heat loss is finding the temperature factor. Write down in the appropriate space of your calculation sheet the temperature at which you wish to keep your home (I have used 67°F for the Dayton home). Next, turn to appendix E, find the section that lists "degree days and design temperatures." Next, refer to the state of Ohio listings and find Dayton. We see that Dayton has a design temperature of 0. Now refer to your city, or a city in your general area that has a similar climate. List your city's design temperature in the appropriate space. Now subtract to obtain the temperature factor. For the Dayton house, $67 - 0 = 67$, which is the temperature factor.

Step 2: We must then determine the "infiltration factor." We begin by measuring your home. First, find the dimensions (in feet) of all the exterior surfaces, including walls, ceiling, doors, windows, etc. Write these measurements in the appropriate spaces in your sample calculation sheet. The Dayton house is single story, $30' \times 40'$, with two doors and seven windows as shown in Fig. 6-1. From the dimensions, calculate the area and perimeter of each door and window.

Write down these calculations in the appropriate spaces. Refer to the calculation sheets shown in Figs. 6-2 and 6-3. Now look in the Appendix E of this guide for the INFILTRATION LOSS FACTORS. Find the type of doors and windows that you have in your home and the value listed under the temperature factor for your house. This value represents the infiltration factor. Write down the value in the appropriate space in your sample calculation sheet. For instance, the example house in Dayton has double-hung metal sash windows with storm windows, and under a temperature factor of 67°, a value of 38 is found and written down for infiltration factor on the sample calculation sheet. The Dayton house had the same size windows as well as the same type. Your house may have different window sizes and types. It is important that you calculate each one individually as each one has a different infiltration factor.

Step 3: Multiply each door and window perimeter (see Fig. 6-4) times its infiltration loss factor to obtain its infiltration loss, and then add up the infiltration losses to get the total infiltration loss. In calculating the Dayton house example, I find that each window has a perimeter of 12 feet times an infiltration loss factor of 38 for an infiltration loss of 456. Therefore, the windows and doors of the Dayton house have a total infiltration loss of 8392 BTU/hour.

Step 4: From the measurements taken in step 2, calculate the gross area of each surface and jot it down in the appropriate space. In the Dayton house, the south wall is 8 feet high by 40 feet wide and has a gross area of 320 square feet. Also calculate the areas of the doors, windows, and other surfaces and jot them down in the appropriate spaces. In order that the doors and windows not be counted twice for conduction losses, these areas must be subtracted from the gross wall area. For the North wall of the Dayton house, one window with an area equal to 8 square feet is subtracted from the gross area of the north wall, which is 320 square feet. This leaves a net area of 312 square feet. The other walls are similarly calculated. After calculating the net areas of all surfaces refer to the appendix of this guide, find the listing for "heat loss factors." Compare your wall, ceiling, floor, windows, and doors with the chart and find the values listed under the

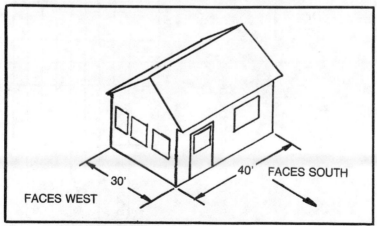

Fig. 6-1. The Dayton house used in the sample calculation.

PART 1

Thermostat: _____70°_____

Design
Temperature: _____- 12°_____
(From Table 6-1)

= _____58°_____ Temperature Factor

PART 2 - INFILTRATION LOSSES:

Window	H (ft)	W (ft)	Area (sq ft)	Perimeter (1 in ft)	Infiltration Factor (From Table 6-2)	Infiltration Loss
S WALL						
DOOR						
W WALL						
E WALL						
N WALL						
DOOR						

TOTAL INFILTRATION LOSS _____

PART 3 - CONDUCTION LOSSES:

	H	W	GROSS AREA	WINDOW & DOOR	NET AREA	HEAT LOSS FACTOR (FROM TABLE 6-3)	HEAT LOSS
S WALL							
N WALL							
W WALL							
E WALL							
CEILING							
FLOOR							
8 WINDOWS W/STORMS							
DOOR							

TOTAL CONDUCTION LOSS _____
Add Infiltration Loss + _____
TOTAL Heat Loss _____

PART 4 - AVERAGE HEATING REQUIREMENT

_____ × 24 divided by _____ = _____ BTU/degree day
Total Heat Loss   Temperature
                                    Factor

_____ × _____ = _____
BTU/degree day   degree days   Loss in BTU/year
                 (From Table 6-3)

Fig. 6-2. Blank calculation sheet for the Dayton house.

67

PART 1

Thermostat: _____ 67 _____

Design
Temperature: _____ 0 _____
(From Table 6-1)

$$\frac{}{} = 67 \quad \text{Temperature Factor}$$

PART 2 - INFILTRATION LOSSES:

	Window	H (ft)	W (ft)	Area (sq ft)	Perimeter (lin ft)	Infiltration Factor (From Table 6-2)	Infiltration Loss
S WALL	#1 door	7	3	21	20	130	2600
	#1 wnd	4	2	8	12	38	456
W WALL	#2 wnd	4	2	8	12	38	456
	#3 wnd	4	2	8	12	38	456
E WALL	#4 wnd	4	2	8	12	38	456
	#5 wnd	4	2	8	12	38	456
	#6 wnd	4	2	8	12	38	456
N WALL	#7 wnd	4	2	8	12	38	456
	#2 door	7	3	21	20	130	2600
						TOTAL INFILTRATION LOSS	8.392

PART 3 - CONDUCTION LOSSES:

	H	W	GROSS AREA	WINDOW & DOOR	NET AREA	HEAT LOSS FACTOR (FROM TABLE 6-3)	HEAT LOSS
S WALL #1 wnd	8	40	320	29	291	12	3492
N WALL #1 wnd	8	40	320	29	291	12	3492
W WALL #2 wnd	8	30	240	16	224	12	2688
E WALL #3 wnd	8	30	240	24	216	12	2592
CEILING	30	40	1200	---	1200	5	6000
FLOOR	30	40	1200	---	1200	5	6000
7 WINDOWS W/STORMS	4	2	8	7	56	38	2128
DOORS (TWO)	7	3	21	2	42	42	1764

TOTAL CONDUCTION LOSS   28,156

Add Infiltration Loss   + 8,392

TOTAL Heat Loss   36,548

PART 4 - AVERAGE HEATING REQUIREMENT

$$\frac{36,548}{\text{Total Heat Loss}} \times 24 = 877,152 \text{ divided by } 67 = 13,091 \text{ BTU/degree day}$$

$$\frac{13,091}{\text{BTU/degree day}} \times \frac{5,622}{\substack{\text{degree days} \\ \text{(From Table 6-3)}}} = \frac{73,597,602 \text{ divided by } 273 = 269,588 \text{ divided by } 24 = 11,232 \text{ per-hour loss}}{\text{Loss in BTU/year}}$$

Fig. 6-3. Completed calculation sheet for the Dayton house.

69

temperature factor. These values are the heat-loss factors and should be jotted down in the appropriate spaces in your sample calculation sheet. In checking the Dayton home, I find that the north wall, which is above grade, has wood siding and ½-inch insulation board, and has a value, under the temperature factor of 67°, of 12. This is jotted down in the appropriate space as the heat loss factor. Remember, different areas of the house may have different construction. For example, a room or rooms may have been added in a remodeling, or possibly the front of the house has a brick veneer. Thus, different constructions have different factors and must be calculated as such.

Now we multiply each net area times its heat-loss factor to get the correct amount of heat loss through each surface. Add these numbers up to get the total heat loss by conduction. From this total we can find the percentage of heat loss through each surface and determine how added insulation, weatherstripping, and storm windows might reduce heat loss.

Step 5: Add the infiltration losses to the heat losses to get the approximate maximum heating requirements in BTU/hour for your home. For the Dayton home, this is 8,392 BTU/hour.

That wasn't so tough, was it? You have just calculated the maximum heating requirements in BTUs/hour. This is the BTU method most often used to calculate the BTUs required for most conventional furnaces.

For solar heating requirements, it is necessary to find the *average* heating requirements per hour. You can accomplish this by calculating how much heat your house requires per degree day and then multiplying by the degree days per season in your locale.

This is fun. You're learning how to save money, not to mention the part that you're playing in reducing our national energy crisis. Stop and consider the effect that solar retrofit would have if everyone did what you are doing.

Step 6: Multiply the total hourly heat loss by 24. Then divide by the temperature factor that we used in Step 1 (this was 67° in the Dayton house). This will give you the BTU lost per degree day. Next, refer to the degree days and design temperature chart found in the appendix section of this guide. Find the number of degree days for your city, or a nearby city. Jot this figure down in the appropriate space. For example, Dayton has 5622. Now, multiply the degree days times the loss per degree day and you have found the total heat loss per year for your house. In the Dayton house we have 36548 BTU/times 24 hrs which, equals 877,152 divided by 67, which equals 13091 BTU/degree day. From Appendix E we know that Dayton has 5622 degree days per year. Therefore, the Dayton house uses 5622 times 13,091 which is 73,597,602 BTU/year.

Practically all the heat utilization occurs between September through May, or the nine-month heating season. Therefore, to find the average daily heating requirements, divide the average heating loss by the number of days in the nine-month heating season, which is 273 days. To find the average loss per hour, divide by 24. We know that the average heating loss is approximately 269,588 BTU/day at the Dayton house. To find the hourly loss, we simply divide the daily loss, 269,588 BTU/day, by 24. This gives us

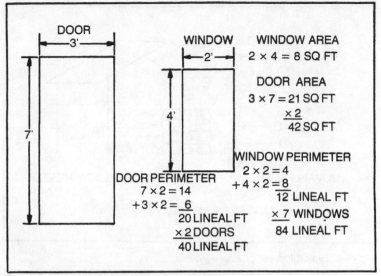

Fig. 6-4. How to calculate door and window perimeters.

an hourly loss of approximately 11,232 BTU/hour. This loss represents approximately 662 gallons of fuel oil per year, or $300, based on current fuel oil costs.

SELECTING A DESIGN

You have already made your predesign list and checked it carefully, noting all variables. You have made a list of all the existing mechanical apparatus that might be used or incorporated into your new system. You have tightened up the old house. Now comes the selection of a solar system for your home.

There are three basic methods of trapping solar radiation for home heating. Their categories are:

- Direct
- Indirect
- Integrated

In direct methods (Fig. 6-5), the sun's rays shine, or penetrate directly into your home. Internal structures, such as adobe walls, concrete walls, and concrete floors, absorb the heat generated and release it when the sun isn't shining. The directly heated home acts as a huge solar collector or heat trap. The direct method is the simplest method, and should be used provided your home meets such basic requirements as adobe walls, concrete walls, or concrete floors.

Indirect methods (Fig. 6-6) for solar heating generally use rooftop collectors with remote or separate storage systems. Heat that is generated by the collector moves from the collector to the storage area or to the rooms by indirect routes. This method usually requires piping or air ducts. Fans

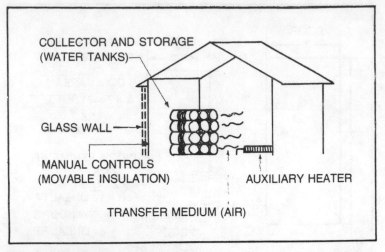

Fig. 6-5. Typical indirect or active system.

and pumps are required to move air, and circulate liquids through the collector and back to the storage area. Another term used to describe indirect systems is *active systems*. The direct, or active system, relies on mechanical power to perform adequately, and is consequently more complex and more prone to failure. Indirect systems are very popular because they require very little owner attention and are very efficient. They are, as a rule, very adaptive and easily installed in most existing homes.

Indirect systems use one or more flat plate collectors. See Fig. 6-8. The collectors are usually mounted on the roof of the home, facing southward. The collectors have one or more glass or plastic cover plates, which allow sunlight to shine through onto a black or dark green absorber. The

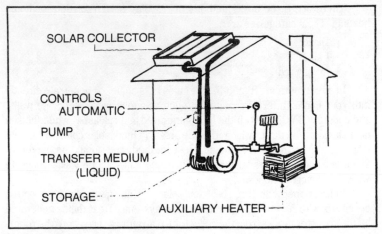

Fig. 6-6. Typical direct or passive system.

72

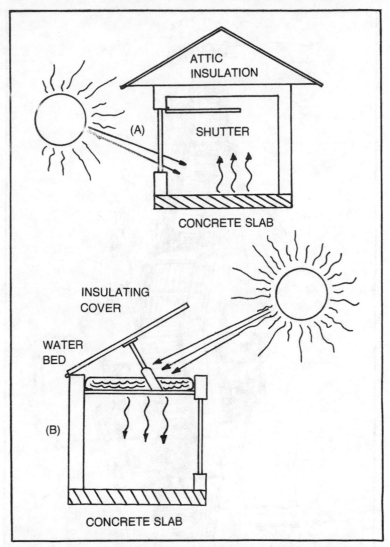

Fig. 6-7. Typical integrated solar concept utilizing natural thermal properties of materials to collect and distribute heat. Wall shutter at (A) and insulating cover at (B).

cover plates reduce the loss of energy through the front, and insulation behind the absorber is conducted to a transfer liquid, or air, which flows in contact with it and carries off the heat.

Another type of indirect system collector is the *concentrating collector*. In concentrating collectors, reflective surfaces such as mirrors, or highly polished metal, concentrate the sun's rays onto a very small area and in an intense manner. This intense, concentrated solar energy is then absorbed

Fig. 6-8. Flat roof installation.

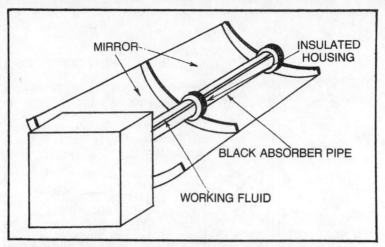

Fig. 6-9. Parabolic reflector. Concentrating collectors such as this one may be used in applications where high temperatures are required. The collector consists of a trough-shaped parabolic reflector that focuses the solar radiation at a point much smaller than the collector area. By focusing the energy collected by a larger area onto a smaller area, higher temperatures can be reached. This type of collector can generate the higher temperatures needed to drive absorption or rankin cycle air conditioning, or produce steam to drive turbines and generate electricty.

by a black or dark green surface surface and converted to heat that is carried off by fluid. This type of collector can produce very high temperatures but usually requires a mechanical device to automatically track the sun. See Fig. 6-9.

Integrated systems (Fig. 6-7) use ingenious adaptations of the natural thermal properties of various materials to collect and distribute the heat that has been collected. In most applications, heat from the sun is directly absorbed and stored in water containers inside the house, water filled bags on the roof, or the concrete walls of the house. The trapped collected heat flows from room to room without the aid of pumps, fans, or ducts.

Notice in Fig. 6-10 that thermal radiation brings heat to the rooms from water filled containers inside the house. This type of system is also referred to as the *passive system*. Figure 6-11 shows the utilization of another commonly used method. Notice how thermal radiation brings heat to the rooms from the warm liquid-filled bags on the roof. Although passive systems frequently require unusual departures from usual building standards, their simplicity results in very effective and reliable home heating.

Now that we have had a quick look at the three basic systems, note the various aspects and principles relative to your home, the feasibility of the system, and your particular requirements. Don't forget, however, that *all* solar heating systems require auxiliary, or backup systems. The backup should be either wood, oil, gas, or electric. Add this requirement to your list, as it is an important factor in selecting your particular system.

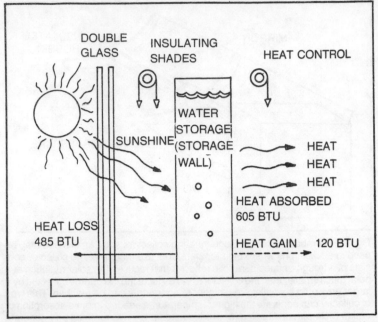

Fig. 6-10. Typical heat storage wall utilizing water. This is a direct or passive system.

WATER SYSTEMS

Solar heating that uses water as the transfer and storage medium is the most common system today. More information is available about the behavior of water systems than about either air or "passive" systems, and most of the designs in this book, therefore, use a water solar heating system.

The basic parts of a typical water system consist of a collector, a storage tank, a system of piping, pumps, and controls for circulating water

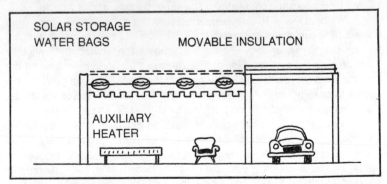

Fig. 6-11. Typical passive system. This particular system was designed by Harold Hay.

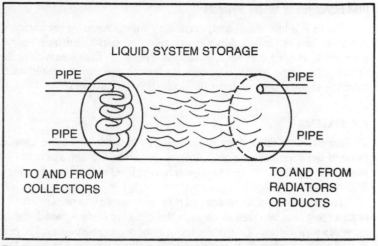

Fig. 6-12. In space heating systems that use a liquid heat transfer medium, the storage system is usually a large tank of water of about 600-1000 gallons or more.

from the storage tank through the collector, and another system for transferring stored heat to the dwelling space, usually a fan that moves air across the storage area.

The collector is like a very thin greenhouse with one or more outer covering layers of transparent glass or plastic; an air space; a non-shiny metal collector surface, which absorbs solar energy striking it through the glass; and a layer of insulation behind the collector surface, carrying away some of the absorbed heat. This water is piped to a storage tank, where it is stored until needed. The tank, or the space in which the tank is located, must be insulated.

Heat from the tank is transferred to the dwelling space by direct convection, by circulating the tank water through ordinary baseboard convectors, by circulating the tank water through a coil in a hot air duct, by fan coil units, or by other equivalent means.

Domestic hot water is preheated by routing the cold feed water through a tank immersed in the solar storage tank.

Among existing examples of water type solar heating systems, details of control cycles vary considerably. Regarding the collection cycle, it is generally true that water from the storage tank is circulated to the collector only when the collector surface is hotter than the storage tank (except when melting snow from the collector).

Advantages of Water Systems

Water is a cheap and efficient heat transfer and storage medium. The circulation of water uses less energy than the circulation of air with corresponding heat content. Water systems have proven that they work well and are easily installed.

Disadvantages of Water Systems

There is a high initial cost, particulary when expensive prefabricated collectors are employed. Maintenance must be performed on a regular schedule to combat corrosion, scale, and freeze-up. Contamination of the domestic hot water supply is possible if a leaking pipe allows treated water from the storage tank to enter the domestic water system.

AIR SYSTEMS

Air systems differ from water systems in using air as the transfer medium between collector and storage area. The storage agent can be water, but typical air system storage areas are filled with stones. See Figs. 6-12 through 6-15.

Large volumes of air (about two cubic feet per minute per surface foot of collector) circulate past or through the collector surface, which can be made of a wide variety of materials, typically light-gauge aluminum. The heat stored in a rock pile can be transferred efficiently to the dwelling space by a forced warm air system. When the collector is functioning, the air system can deliver heat directly from the collector to the dwelling space.

The preheating of domestic hot water is not usually practical by using heat from the storage bin. Usually, a pre-heat coil is located in the return duct from the collector. See Fig. 6-16.

Advantages of Air Systems

There is no problem with corrosion, blockage, or freezing. The domestic hot water supply is not subject to contamination by contact with the storage area or transfer medium, as in some water systems. Air leakage will not damage the building as opposed to the damage that can occur with water or other fluids.

Table 6-1. Infiltration loss factor.

WINDOWS	TEMPERATURE FACTOR							
	40	50	60	65	70	75	80	85
Double Hung Wood Sash- No Weatherstripping, Poor Conditions	23	28	42	45	50	53	57	66
Double Hung Wood Sash- Weather Stripped or with Storm Sash	17	20	25	28	30	32	34	36
Double Hung Metal Sash- Weather Stripped or Storm Sash	25	30	35	37	40	45	50	55
Casement Windows	35	45	55	60	65	70	75	80
DOORS: All types with or without Storm Sash	80	100	120	130	140	150	160	170

Table 6-2. Heat loss factor of houses.

WALLS:	40	50	60	65	70	75	80	85
WOOD SIDING, ABOVE GRADE								
Tar Paper, Wood Sheathing, Lath, 3½" Insulation, Plaster	4	5	5	6	6	7	7	8
Same, no Insulation	10	13	15	16	18	19	20	21
Tar Paper, Wood Sheathing, Plaster Board, and ½" Insulation Board	8	10	11	12	13	14	15	16
BRICK-8"								
Bare Wall	20	25	30	33	35	38	40	43
Brick, Furring, Lath, Plaster	12	15	18	20	21	23	24	26
Brick, Furring, ½" Insulation, Lath, Plaster	9	11	13	14	16	17	18	19
BRICK-12"								
Bare Wall	14	18	22	23	25	27	29	31
CONCRETE BLOCK-8"								
Block, Furring, Lath, Plaster	13	16	19	21	22	24	26	27
Block, Furring, ½" Insulation, Lath, Plaster	10	12	14	16	17	18	19	20
DOORS 1½"	20	25	30	32	35	37	40	43
With Metal Storm Door	13	16	20	21	23	24	26	28
BASEMENT FLOOR								
Concrete Slab	2	2½	3	5	7	8	10	12
CEILING WITH ATTIC ABOVE								
Unfloored, ventilated, no Insulation	14	18	21	22	24	26	27	29
Floored, Unventilated, no Insulation	9	11	13	14	15	16	17	18
Floored, Unventilated, 3½" Insulation	3	4	4	5	6	7	7	8
Floored, Unventilated, 6" Insulation	2	2	3	3	3	3	4	4
BASEMENT WALLS								
8" Concrete, Below Grade	2	2	3	3	4	4	5	5
8" Concrete, Above Grade	28	35	42	46	49	53	56	60
8" Cinderblock, Above Grade	17	21	25	27	29	32	34	36
WINDOWS								
Single Glass	45	56	68	73	79	85	91	96
Single with Storm Windows-can be plastic	22	27	34	37	40	43	45	48
Insulating Glass, ¼" Air Space	26	32	39	42	45	48	52	55

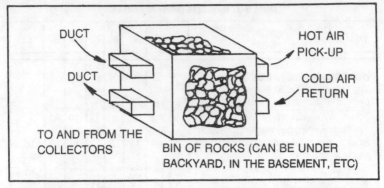

Fig. 6-13. In systems that use air as a heat transfer medium, the storage is usually a bin of large gravel or fist-sized rock. Hot air flows through the space between the 1 to 2-inch gravel and heats it. In this case, the bin must be at least 2½ times as large as the tank used in a water storage system. Another way of putting this is that there should be one-half cubic foot of rock for every square foot of collector.

Disadvantages of Air Systems

Ductwork is necessary as the transport mode. Air, having a lower thermal capacity than water, requires more energy to transfer heat. Air systems are more expensive because they are more complex and difficult to install in an existing house.

PASSIVE OR INHERENT SYSTEMS

Passive is the term used to describe a number of interesting solar designs which more directly involve the construction of the building and the

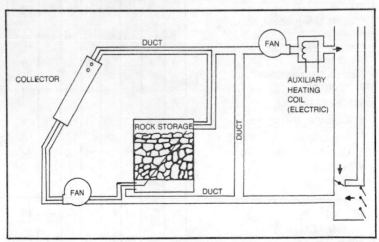

Fig. 6-14. Heat storage from collector using the warm air system. The airspace requires no heat, and the collector temperature exceeds storage temperature.

Table 6-3. Climate data for certain cities.

CITY	DESIGN TEMPERATURE	APPROXIMATELY DEGREE DAYS/YEAR
ATLANTA	+18	2,961
BALTIMORE	+12	4,654
BIRMINGHAM	+19	2,551
BOSTON	+6	5,634
BUFFALO	+3	7,062
CHARLESTON	+26	1,794
CHICAGO	−4	6,155
CLEVELAND	+2	6,351
DALLAS	+19	2,363
DENVER	−2	6,283
DETROIT	+4	6,232
HOUSTON	+28	1,396
INDIANAPOLIS	0	5,699
KANSAS CITY	+4	4,711
LOS ANGELES	+41	2,061
MIAMI	+45	141
MILWAUKEE	−6	7,635
MADISON	−9	7,863
MINNEAPOLIS	−14	8,382
NEW ORLEANS	+32	1,385
NEW YORK	+11	4,871
OKLAHOMA CITY	+11	3,725
PHILADELPHIA	+11	5,144
PITTSBURGH	+5	5,987
PORTLAND, MAINE	−5	7,511
PORTLAND, OREGON	+21	4,635
SAN FRANCISCO	+42	3,001
SEATTLE	+28	4,424
ST. LOUIS	+4	4,900
WASHINGTON, D.C.	+16	4,224
DAYTON	0	5,622

behavior of the occupants with the solar heating and cooling process. It is evident that the comfort level of a dwelling can be increased by careful insulation, construction, and orientation of the building. In passively solar heated houses, an attempt is made to refine the design enough to achieve modern comfort standards with a minimal utilization of auxiliary heating methods.

By storing the daily excess of solar heat, it is possible to approach modern comfort standards, especially if you are located in a climate where daily sunshine and few cold periods are the norm. See Figs. 6-17 and 6-18.

Nearly every passive design presently employed demands that changes be made in the living patterns of the occupants. Most homeowners are reluctant to make such changes because the solar heating concept is perceived as a way to keep their present living patterns without using nonrenewable resources. Understanding this strongly held consumer pre-

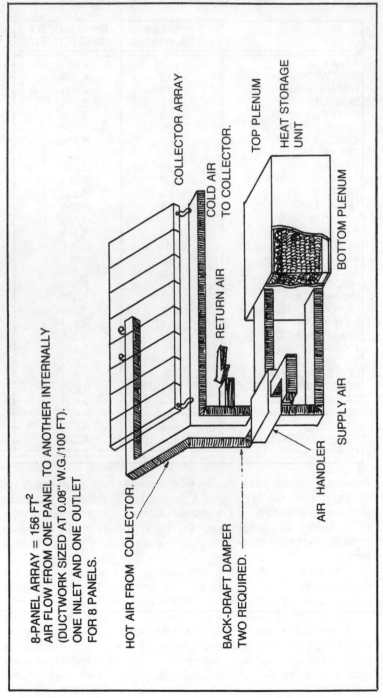

8-PANEL ARRAY = 156 FT^2
AIR FLOW FROM ONE PANEL TO ANOTHER INTERNALLY
(DUCTWORK SIZED AT 0.08'' W.G./100 FT).
ONE INLET AND ONE OUTLET
FOR 8 PANELS.

COLLECTOR ARRAY

COLD AIR
TO COLLECTOR.

RETURN AIR

TOP PLENUM

HEAT STORAGE
UNIT

BOTTOM PLENUM

HOT AIR FROM COLLECTOR.

BACK-DRAFT DAMPER
TWO REQUIRED.

SUPPLY AIR

AIR HANDLER

Fig. 6-15. Typical warm air system.

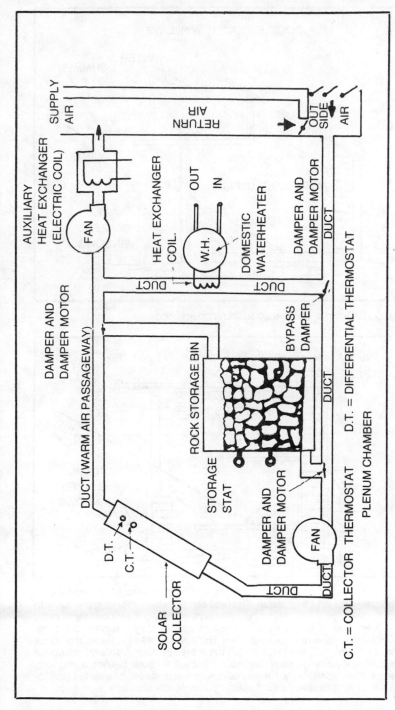

Fig. 6-16. Typical solar warm air heating system.

C.T. = COLLECTOR THERMOSTAT   D.T. = DIFFERENTIAL THERMOSTAT

83

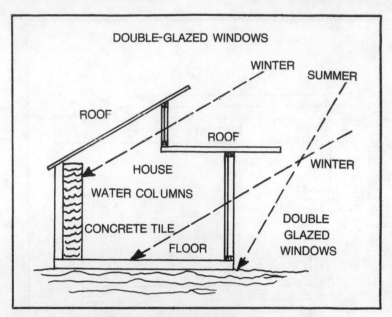

Fig. 6-17. Direct or passive solar utilization in a home

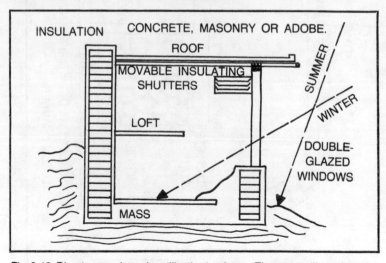

Fig. 6-18. Direct or passive solar utilization in a home. The mass will reradiate the heat back into the living space. The heat can be retained for long periods with movable window insulation. In the summer, the building is kept cool by blocking the direct rays of the sun with the use of appropriately designed overhang, movable insulation or deciduous trees. Because the mass is kept out of direct sun, it remains cool and helps to cool the entire structure. Auxiliary heat from a conventional heating system provides a backup for solar heating during long periods of cloudiness. The primary advantages of direct use of solar are simplicity, low cost, reliabilty, durability, and opportunity for creativity.

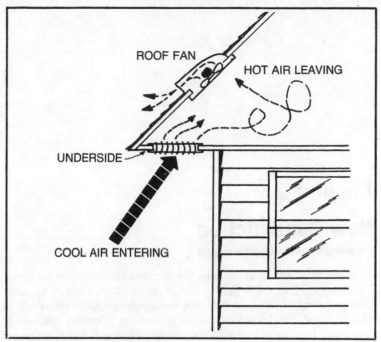

Fig. 6-19. Typical powered roof vent fan.

ference, solar advocates perceive passive solar heated homes in the northern areas of the United States to be marginally acceptable to the average homeowner, for the following reasons:

- In those designs utilizing large areas of glass facing southward, loss of privacy, overheating, damage to furniture, and glare present problems.
- When compared with collectors located high on the roof, the vertical wall collectors reaching the ground, which are common to many passive solar designs presently used, will require a decrease in the density of currently used building practices in order to avoid interference from neighboring homes, trees, fences, driveways, etc. Decreased densities will require greater energy consumption for transportation and other necessary services.

ATTIC COOLING

Powered roof vents with thermostatic controls are most effective when used in conjunction with soffit vents. An easy-to-install powered vent can lower attic temperatures up to 30 degrees, reduce cooling loads on a home, and prolong roof life.

See Fig. 6-19. Remove shingles from between two rafters, sabersaw a hole for the vent. Then slide the vent into place under the shingles and nail in place. Inside, wire the fan to a junction box.

Chapter 7
New Construction

Solar energy utilization is cost effective for many applications in the United States today. For new buildings, simple design considerations for solar energy utilization can heat and cool most buildings quite effectively at minimum cost. The following five basic solar design principles which we go into detail later should be incorporated into all new buildings wherever possible:

- Insulate and weatherstrip thoroughly.
- Orient the long axis of the building so it faces south.
- Place most windows on the south side for heat gain.
- Provide an overhang on south glass for summer shading.
- Cover the roof with a light color surface material to reject heat.

Direct solar is the most cost effective method for heating and cooling. The buildings are designed so they accept or reject heat directly without the use of solar hardware systems. The energy storage and transfer system is often the structure itself. It collects and radiates the energy throughout the building naturally.,

Indirect or active solar for air conditioning is currently not cost effective for single family residences or small commercial buildings. It may achieve cost effectiveness for large primary commercial applications.

SOLAR CELLS

All of the above solar energy uses are for heating and cooling. Solar cells are used for photovoltaic electricity generation. Presently they are used only for very remote and specific applications.

COST OF SOLAR APPLICATIONS

The economic attractiveness of each solar application will depend upon local setting, orientation, geographical location, climatic conditions, and the

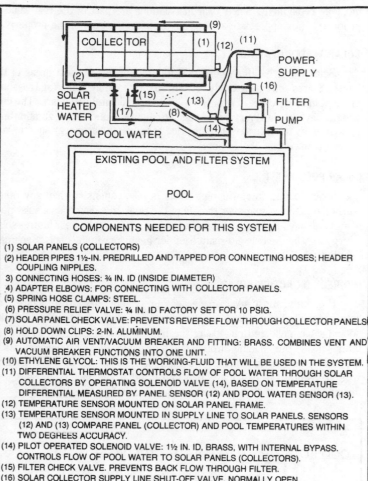

COMPONENTS NEEDED FOR THIS SYSTEM

(1) SOLAR PANELS (COLLECTORS)
(2) HEADER PIPES 1½-IN. PREDRILLED AND TAPPED FOR CONNECTING HOSES; HEADER COUPLING NIPPLES.
3) CONNECTING HOSES: ¾ IN. ID (INSIDE DIAMETER)
4) ADAPTER ELBOWS: FOR CONNECTING WITH COLLECTOR PANELS.
(5) SPRING HOSE CLAMPS: STEEL.
(6) PRESSURE RELIEF VALVE: ¾ IN. ID FACTORY SET FOR 10 PSIG.
(7) SOLAR PANEL CHECK VALVE: PREVENTS REVERSE FLOW THROUGH COLLECTOR PANELS
(8) HOLD DOWN CLIPS: 2-IN. ALUMINUM.
(9) AUTOMATIC AIR VENT/VACUUM BREAKER AND FITTING: BRASS. COMBINES VENT AND VACUUM BREAKER FUNCTIONS INTO ONE UNIT.
(10) ETHYLENE GLYCOL: THIS IS THE WORKING-FLUID THAT WILL BE USED IN THE SYSTEM.
(11) DIFFERENTIAL THERMOSTAT CONTROLS FLOW OF POOL WATER THROUGH SOLAR COLLECTORS BY OPERATING SOLENOID VALVE (14), BASED ON TEMPERATURE DIFFERENTIAL MEASURED BY PANEL SENSOR (12) AND POOL WATER SENSOR (13).
(12) TEMPERATURE SENSOR MOUNTED ON SOLAR PANEL FRAME.
(13) TEMPERATURE SENSOR MOUNTED IN SUPPLY LINE TO SOLAR PANELS. SENSORS (12) AND (13) COMPARE PANEL (COLLECTOR) AND POOL TEMPERATURES WITHIN TWO DEGREES ACCURACY.
(14) PILOT OPERATED SOLENOID VALVE: 1½ IN. ID, BRASS, WITH INTERNAL BYPASS. CONTROLS FLOW OF POOL WATER TO SOLAR PANELS (COLLECTORS).
(15) FILTER CHECK VALVE. PREVENTS BACK FLOW THROUGH FILTER.
(16) SOLAR COLLECTOR SUPPLY LINE SHUT-OFF VALVE. NORMALLY OPEN.
(17) SOLAR COLLECTOR RETURN LINE SHUT-OFF VALVE. NORMALLY OPEN.
(18) IN-LINE PUMP. CHECK BUYER'S GUIDE.
(19) SWIMMING POOL FILTER. CHECK BUYER'S GUIDE.
SOLAR HEATING SYSTEM FRAMING MATERIALS
(1) SUPPORT FRAMING: WOOD OR ALUMINUM.
(2) CONTINUOUS HOLD-DOWN BATTENS: ALUMINUM. MUST BE ABLE TO SATISFY HIGH-WIND LOAD CONDITIONS AND MEET THE MOST STRINGENT BUILDING CODES.

Fig. 7-1. Typical solar heating system for a swimming pool.

price of competing energy sources. People living in areas with greater temperature extremes who use large amounts of energy for heating and cooling often realize more immediate savings than those living in more temperate climates.

The initial investment in a solar system can be amortized as part of an increase in the purchase price, and be paid for with the down payment and mortage repayment. Since solar installations are part of the real value of property, they appreciate at the same rate as the rest of the property.

SOLAR WATER HEATING

Solar water heating is practical for new homes in most areas of the United States and can be easily retrofitted onto existing homes at a reasonable cost in many cases. Paybacks will be approximately 10 years. The cost and the paybacks will vary by the specific requirements of each situation and, of course, by the rate at which the price of conventional energy sources rise (which is uncertain at this time).

SOLAR POOL HEATING

Solar heating for swimming pools is less espensive than any other method of pool heating over the life of the pool. In most cases a solar pool heater will pay for itself within five to seven years. In the near future, solar energy may be the only alternative left for heating swiming pools. See Figs. 7-1 through 7-3.

INDIRECT OR ACTIVE SOLAR

Presently, most solar space heating systems are of the indirect or active type. Indirect solar is a solar heating or cooling system in which the solar heat is collected outside of the building and transferred by fans or pumps inside the building through ducts or pipes. Recent developments in the solar energy field demonstrate that indirect solar will be most practical when retrofitted to existing homes and in other specific situations where direct solar cannot accomplish the required heating. See Fig. 7-4.

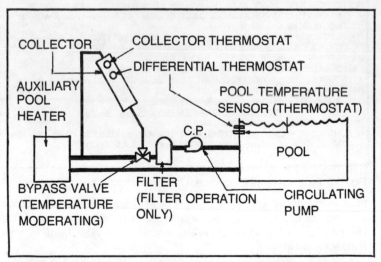

Fig. 7-2. Simple pool heater. This system may be manually or automatically controlled.

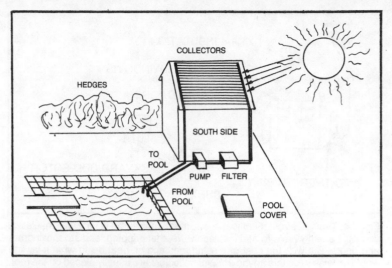

Fig. 7-3. Solar heating your pool.

FIVE BASIC SOLAR DESIGN PRINCIPLES

Implementing these five simple principles could save you up to 50 percent of your total heating and cooling costs. See Fig. 7-5.

- Insulate and weatherstrip the building thoroughly. At minimum, most state laws require in new homes insulation with R-11 value in the walls and R-19 value in the roof. Be sure to examine the energy conservation standards of your state, although it makes sense to exceed state requirements.
- Orient the long axis of the building so it faces south. See Fig. 7-6.
- Place most of the windows on the south side of the building and provide shading by some method.
- Build an appropriate overhang on the south side that will block out the high summer sun yet will permit entrance of winter sun, as shown in Fig. 7-7. An equation for estimating the optimum length of overhang is:

$$\text{Overhang} = \frac{(\text{latitude in degrees}) \times (\text{window height in inches})}{50}$$

where latitiude can be gotten from a road map and the height of a window is equal to the distance between the bottom of the overhang and the bottom of the window.

Cover the roof with a light color surface material. To meet greater than 50 percent of your heating and cooling needs with solar, see the following section on direct or passive solar use.

DIRECT OR PASSIVE SOLAR

The best approach for heating and cooling buildings is to do it as simply as possible, and to use existing building materials and technology. *Direct* or

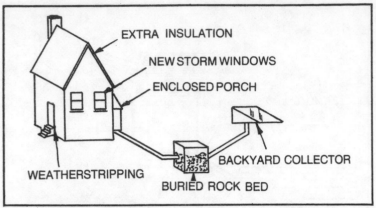

Fig. 7-4. Typical retrofit modifications. Unless your home is very well insulated, you will certainly have to add insulation, weatherstripping, and storm windows and doors. But with the cost of electric, gas and oil heat being what it is, you would be wise to do this anyhow. Solar collectors are usually placed on the roof, but they can be attached to a wall or erected in a back yard. If you add solar equipment to your existing heating system, you may have to allow for piping or duct work connections. Storage tanks or bins are usually in basements or buried outside in a convenient location. The heat from your collector and/or storage facility can reach the rooms of your house in two ways. It can circulate through a forced air duct system which distributes the warm air. Or it can be circulated as hot water in radiators or baseboard units, with the water being preheated by solar and brought up to the high temperature needed by the backup system. In many instances, this means that your present heating system can be adapted to distribute solar-generated heat.

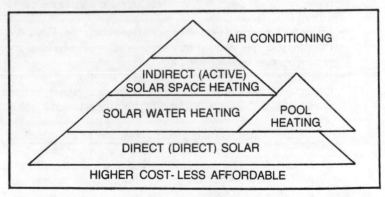

Fig. 7-5. This illustrates the cost of new-building solarization. The lower cost solar applications are at the bottom of the pyramid. Direct solar applications are the most affordable and therefore occupy the largest area of the pyramid. There are, however, significantly more elaborate direct solar systems that can be more expensive. Indirect solar air conditioning is the highest cost, least affordable, solar building application. The other solar applications fill in the middle of the pyramid. Retrofit of solar systems onto an existing building or buildings is hard to generalize because it is usually a more complex matter, but in many cases the order of costs will remain the same.

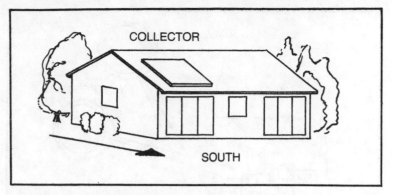

Fig. 7-6. South view with summer shading.

passive solar utilizes this approach. Direct solar buildings are designed so they accept or reject heat directly without the use of solar hardware systems. The energy storage and transfer system is often the building itself. It collects and radiates the energy throughout the building naturally.

Many primitive civilizations practiced direct solar design on their buildings. The Indians of Mesa Verde in New Mexico constructed their buildings utilizing the principles of direct solar heating and cooling as early as 1200 A.D. To this day they are still heated and cooled naturally because they respond to the physical properties of nature. During the winter, when the

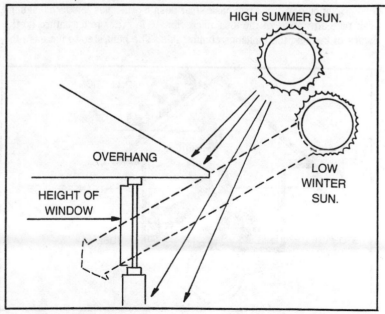

Fig. 7-7. Overhang example.

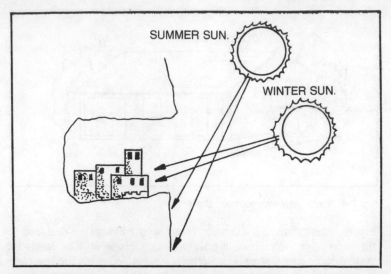

Fig. 7-8. An ancient civilization concept of direct or passive solar for heating and cooling.

sun is low in the sky, the warming rays can enter and heat the structures. During the summer, when the sun is high in the sky, sunlight cannot enter the interior of the building, so the buildings are kept relatively cool. See Fig. 7-8.

Beginning with the five basic solar design principles, modern buildings can take advantage of the local microclimate in order to let nature do the work of keeping the buildings comfortable. The next step to increase the

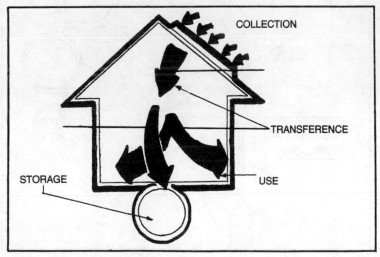

Fig. 7-9. A diagram showing solar collection, transference, use and/or storage.

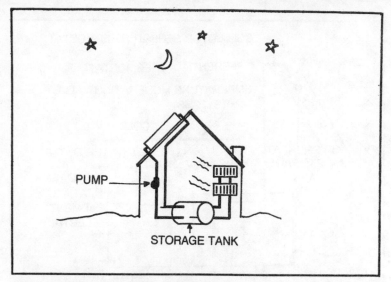

Fig. 7-10. Typical nighttime solar utilization. All day heat is generated in the collectors. This heat is stored in the storage system tank or bin. At night, it is transferred from the storage facility to the areas of the house that need heat.

heating and cooling potential of the building is to increase the thermal mass. This can be accomplished by using dense materials inside the building, such as concrete, masonry, adobe, rocks, and water. These materials are used because they have a high capacity to store heat. For heating, the south windows should be designed in a manner to allow the sun's rays to enter the structure and directly heat the mass.

MODERN SOLAR HOMES

A modern solar utilization method is shown in Fig. 7-9. The mass will radiate the heat back into the living space. The heat can be retained for long periods with movable window insulation. In the summer, the building is kept cool by blocking the direct rays of the sun with the use of appropriately designed overhang, moveable insulation, or deciduous trees. Since the mass is kept out of direct sun, it remains *cool* and helps the entire structure cool. Auxiliary heat from a conventional heating system provides a backup for solar heating during long periods of cloudiness.

The major advantages of direct use of solar are simplicity, low cost, reliability, durability and opportunity for creativity. See Figs. 7-10 through 7-14.

SOLAR WATER HEATING SYSTEMS

Solar water heating is in many cases a cost effective and practical solution for heating water. Solar water heating is relatively simple and can be retrofitted onto existing buildings or included in the design of new buildings.

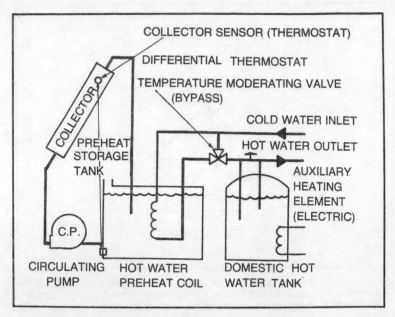

Fig. 7-11. Typical solar water preheater. If the collector temperature is greater than storage temperature, the pump is energized. Makeup water for domestic hot water system is preheated as it passes through the coil in the solar storage tank. A temperature moderating valve may be used to regulate the maximum water temperature from the preheat coil.

THERMOSIPHONS

A simple solar water heating system is called a thermosiphon. It operates on the principle that cold water will sink in a water tank and thereby cause hot water to rise. The water heated in the solar collector will flow up into the storage tank, because warm water rises, just as warm air rises. The

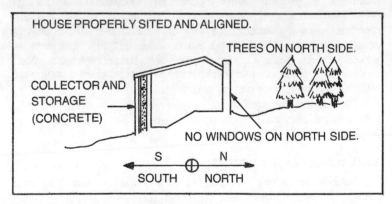

Fig. 7-12. The "Trombe wall" new home or building design, named for its developer, Felix Trombe, is often called a passive system.

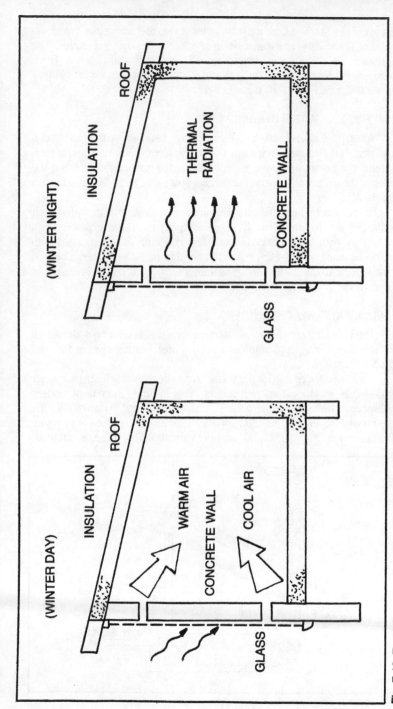

Fig. 7-13. Typical passive or direct solar system using a concrete wall collector method.

95

bottom of the storage tank must be at least two feet above the top of the collector. This will prevent circulation of water in the wrong direction. The thermosiphon system eliminates the need for pumps and controls. However, where freezing is a factor, a closed system with a heat exchanger may be needed. See Figs. 7-15 through 7-17.

PUMPED SOLAR WATER HEATING

Where it is not feasible to place a storage tank, above the collector, a small pump may be used to circulate the water. Combined with a heat control system, the pump will move water through the collector only when the water in the collector is warmer than the water in the tank. This is shown in Fig. 7-18.

In locations where freezing is common, a dual system with a heat exchanger is recommended. The heat exchanger system requires only a single tank with an auxiliary heater. The collector system is filled with antifreeze, and the heat exchanger is isolated from the hot water. The heat is transferred to the water through an immersed heating coil, as is illustrated in Fig. 7-19.

A SOLAR WATER HEATING SYSTEM

The following are the additional questions which must be addressed if you are considering application of a solar water heating system for your home or business.

What is your demand for hot water? Average daily residential hot water usage equals 20-40 gallons per person. This includes the use of modern appliances, such as washing machines, dishwashers, etc. Average daily hot water usage for an office building or business equals two gallons per person. This is for washing hands, and janitorial clean-up. Of course, a cafeteria,

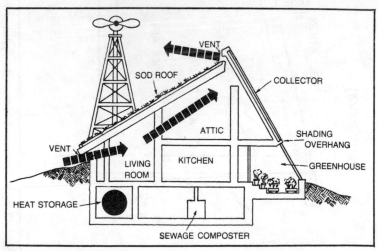

Fig. 7-14. Indirect and direct solar systems in combination.

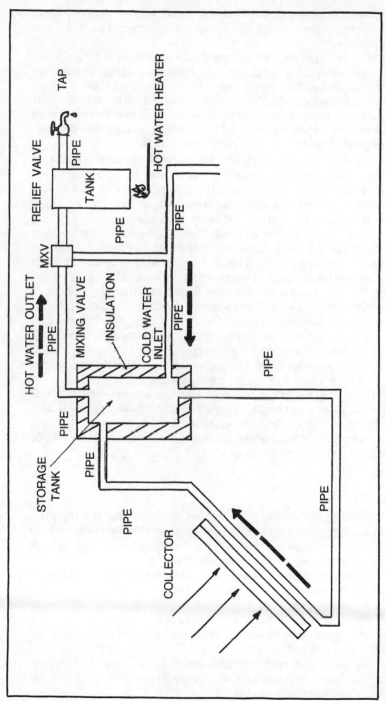

Fig. 7-15. A thermosiphon.

97

laundromat, or laboratory would increase the hot water demand considerably. Monthly water bills can give you precise information on your water consumption.

How much can you afford to spend on a solar water heating system? The higher the approximate daily use, the higher the potential for realizing a significant savings. The average cost of a residential solar water heating system will be between $1,200 and $2,000. This cost can be cut by doing the installation yourself. A family of four would need a storage tank of about 80 gallons and from 40-60 square feet of solar collector to supply their domestic water heating needs.

Why do you want a solar heating system? If your primary interests are energy conservation and cost effectiveness, you will next have to ask yourself how long a period of time will be reasonable for a payback on your investment. If you want a solar water heating system for hobby, ethical, or patriotic reasons, the cost may not be as much of a concern.

Where do you put the solar collectors? The roof is usually the most practical location for collectors, although they can be mounted almost any place: on the ground, on the garage, on a storage shed, or on exterior walls. Keep in mind that the more structure required to support the collectors, the more the total system will cost. The degree of tilt for the collector is approximately equal to the latitude where the building is located. Under certain conditions it may be practical to vary the pitch of the collector by a few degrees. In order to optimize for winter, the collector can be mounted at a steeper angle. If the pitch of an existing roof is only a few degrees more or less than the optimum, it would be most practical to mount the collectors on the roof even though it is not the optimum angle.

If the answers to the following questions are yes—and relatively easy—then solar water heating is likely to be cost effective for you. If there are any questions you cannot answer, do some of your own research. Check with contractors, or solar dealers and manufacturers or others who may be able to help you answer these questions.

Collectors

Are there any significant obstructions to incident sun? It is important that the collectors face as close to due south as possible. However, they can be effective if they are as much as 15 degrees off due south. Also, is there sufficient area to accommodate the solar collector?

Will the roof support the additional weight of solar collectors? In most cases, placing collectors on the roof will not necessitate structural modifications for their support.

What is the ease of mounting and tying down the collector supports? And what is the ease of waterproofing the new roof jacks, structural penetrations, and such?

Will the system operate without interfering with the operation, replacement, and maintenance, of existing equipment? Will the system be protected from potential vandalism?

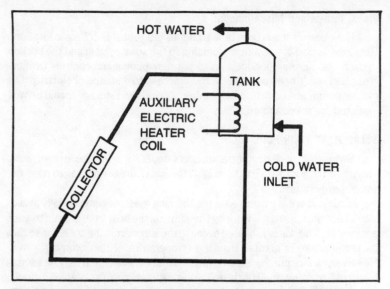

Fig. 7-16. A thermosiphon water heater. The hot water is lighter than the cold water. Settling of the cold water and rising of the warm water induces natural circulation in this type of system.

Storage

Is there adequate space for an additional storage tank? Is it possible to locate the storage tank close to the backup water heating system and also close to the collectors?

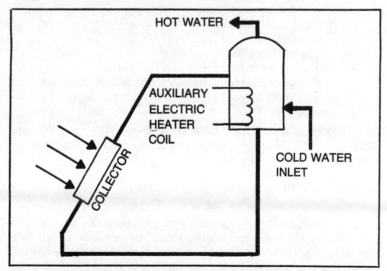

Fig. 7-17. A solar-powered thermosiphon water heater. No controls are required except for the auxiliary heat.

Pipes, Pumps and Miscellaneous

How easy is it to route new piping to the probable collector location? How easy is it to connect new plumbing to the solar system and the backup system? Is there a good location to put new pumps and controls (a thermosiphon won't need pumps)? Is there access to a source of electricity to run the pumps and controls? Remember, all pipes and storage should be well insulated for maximum efficiency.

SOLAR HEAT YOUR POOL

Swimming pool heating is an ideal application for the use of solar energy. If the pool is in direct sunlight, the sun is already helping to raise the water temperature.

Today, there are many solar pool heating systems commercially available. These solar systems work by transferring the heat from the sun to your pool water. The water is heated because the sun warms the collector so that its temperature is greater than the temperature of the incoming water. However, before purchasing a commercially available unit, it may be advisable to utilize some or all of the following methods to solar heat your pool.

A conventional solar pool heater can be a do-it-yourself project or it can be installed by a solar pool heating contractor. A do-it-yourself solar pool heater can be built for under $500. Commercial systems run $1,000 to $3,000. The temperature change achieved by solar pool heaters will depend on numerous factors: collector area, volume of water in the pool, and amount of available sunshine.

If you decide to hire a solar dealer to install a commercial system, here are some suggestions:

- Be sure the installer is a licensed contractor. Check with your local Better Business Bureau.
- Compare prices.
- Compare warranties.
- Investigate the experience of past customers.
- Don't expect miracles. The solar collector will only work when there is adequate sun.
- Have fun.

To locate solar collector manufacturers, check in the Buyer's Guide in this book and the "Yellow Pages" under solar energy, or contact local pool companies.

INDIRECT OR ACTIVE SOLAR FOR SPACE HEATING

Indirect systems can be applied to new buildings or retrofitted onto existing buildings. They are generally more appropriate for apartment buildings, schools, and commercial buildings, but they are currently most popular for single family dwellings. Close coordination between the designer and the engineer is required to design an indirect solar energy system that is not overly complex and costly.

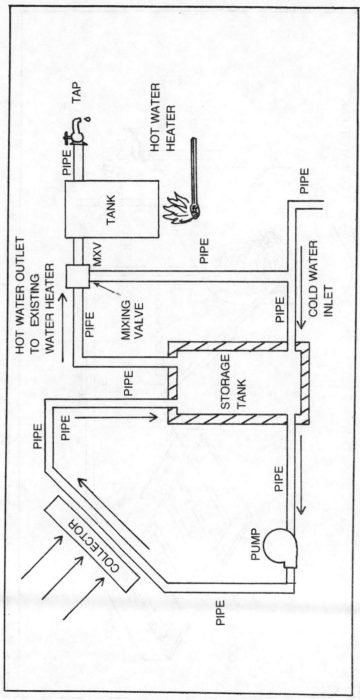

Fig. 7-18. A pumped solar water heater. When it is not feasible to place the storage tank above the collector, a small pump may be used to circulate the water. Combined with a heat control system, the pump will move the water through the collector only when the water in the collector is warmer than the water in the tank.

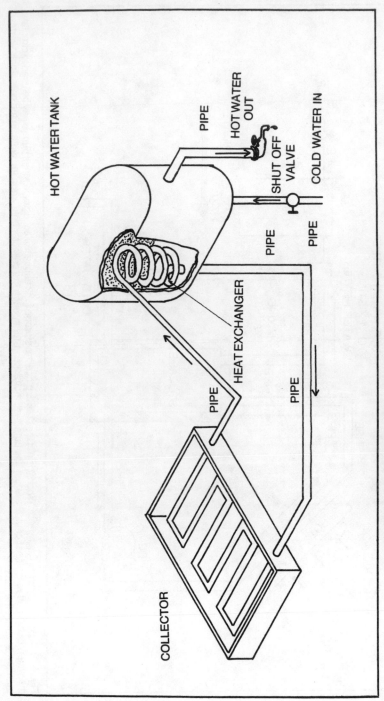

Fig. 7-19. Typical hot water heater with heat exchanger inside tank.

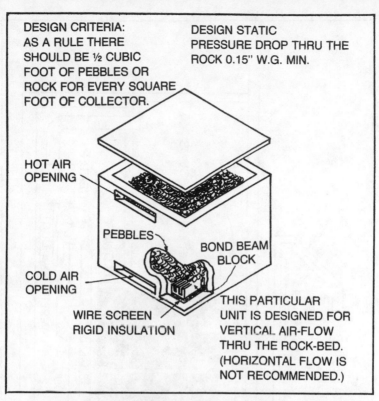

Fig. 7-20. Pebble bed heat storage unit. The heat storage container can be constructed of any of the following materials: plywood on 2 × 4 or 2 × 6 studs; poured reinforced concrete; concrete block or other masonry materials. The storage bin should be constructed so that it is air tight and insulated to meet at least R-11 standards. The air flow through the pebble bed should be vertical.

There are two equally effective mediums that can be utilized to collect, transfer, and store solar heat: air and water. Water is currently the most popular medium utilized. Both air and water should be investigated in order to arrive at the most cost effective solution. For a retrofit application, the existing heating and cooling system will determine which is the best medium to use. Forced air circulation is most compatible with air systems but can also be used with liquid systems. Hot water radiant systems, such as baseboard radiators, work well with liquid systems. Auxiliary heat from a conventional heating system provides a backup for the solar heating during long periods of cloudiness.

AIR COLLECTOR/ROCK STORAGE SYSTEM

The air collector/rock storage system circulates air through the solar collectors to carry the heated air to storage or directly to the building for immediate use. These systems most often use a flat-plate collector located

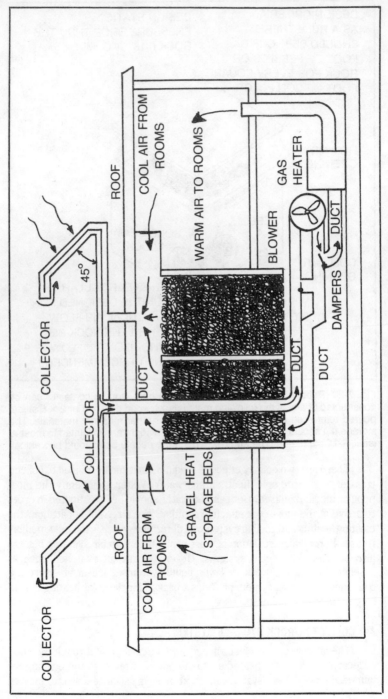

Fig. 7-21. Typical heating system utilizing an indirect system with a warm air concept and gravel storage.

COLLECTOR

COLLECTOR

COLLECTOR

45°

ROOF

COOL AIR FROM ROOMS

WARM AIR TO ROOMS

ROOF

COOL AIR FROM ROOMS

GRAVEL HEAT STORAGE BEDS

DUCT

DUCT

DUCT

DUCT

DAMPERS

BLOWER

GAS HEATER

on the roof and a bin of one to three-inch rocks for storage. Hot air flows through the spaces between the rocks and heats them. A bin of rocks must be about 2½ times the size of a water tank of equal heat storage capacity. See Fig. 7-20. Air from the cold end of the rock storage bin is blown up to the lower end of the collector, heated, drawn off from the hot upper end, and returned to the bin. When the living space of the house needs heating, dampers in the air ducts are adjusted and hot air is blown from the storage bin into the living space. Heating coils from the auxiliary system are used to supply some or all of the heat needed. The same thermostat controls both the solar heating system and the auxiliary heating system.

LIQUID COLLECTOR/LIQUID STORAGE SYSTEM

In the liquid collector/liquid storage system, hot water from the collectors can circulate directly through the heating system or be sent to the heat storage tank. A heat transfer fluid (usually water with antifreeze and anticorrosion additives) is pumped through the collector, through the storage tank, and back to the collector. Liquid from the storage tank is pumped through a heat exchanger coil where it heats the living spaces. Storage is provided by a large tank holding 500 to 1000 gallons which is usually located in the basement or buried outside. A thermostat sets the temperature in living space for both the solar and the auxiliary systems.

There are advantages and disadvantages to both the air and liquid systems. The advantages of air systems are that they use relatively simple hardware and there is no potential of leaks. See Fig. 7-21. The disadvantages are the large ducts and storage systems required. The advantages of a liquid system are that liquid systems require less than half the storage volume of an equivalent air system and smaller pipes for heat transfer. The

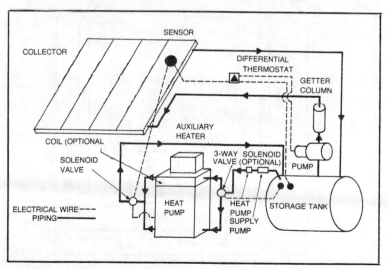

Fig. 7-22. Typical solar space heating design.

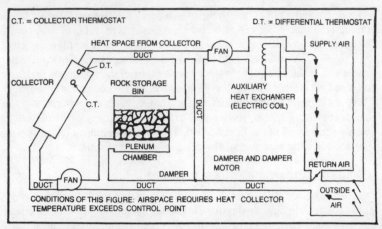

Fig. 7-23. Solar warm air heating. The air space requires heat, and the collector temperature exceeds the control point in the illustration.

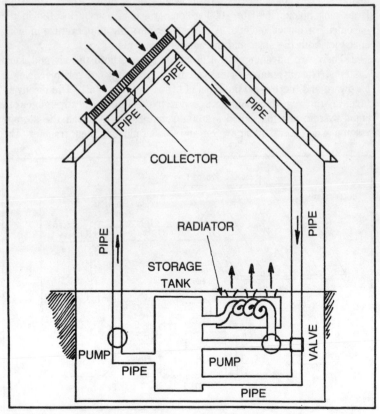

Fig. 7-24. A simple do-it-yourself solar space heater using a water system.

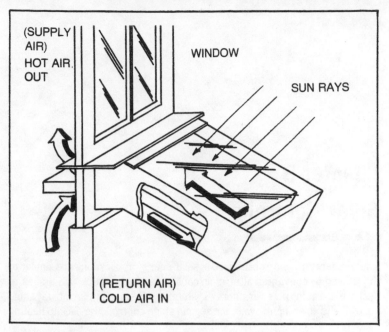

Fig. 7-25. Window box.

disadvantages are that water systems require more complex plumbing and hardware. See Fig. 7-22. A typical air system is shown in Fig. 7-23, and a typical water system is shown in Fig. 7-24.

SIMPLE DO-IT-YOURSELF SOLAR SPACE HEATING

A simple way for almost anyone to solar heat a building is with a solar window box, as shown in Fig. 7-25. Whether you're low on money, a renter, or may be moving soon, the solar window box can help heat your house with the sun. This solar unit is attached to the window and can be taken with you when you move. It consists of two compartments. The lower layer brings in the cool room air. The top is painted black or dark green and as the air at the bottom of the collector heats, it rises to the top and back into the room. See Fig. 7-25.

Chapter 8
Solar Controls

The temperature controls utilized in solar energy applications are similar to those used in conventional heating/cooling systems where two stages of heat are used. In the solar energy system, the first room thermostat stage controls the solar input, while the second stage controls the backup heating system.

Solar heat control thermostats for any medium (water, air, etc.) are similar to the thermostats used in conventional systems, and have proven to be equally reliable.

A solar energy system requires a differential temperature control to monitor the temperature difference between the collector and storage facility temperatures. Heat exchange is permitted *only* if the collector is hotter than the storage facility.

Standard limit controls perform the same function as in conventional systems, limiting the critical functions as required.

In hydronic (water, water combinations) solar systems, standard circulator control equipment (such as relays and transformers to allow control of circulators with low voltage thermostats) is needed, as in the conventional hydronic system. Standard hot water valve and valve actuators are employed as in any such system.

In hot-air solar systems, dampers, motors, sensors, and other such equipment correspond to those needed in conventional systems.

The standard complement of relays, transformers, timers, contactors, sequencers, and other such equipment is required, as in conventional systems.

This control initiates control action whenever the controlled medium temperature crosses the controller set point. By selecting the proper switching action, these thermostats can provide freeze or high temperature protection, or initiate operation at preselected temperatures.

This control may be used to automatically alter a control point as the outdoor temperature changes. For example, when applied to the storage

Table 8-1. Honeywell Heating System Devices.

DESCRIPTION	ORDER NO. HONEYWELL	REMARKS
Thermostat, two stage room	T 872	Controls 1 or 2 stages of low voltage heating and cooling.
Thermostat, single stage room	T 882	Provides control and auto. setup or setback of 1 stage of low voltage heating and cooling.
Thermostat, single stage room	T 87	Provides one-stage control of low voltage heating and cooling.
Thermostat, single stage room	T 651	Provides one-stage control of line voltage heating and cooling.
Thermostat, outdoor	T 238	Self-contained mercury switch thermostat.
Thermostat, (Aquastat)	L4008, LS8008	Capillary type sensor suitable for semiremote outdoor temperature sensing.
Thermostat	T 675, T 678	Capillary type sensor providing fast response and double-throw capability.
Thermostat, differential temp.	R 7406	Measures diff. temp. using electrical sensors.
Thermostat, collector	R 7406	Ideal where sensor is in remote location.
Thermostat, (Aquastat)	L4008	Capillary type sensor suitable for semiremote location in air or hydronic systems.
Thermostat, (Aquastat)	L4006	Immersion type sensor suitable for hydronic systems.
Thermostat, (Aquastat)	LA409	Suitable for direct surface mounting on piping.
Thermostat (Dual Aquastat)	L4031	Provides 2 control functions; capillary type sensors suitable for semiremote locations in air or hydronic systems.
Valves	V4044	Family of diverting valves suitable for low Cv residential applications. (Straight-through models also available.)
	V5013	Family of diverting and mixing valve suitable for large applications. (Straight-through models also available.)
Dampers	D524	Single blade for in-duct installations.
	D640/D641	Louvered damper for controlling inlet or exhaust flow.
Economizer	W859	Controls dampers so as to minimize energy consumption in cooling mode.
Motors	M644	For use with single blade damper (D524).
Motors	M845	2-position, spring-return motor for use with dampers or valves.
Motors	M436	Spring-return motor for 2-position zone or damper control.
Motors	M835	2-position damper motor for zone control.
Motors	M833	Heat-actuated damper motor for zone control.
Relays (contactors)	R8222	General purpose switching relay-1-or 2-pole.
	R8230	Medium duty switching relay-1-2-or 3-pole.
	R8243	Light duty contactor-2-pole.
Controller, reset	T475	Automatically raises storage temp. as outdoor temperature falls.
Timer	S659	Provides 24 hour on-off timing of system with spring-wound backup feature.
Transformers	AT72, AT87, AT88	Provide low voltage for use in control circuits.

system, the maximum storage temperature may be automatically lowered in warm weather when the home heating demand is low. The system may then be shut down to conserve electricity when sufficient heat energy has been stored.

Timers are often used in solar systems to establish the minimum operating time of the system. During initial operation, this prevents short cycling of the circulators. By the end of the timer interval, the temperature within the various flow loops should be stabilized and the locked on feature provided by the timer is no longer needed.

Because most solar systems can store energy, it is possible to operate from this stored energy during hours of peak electrical power consumption. In many areas of the country, off-peak electrical rates are favorable enough to justify operating from storage during off-peak periods. Electrical powered timers with spring wound backup may be used to establish the proper time frame reference for such systems.

Hydronic solar systems use valves to control flow within the system. Because solar systems utilize multiple piping loops (examples: collector-load, collector-storage, collector-purge, storage-load), for the different operating modes of the system, valves are needed. These valves are often diverting or three-way rather than the straight through or two-way valves used in most residential applications. These valves are automatically positioned or set by the thermostats and control logic provided with the system. Electrically operated actuators are most commonly used to operate these control valves.

Solar warm air systems make use of dampers to divert air within the system. These damper systems are more elaborate than conventional warm air systems because there are generally more operating modes. Standard dampers and electrically operated damper motors may be used for these applications. The damper motors are operated by thermostats and system logic in the control system.

Good solar practices demand that energy be conserved wherever possible. Most solar fitted homes have better than average insulation. Remember that adequate insulation is a must. While this prevents extreme heat or cold from rapidly penetrating into the home, it also prevents the outside ambient from influencing the inside conditions, even when the outside conditions are favorable. In some locations, the prevailing evening conditions can provide cool air to condition the living space during much of the summer.

An economizer is a system that decides when outside conditions can be used to cool the indoor space. The economizer operates an outside damper system to use this outside air.

Economizer systems are particularly effective at reducing the cooling load when evening temperatures drop. The use of fresh outside air also improves air quality, which can be a real problem in well-insulated solar structures.

Relays are extensively used to convert low energy level signals for other uses, or to provide ON-OFF regulation of control devices such as valves, fans, and circulators. Through sequential use of the contacts in thermostats, controllers, and relays, system operation may be initiated or stopped.

Many of the standard control devices, such as space thermostats, use low-voltage (24-30 volt) control circuits for safety and economic reasons. A typical transformer converts line voltage (120 or 240 volt) to 24 volts for use within the control circuits. Some control devices may contain a built-in transformer to power the control circuit.

The *two-stage space thermostat* measures air temperature in the conditioned space (the load). The first stage generally operates the solar system. The second stage generally operates the backup heating system (heat pump, gas, oil or electric furnace, or boiler). A cooling control, may also be included on this thermostat.

The *outdoor thermostat* changes system operation in response to outdoor (or pool) temperature. It can bring in supplementary heating or alter fan speed if desired.

The *differential temperature thermostat* (control) measures temperature difference (ΔT) between two media, such as collector/storage or storage domestic hot water. If a difference exists, a pump or fan may be operated to transfer energy from the hotter medium to the cooler one.

The *collector temperature thermostat* determines if the collector is warm enough to provide heat directly to the load.

The *collector overtemperature thermostat* alters system operation when overtemperature conditions occur that might be damaging to some part of the system. Not necessarily mounted on the collector.

The *storage thermostat* determines if storage temperature is high enough to provide heat directly to the load.

The *low temperature thermostat* is used on water systems without antifreeze protection. It initiates a system action to prevent freezeup, such as draining the collectors.

The *valve* controls fluid flow through piping loops. Diverting valves have a single inlet and divert flow to either of two outlets. These valves are common in most solar systems. Mixing valves have two inlets and a single outlet. Straight through valves modulate or shut off flow.

Dampers divert or shut off flow in air duct systems. *Economizers* are automatically controlled outside dampers that makes use of outdoor temperatures and humidity levels to reduce system operation whenever possible. They are often used to reduce cooling demands. The *motor* is electrically operated and used to operate valves or dampers in response to a control signal.

This concludes the definition of controls. I would like to leave the do-it-yourselfer with this thought. Your controls are an integral part of your system. Do not attempt to save money at the expense of controls. Once you have selected a particular solar system for your application, look in the "yellow pages" of your telephone book. Or contact the local Honeywell distributor, make an appointment, and take your basic system outline to him. He will help you to select the proper controls for your system.

Chapter 9
Safety

I cannot place enough importance on safety. As you begin to explore the nooks and crannies of your home or building in preparation for your solar-retrofit, be careful. Adequate lighting is a must. Following is a list of a few essential safety items:

1. An explosion-proof flashlight.
2. A stepladder (never climb on top of chairs, bookcases, and such.
3. Work gloves.
4. Safety shoes or boots.
5. Safety glasses or goggles.
6. An approved face mask if you are going to work around insulation or heavy dust-laden areas.
7. Good tools. No mushroomed heads, broken or cracked handles, or chipped screwdriver blades.
8. All tools that have cutting edges should be sharp: saws, chisels, knives, drill bits, etc.

POWER TOOLS

In order to make your job easier, you will probably need several power tools, such as an electric power saw and an electric drill motor. A power saw utilizing a 7¼-in. blade should be sufficient. A drill motor with a ⅜-in. chuck should fulfill that requirement. These tools can be purchased at any local hardware store or building center. Buy power tools that incorporate the latest advances in safety devices, such as a built-in *ground fault interruptor* (GFI).

In using extension cords, make sure that the cord is heavy enough to supply your power tool with adequate power and that it doesn't heat-up.

Also, check and make sure that the extension cord has no frayed places, exposed wires, and such. Check to see that the cord has a ground wire and a working ground prong on the male end.

Respect power tools. NEVER remove safety devices! Change saw blades and drill-bits when they become dull.

THE ATTIC

A word of caution to those of you who may be venturing into an attic for the first time. Be careful of your footing. A misstep and you could fall through the ceiling, or at least put a hole in the ceiling. One trick that I use when venturing into a strange attic is to sit down for a few moments and thoroughly orient myself. I do this by shining my explosion-proof flashlight everywhere until I feel confident, taking special notice of the walkway planking that is found in most attics.

Good ventilation in an attic is a must, especially in the summer months. Pace your work in an attic. If you get hot, take a break.

If you become dizzy, sit down immediately; call for someone to help you out of the attic.

HANDLING ELECTRICAL CIRCUITS

Always disconnect the electrical power and make sure no one can turn it on while the electrical components of any electrical part, motor, switch, solenoid valve, etc. are being checked, serviced, repaired, installed, or replaced!

All of us can see or hear what electricity can do, such as light, power, heat, and communications. It is hard to be alert against the dangers of electricity, because this energy is hidden in the wires (conductors). What causes electrical energy to hurt and even kill people is that the human body or parts of the body can become an electrical conductor. When this happens, all too often the electricity will burn part of the body and/or cause muscle spasms, injure the nervous system, stop the heart from beating, or similar traumas.

When anyone feels the shock, it is too late.

You cannot be too careful. You can avoid being electrically shocked, however, if you remember and practice just a few safety measures.

- Test the system with a voltmeter to make sure it has no potential (power off and no charged capacitor in the circuit).
- Insulate the body as much as possible. Use tools with insulated handles. Be sure the material you are standing on is an insulator (wood, concrete, etc.) and that the material is dry. If a damp situation cannot be avoided, wear rubber gloves and rubber boots.
- Voltages above 24 volts can cause current to flow through parts of the body. Remember, most circuits are at least 120 volts and 15 amperes. Only 0.025 of an ampere (25 milliamperes) across the heart can kill.

- Lock the switches open to prevent someone from closing them during installation or service operations. The switch should also be tagged to warn other people. Or, you can remove the fuses and put them into your pocket or tool kit. Put a note on the switch and fuse box to inform people not to close the circuit.
- Always short a capacitor with a resistor before touching its terminals. If it is charged, it may discharge 200 to 500 volts into a person.
- Replace worn electric wires or those which have brittle insulation. Poor insulation will crack when the wire is bent into a tight loop.
- Use only screwdrivers with completely insulated handles (wood or plastic). Use only wrenches and pliers with insulated handles. This habit is double insurance against electrical shocks.
- Always use instruments to check a circuit to see if it is electrically charged before handling wires, terminal, or parts. Such instruments can be purchased at local hardware stores or building centers.
- Always solder or crimp solid metal terminals on the ends of stranded wire. Avoid using stranded wire ends to attach the wire to the terminals.
- Electrically ground all metal parts of a heating or cooling system to eliminate any danger of receiving a shock if the circuit should become shorted to the frame of a cabinet or a part of the mechanism.

HANDLING TOOLS AND SUPPLIES

Always pull a wrench (instead of pushing) to prevent possible injury to the hands if the wrench should slip. It is recommended that a hoist be used in lifting heavy components, or materials which weigh over 60 lbs. Always use leg muscles when lifting objects; never use back muscles. Make certain that the work area is clear and uncluttered.

Always wear safety glasses when working with tools.

Avoid putting hands near revolving fans, motor pulleys, or motor belts. Put safety guards on powered moving objects such as flywheels, belts, pulleys, fans, etc.

One should never breathe fumes of any kind. Do not neglect the use of a gas mask when working in dust-laden areas (you may experience such an area in the attic when you insulate). Good ventilation is of VITAL importance.

Use only non-toxic materials for cleaning, and avoid skin contact and breathing the fumes. Use soldering materials and brazing alloys which *do not* contain cadmium.

"Mushroom" heads should be removed from chisels and punches by grinding, as these parts may fly when struck with a hammer and may cause serious injury . Do not use a screwdriver as a chisel; do not use a chisel as a crowbar. Always dispose of broken or worn out tools. Only use files with handles; otherwise, the tang may injure the hands. Keep the work area clean. Pick up tools that aren't being used for that particular job and put them back into the tool kit, or in someone designated tool area. Wear safety shoes if heavy objects must be carried or if heavy objects may fall.

When working on roof tops observe all safety rules for ladders:

- Safety fastened at bottom.
- Safety fastened at top.
- Ladder should extend above roof edge.
- Do not carry objects when moving up or down a ladder. Instead, use a rope hoist, with rope control from both top and bottom (a two-person job).

Safety on the roof:

- Avoid removing or opening solar collector lids in a high wind.
- Avoid standing on solar collector tops.
- Avoid standing in water when checking or working on electrical circuits.
- Avoid skin contact with any chemical fluids (heat transfer fluid, such as silicone fluids, hydrocarbon oils, glycol/water mixtures, and alcohol).

SERVICING HEATING EQUIPMENT

When wood, coal, gas or oil furnaces are used as secondary heating systems, it is absolutely essential that *none* of the fumes (products of combustion) become mixed with the air in the building.

Safety controls for a heating or cooling system should never be removed and bypassed to keep a system operating, because dangerous conditions or damage to the system may result. It is essential that a heating system have enough capacity to heat a structure without taxing or overheating the heating system. The heating system should be slightly oversize— never undersize.

Coal, oil, and fuel-gas furnaces use fires in a confined area. The fuel must be stored safely and fed in a safe manner to the firepot of the furnace. Also, means must be provided to shut down the unit, if the fuel flow ceases; if any part of the system overheats; if all the products of combustion gases cannot exit from the building; or if combustion ceases.

Remember that if fuel is in the presence of air and an ignition source exists, a fire will result. By inspection, *always* make certain that the firepot is free of gas fumes and/or oil before starting up a system.

The gas piping system must be leakproof. Use soapsuds to check for leaks.

Never Use An Open Flame, Such As A Match

An explosion may occur. Use an explosion-proof flashlight or an explosion-proof extension lamp when inspecting a furnace.

Be careful when working with metal duct material. Use gloves with metal inserts.

Practice these safety tips!

IMPORTANT

It is recommended that all electrical work be contracted to a licensed professional electrician. This recommendation is made in respect to safety, and local and state electrical codes. Such codes often require that all electrical work be performed by licensed professionals and that the work be inspected.

Chapter 10
Putting It Together

By now, you've acquired a pretty thorough knowledge of solar heat systems. It has been mostly theory, though, and all the theory in the world—by itself—won't heat the water in your house. Accurate solar theory combined with good construction practices, however, will. In this chapter, we finally put it all together: the collectors, the mounts, the plumbing, the safety measures, the insulation, and all the rest.

HOW TO SOLDER

The most important rule in soldering or sweating copper pipe or tubing is to make sure that the area in which you are soldering is clean; i.e., clean the inside of the fitting and the end of the pipe. You can use plumber's sand cloth or .00 emery cloth as the cleaning tool. After cleaning, apply a small amount of flux onto the cleaned areas. Join the fitting to the pipe and work the joined pieces into the position that you wish to permanently maintain. Now ignite your propane torch and adjust the flame to a medium flame. Apply the tip of the flame onto the fitting rather than the pipe. In a few seconds try your wire solder on the heated lip area of the fitting where the outer edge of the fitting ends. If the fitting is hot enough, the solder will melt and be sucked up into the fitting. When this occurs, make sure that the solder runs well up and into and around the fitting. Remove the flame. Let the heated area cool off before attempting to move it. If you move the soldered pieces before they are cooled, the fitting will probably leak.

Experience is the best teacher in this art, so hang in there. Generally, you can examine the soldered area closely and determine what kind of a job you have. Try to get a good finished solder on each fitting (joint). See Fig. 10-1.

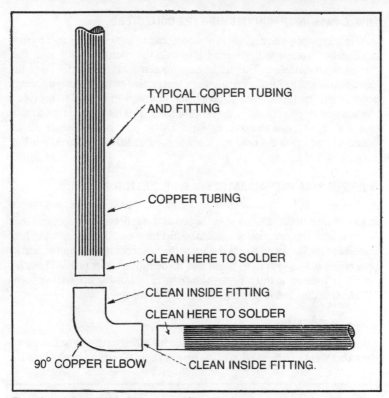

Fig. 10-1. An example of how to solder.

It is difficult to have to resolder a fitting once you have placed water in it. But if this is the case, drain all the liquid out, heat the fitting again, and apply flux, or "clean" as they say in the business. When the solder in the fitting begins to melt and run, apply a little more flux and then apply the wire solder again. Be careful not to overheat the fitting. If you still have a leak, drain all the liquid out, heat the fitting again until it can be worked off the end of the pipe, clean the end of the pipe and the inside of the fitting, and begin the process over.

Materials Needed

- Copper tubing and fittings.
- A small propane torch (can be bought at your local hardware store or building center).
- A roll of plumber's 50/50 or 95/5 wire solder.
- Soldering flux (plumber's).
- A roll of plumber's cloth or .00 emery cloth.

NOTE: Block solder will be needed to bond or solder the copper tubing to the copper sheet. A thinner's iron should also be employed.

SINGLE PASS ROOF MOUNTED AIR-TYPE COLLECTORS

In some applications, air-type collectors are preferred for roof mounting because water-type collectors increase the roof load to a point that threatens roof design. The single pass roof mounted collector uses the existing roof and its insulation to lower construction costs. Usually a sheet of polyethylene material, such as construction visqueen is used to provide a moisture barrier and to cover the roof shingles. This also lessens the friction that the air, which is the working-fluid, has to pass over. The air passes beneath or on top of the collector absorber and in either direction. See Fig. 10-2.

MULTIPLE PASS ROOF MOUNTED AIR-TYPE COLLECTORS

The multiple pass system is more efficient than the single pass system. In this system the air passes over the top of the collector absorber and then underneath. This increases collector efficiency by allowing greater heat transfer to the incoming air, as the top of the absorber plate is hotter than its underside. It also lowers the heat loss through the cover plate. The holes distributing the air to the collector should be of increasing size as they travel further from the inflow, or air inlet. See Fig. 10-3.

STORAGE SYSTEMS

Storage system design criteria should be based on the same considerations that went into the design of the type of system you are employing. The

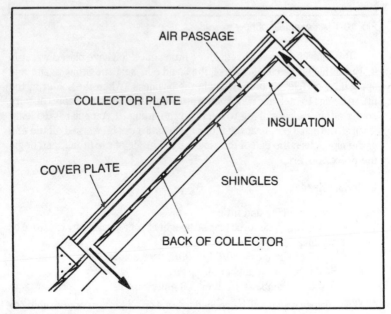

Fig. 10-2. Single pass roof mounted collector.

storage system should be located inside the physical structure of the building, if possible. There are two good reasons for this: convenience in retrofit (it is less costly and less troublesome to utilize a storage facility inside the physical structure of the building); any heat loss from the storage system will be lost to the building.

The insulation of the storage system should be effective to minimize any heat loss. The amount of insulation required, of course, depends on the temperature differential between the inside and the outside of the storage facility. At normal operating temperatures (150° to 190° F) and a moderately heated house (70°F), from six to eight inches of fiberglass insulation should be used. Moreover, the walls of the storage facility, if made of wood, cement, or concrete block, can also add effective insulation. Heat loss can also be minimized by employing certain building techniques, such as making the storage system a cube.

The size of the storage system depends on several variables: the storage medium used, the size of the building to be heated, the number of collectors used, the location of the house, the location of the storage system, and the amount of reserve heat to be stored. For example, we know that a 3000-square foot house in Northern Minnesota, employing 1500 square feet of collector surface, will require a larger storage facility than a 1000-square foot house in Southern Ohio, employing 500 square feet of collector surface. By the same rule, we know that another house right down the street from the house in Northern Minnesota—even though it is the same size and employs the same amount of collector surface—will require a larger storage facility if the owner wishes to contain a larger heat reserve. His neighbor may have a system designed to supply 24 hours of reserve heat, and he may have a system designed to store 48 hours of reserve heat. Thus, his system will be larger.

In a sunny temperate location, and utilizing 1½ to 2½-inch rocks as the storage medium, one cubic foot of rocks can supply 25 cubic feet of house with heat for 24 hours; therefore, 350 cubic feet of rocks will supply an 8000 cubic foot house with one day's heat and 700 cubic feet will supply two days of reserve heat. One cubic foot of water can store about three times as much heat as a cubic foot of rocks (one third the volume will provide the same amount of storage capacity). A cubic foot of rock will store about 20 British thermal units per degree F; water stores 62.5 BTU per degree. A pile of two-inch rocks is approximately one-third empty space.

Water storage systems require a good, well insulated container, a pump, and piping. This is necessary in order to maintain circulation.

Rock storage systems need less insulation, but they have to be larger in mass. Rocks should be washed and cleaned prior to their placement in the container. Air filters, like those used in air conditioning systems, should be placed in both the discharge and return air duct. Rocks should also be dry prior to their placement.

The best place for storage system location is the basement or mechanical room, but if this isn't feasible, a system underneath the floor would be just as effective. If this isn't possible, a hole should be dug in the ground out

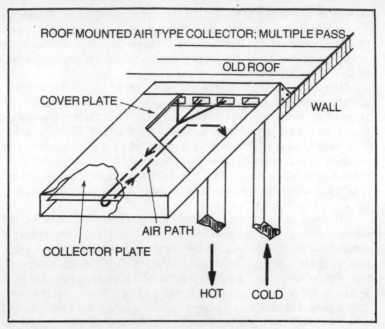

Fig. 10-3. Multiple pass roof mounted air type collector.

in the side or back yard and the system placed there. Be careful to seal the system container against water seepage and/or moisture.

Storage systems can and are often placed in the attic. Be sure to take into consideration the weight of the filled container. Support it accordingly, paying particular attention to not only the support structure platform, but also the support structure that bears the overall platform. Water is very dense.

Several other points should be remembered in utilizing water systems. A pressure relief valve should be installed on the outlet side of the collector. This is a safety device that will protect the system in the event of a pump failure or collector overheating. A water filter should be installed in the system at a point that is easily accessible. Gate valves should be installed on both sides of the filter, which allow the owner to valve-off the filter and perform periodic maintenance. Gate valves should also be installed immediately before and after the water pump and on the inlet and outlet side of the collector, for the same reason.

On an air system, filters should be checked and cleaned every 30 days. Damper motors should be checked periodically and any moving parts oiled with a light household oil. Collector covers should be cleaned at least every other month to maintain a high degree of efficiency. Also, the absorbers should be inspected and cleaned. If the paint of the absorber surface is showing signs of wear in the form of cracks or peeling. the surface should be cleaned, sanded, and repainted. Be especially careful to reseal the collector, as moisture may form on the bottom of the covers and thereby dilute the sunlight entering.

If the working fluid is water or an antifreeze solution, a drain cock should be installed at some low point in the piping system. This is a safety precaution. In locations where possible freezing might occur, antifreeze strength tests should be made every month. All systems that contain an antifreeze solution should be tested every six months for pH (acidity content). Testing equipment can be purchased from swimming pool dealers listed in the Buyer's Guide.

All exposed piping should be well insulated. I have found that Armorflex or Rubberoid insulation material is excellent for this type job. These products can be purchased from air conditioning and refrigeration wholesale dealers. See the Buyer's Guide or check your telephone "Yellow Pages" for such dealers.

For the do-it-yourselfer, I have found that a local scrap metal dealer will usually have a suitable tank at a reasonable price. I have also found that most sheet metal firms will gladly bond or solder the copper tubing to the sheet copper (absorber plate) for a small price. Remember this if you have trouble in finding a tank.

COLLECTOR ANGLE

The collectors can be located anywhere near the house or on the roof as long as they face south and have an unobstructed view of the sun. They must also be mounted at the correct angle from the horizontal in order to maximize the efficiency of the collector. See Fig. 10-4.

The optimum angle changes with the geographic location. A rough rule of thumb sometimes used for a starting point is that the angle of the collector

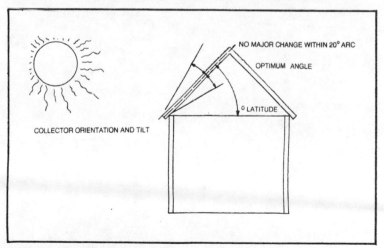

Fig. 10-4. Collector tilt for domestic hot water. The optimum collector tilt for domestic water heating alone is usually equal to the site latitude. Variations of 10° on either side of the optimum are acceptable.

from the horizontal should equal the latitude in degrees. The collector angle is important, because an improperly angled collector requires more surface area to collect the same amount of energy.

Depending on the application of the solar system, different collector angles should be used for a given location. When a summer cooling load is most important, the collector angle can be reduced (latitude − 10°) to catch the summer sun higher in the sky. During winter, the sun is low in the sky and collectors will be more effective for heating if their angles are increased to face the winter sun. Changes in collector angles of 10° or 15° for certain applications are common.

Chapter 11
How to Mount Solar Collectors

The mounting of collectors on existing roofs can create problems and lead to roof leaks, if the hardware attachments are not properly mounted. In general the following materials are needed as hardware for an installation of a lightweight solar collector (up to 1000 lbs).

- ½-in copper pipe with the amount depending on the increase and distance from the storage to the collector.
- Two ½-in gate valves.
- Elbows, tees, couplings and bibs. Count the number of times that you need to make turns or tees. Also count the number of times you need to couple pieces of pipe togather.
- Pipe insulation (either Armstrong Armaflex or Rubatex). Include Armaflex glue or some other insulation glue and a roll of duct tape.
- Plastic roofing cement, solder, solder paste, small roll of sandcloth and a Benezine torch. Propane torch, oxygen/acetylene , etc.
- Gray or white mortar mix if concrete tile roof.
- Old rags, a hammer, various size wrenches (3/8, 1/2, 5/8, and 9/16-in open end).

The distance between roof rafters and the direction which the roof faces will determine the location of the struts or mounting hardware. For a 10-ft horizontal collector with the rafters running north-south, the brackets may be fastened 8 ft apart. The vertical distance up the rafters will be determined by the slope of the roof. For a 4/12 pitch in New Orleans, for instance, The brackets should be 42 inches apart, but this distance will vary with geographic latitude. This information will be supplied by manufacturers.

The first step before installing the mounting hardware is to properly prepare the roof area. For asphalt shingle roofs, mount the collector on a flat spot. If this is not possible, cut off part of one shingle. If working with concrete tile, remove part of the tile to expose the slate. For a tar and gravel roof, remove as much gravel as possible and soften the roof tar with a paint thinner.

Use a pitch pan made of copper (usually supplied by the manufacturer). If you built your collector, you can buy a pitch pan from a sheet metal shop or a roofing wholesaler. The pitch pans should be large enough to completely cover the area that the brackets cover, allowing enough to curl over and to be filled with roofing mastic or cement.

The pitch pan is fastened in place with small lag screws. Fasten the pitch pan by placing the pan on the rafter drill pilot holes through the copper pan and into the rafter approximately ⅜ to ½ in deep. Start lag screws into each hole, and be careful to line up holes in the center of the rafter studs.

After pans have been securely fastened, place a spreader block, a ⅜-in piece of plywood into the bottom of the pan, making sure that the block is resting evenly on the top of the rafter. This will allow you to add more weight on the rafter. Spreader blocks can be installed by drilling holes through the block and lagging the block down with the pan. After the pan and the spreader block have been placed and lagged securely, fill the pitch pan with pitch or roofing cement. Be sure that brackets and lag screw tops are covered well; you don't want water seeping down around the threads of the lag screws. The underside of the pan should be covered with roofing mastic to guarantee a secure seal.

In some installations the pitch pan can be eliminated by placing tar tape under the brackets and silicone seal on the screw heads that fasten the bracket to the roof. Run the piping through a carefully drilled hole through the roof, making sure that the pipe is well insulated. Use Armaflex, or Ruberoid, or Rubertex. Make sure that the hole drilled through the roof is small enough to allow for a tight fit of pipe and insulation. Where possible, try to keep supply and return close to the surface of the roof, especially when long runs of more than five ft. are used.

Be careful that the pipe entrance through the roof is well covered with roofing cement or a proper roofing mastic. The final step in mounting the collector may vary with each collector. Where you can, place the collector on a strong back (a strong back is a piece of ¼-in angle iron, 2 by 2 in).

After you know the correct dimensions of your collector, you can have a local welding shop make the strong back and brackets to your specifications. If you buy a collector, the kit should include these pieces. The strong back should be angled with the struts. Pilot holes are drilled into the side of the collector. Be sure not to drill or penetrate your pilot hole completely through the side of the collector.

Glossary

absorbent—The less volatile of the two working fluids used in an absorption cooling device.

absorber—The blackened surface in a collector that absorbs the solar radiation and converts it to heat energy.

absorptance—The ratio of solar energy absorbed by a surface to the solar energy striking it.

active system—A solar heating or cooling system that requires external mechanical power to move the collected heat.

air-type collector—A collector with air as the heat transfer fluid.

altitude—The angular distance from the horizon to the sun.

angstrom— 00000001 centimeters.

ASHRAE—The American Society of Heating, Refrigerating, and Air Conditioning Engineers, Inc.

auxiliary heat—The extra heat provided by a conventional heating system for periods of cloudiness or intense cold, when a solar heating system cannot provide enough.

azimuth—The angular distance between true south and the point on the horizon directly below the sun.

British thermal unit (BTU)—The quantity of heat needed to raise the temperature of one pound of water one degree Fahrenheit.

calorie—The quantity of heat needed to raise the temperature of one gram of water one degree Celsius.

coefficient of heat transmission (U-value)—The rate of heat loss in BTU per hour through a square foot of a wall or other building surface when the difference between indoor and outdoor air temperature is 1°F.

collector—Any of a wide variety of devices used to collect solar energy and convert it to heat.

collector efficiency—The ratio of heat energy extracted from a collector to the solar energy striking the cover, expressed in percent.

concentrating collector—A device which uses reflective surfaces to concentrate the sun's rays onto a smaller area, where they are absorbed and converted to heat energy.

conductance—A property of a slab of material equal to the quantity of heat in BTU per hour that flows through one square foot of the slab when a 1°F temperature difference is maintained between the two sides. tween the two sides.

conduction—The transfer of heat energy through a material by the motion of adjacent atoms and molecules.

conductivity—A measure of the ability of a material to permit heat flow through it.

convection—The transfer of heat energy from one location to another by the motion of fluids which carry the heat.

corona—The luminous area around the sun; seen only during solar eclipses.

cover plate—A sheet of glass or transparent plastic that sits above the absorber in a flat-plate collector.

degree-day—A unit that represents a 1°F deviation from some fixed reference point (usually 65°F) in the mean daily outdoor temperature.

design heat load—The total heat loss from a house under the most severe winter conditions likely to occur.

design temperature—A temperature close to the lowest expected for a location, used to determine the design heat load.

diffuse radiation—Sunlight that is scattered form air molecules, dust, and water vapor, and comes from the entire sky vault.

direct methods—Techniques of solar heating in which sunlight enters a house through the windows and is absorbed inside.

direct radiation—Solar radiation that comes straight from the sun, casting shadows on a clear day.

double-glazed—Covered by two panes of glass or other transparent material.

dyne—The basic unit of force of the centimeter-gram-second (cgs) system of measurement. Defined as the force required to give a mass of one gram an acceleration of one centimeter per second.

energy—Energy is often defined as the ability to do work. It is a conserved quantity which is neither created nor destroyed. It can, however, be converted from one form to another or interconverted with matter according to Einstein's equation: $E = mc^2$ where m is mass and c is the speed of light.

emittance—A measure of the propensity of a material to emit thermal radiation.

ERG—A unit of work or energy of the cgs system. The work done when a continuous force of one dyne produces a displacement of one centimeter in the direction of the force.

eutectic salts—A group of materials that melt at low temperatures, absorbing large quantities of heat.

flat-plate collector—A solar collection device in which sunlight is converted to heat on a plane surface, without the aid of reflecting surfaces to concentrate the rays.

forced convection—The transfer of heat by the flow of warm fluids, driven by fans, blowers, or pumps.

fossil fuels—Combustible substances of organic origin laid down in the past geologic ages; hydrocarbons; formed through the decay of vegetation under heat and pressure; coal, oil, and natural gas.

geothermal power—Utilization of the potential energy of water in lakes and rivers to power generators, heat water, etc.

glauber's salt—Sodium sulfate ($Na_2SO_4.10H_2O$), a eutectic salt that melts at 90°F and absorbs about 104 BTU per pound as it does so.

gravity convection—The natural movements of heat through a fluid that occurs when a warm fluid rises and cool fluid sinks under the influence of gravity.

header—The pipe that runs across the top or bottom of an absorber plate, gathering or distributing the heat transfer fluid to or from the grid of pipes that run across the absorber surface.

heat capacity—A property of a material, defined as the quantity of heat needed to raise one cubic foot of the materail one degree Fahrenheit.

heat exchanger—A device, such as a coiled copper tube immersed in a tank of water, that is used to transfer heat from one fluid to another through an intervening metal surface.

heating season—The period from about October 1 to about May 1, during which additional heat is needed to keep a house warm,

heat pump—A mechanical device that transfers heat from one medium (called the heat source) to another (the heat sink), thereby cooling the first and warming the second.

heat sink—A medium or container to which heat flows (see heat pump).

heat source—A medium or container from which heat flows (see heat pump).

heat storage—A device or medium that absorbs collected solar heat and stores it for periods of inclement or cold weather.

heat storage capacity—The ability of a material to store heat as its temperature increases.

hydroelectric power—Utilization of the potential energy of water in lakes and rivers to power generators.

indirect system—A solar heating or cooling system in which the solar heat is collected exterior to the building and transferred inside using ducts or piping and usually fans or pumps.

infiltration—The movement of outdoor air into the interior of a building through cracks around windows and doors or in walls, roofs, and floors.

infrared radiation—Electromagnetic radiation, whether from the sun or a warm body, that has wavelengths longer than visible light.

insolation—The total amount of solar radiation—direct, diffuse, and reflected—striking a surface exposed to the sky.

insulation—A material with high resistance of R-value that is used to retard heat flow.

integrated system—A solar heating or cooling system in which the solar heat is absorbed in the walls or roof of a dwelling and flows to the rooms without the aid of complex piping or ducts.

langley—A measure of solar radiation equal to one calorie per square centimeter.

latitude—Referring to a point on the earth; the angle formed by a line intersecting the core (center) of the earth and the point on the surface of the earth, and the plane cutting the earth at the equator.

life-cycle costing—An estimating method in which the long-term costs, such as energy consumption, maintenance, and repair, can be included in the comparison of several system alternatives.

liquid-type collector—A collector with a liquid as the heat transfer fluid.

longitude—Referring to point on the earth; the angle formed by the intersection of a line from the center of the earth to the point on the surface of the earth, and the plane cutting vertically through the center of the earth and the prime meridian at Greenwich, England. May be measured as either time or degrees.

natural convection—See gravity convection.

nocturnal cooling—The cooling of a building or heat storage device by the radiation of excess heat to the night sky.

passive system—A solar heating or cooling system that uses no external mechanical power to move the collected solar heat.

percentage of possible sunlight—The percentage of daytime hours during which there is enough direct solar radiation to cast a shadow.

photosynthesis—The conversion of solar energy to chemical energy by the action of chlorophyll in plants and algae.

photovoltaic cells—Semiconductor devices that convert solar energy into electricity.

radiant panels—Panels with integral passages for the flow of warm fluids, either air or liquids. Heat from the fluid is conducted through the metal and transferred to the rooms by thermal radiation.

radiation—The flow of energy across open space via electromagnetic waves, such as visible light.

reflected radiation—Sunlight that is reflected from surrounding trees, terrain, or buildings, onto a surface exposed to the sky.

refrigeration—A liquid, such as freon, used in cooling devices to absorb heat from surrounding air or liquids as it evaporates.

resistance, (R-value)—The tendency of a material to retard the flow of heat.

retrofitting—The application of a solar heating or cooling system to an existing building.

risers—The flow channels or pipes that distribute the heat transfer liquid across the face of an absorber.

R-value—See resistance.

seasonal efficiency—The ratio of solar energy collected and used to that striking the collector, during an entire heating season.

selective surface—An absorber coating that absorbs most of the sunlight hitting it but emits very little thermal radiation.

shading coefficient—The ratio of the solar heat gain through a specific glazing system to the solar heat gain through a single layer of clear, double-strength glass.

shading mask—A section of a circle that is characteristic of a particular shading device. This mask is superimposed on a circular sun path diagram to determine the time of day and the months of the year when a window will be shaded by the device.

solar house or solar tempered house—A dwelling that obtains a large part, though not necessarily all, the heat from the sun's rays.

solar radiation—The radiation of the sun; a very large band of electromagnetic radiation. The visible part of this spectrum ranges from long red to short violet. The direct illumination of the sun is approximately 6,500 foot candles.

specific heat—The quality of heat, in BTU, needed to raise the temperature of one pound of a material one degree Fahrenheit.

sun path diagram—A circular projection of the sky vault, similar to a map, that can be used to determine solar position and to calculate shading.

temperature—Temperature means intensity of heat and is relative, like time. When defined from an absolute zero or state of no energy, that point becomes zero degrees Kelvin. This temperature is unattainable. Zero degrees Celsius (the freezing point of water) is 273.16 degrees Kelvin. The boiling point of water is 100 degrees Celsius and corresponds to 212 degrees Fahrenheit. The formula for conversion of Fahrenheit to Celsius is $F = 9/5C + 32$.

thermal capacity—The quantity of heat needed to warm a collector up to its operating temperature.

thermal mass (thermal inertia)—The tendency of a building with large quantities of heavy materials to remain at the same temperature or to fluctuate only very slowly; also, the overall heat storage capacity of a building.

thermal radiation—Electromagnetic radiation emitted by a warm body.

thermodynamics—Science concerned with the conversion of heat to energy flows from a high state to a lower state (that is, heat flows from a energy flows from a high state to a lower state. (that is, heat flows from a hotter body to a colder body); and all energy states tend toward entropy or randomness and every substance has a finite positive entropy that becomes zero at the temperature of absolute zero.

thermosiphoning—See gravity convection.

tilt angle—The angle that a flat collector surface forms with the horizontal.

trickle-type collector—A collector in which the heat transfer liquid flows down channels in the front face of the absorber.

tube-in-plate absorber—An aluminum or copper sheet metal absorber plate in which the heat transfer fluid flows through passages formed in the plate itself.

tube-type collector—A collector in which the heat transfer liquid flows through metal tubes that are wired, soldered, or clamped to the absorber plate.

ultraviolet radiation—Electromagnetic radiation, usually from the sun, with wavelengths shorter than visible light.

unglazed collector—A collector with no transparent cover plate.

U-value—See coefficient of heat transmission.

Appendix A
Solar System Examples

Fig. A-1. Archimedes used the sun to set fire to the attacking Roman fleet.

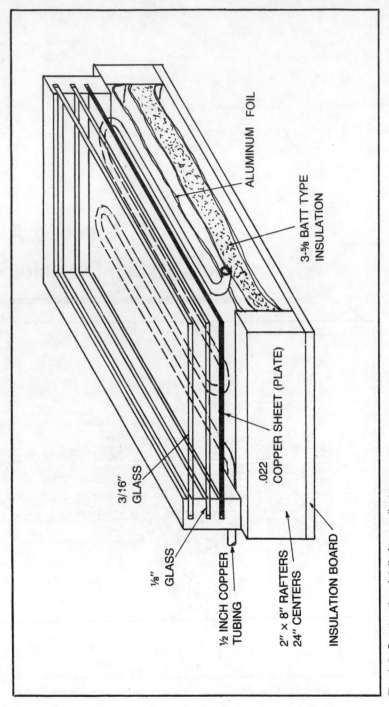

ALUMINUM FOIL

3-5/8 BATT TYPE
INSULATION

.022
COPPER SHEET (PLATE)

INSULATION BOARD

3/16" GLASS

1/8" GLASS

1/2 INCH COPPER TUBING

2" × 8" RAFTERS
24" CENTERS

Fig. A-2. Construction details for a collector.

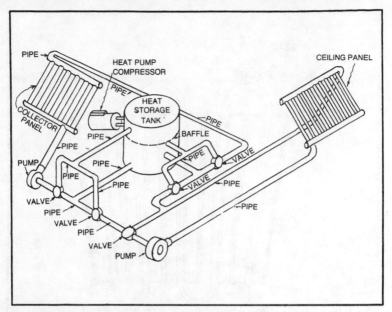

Fig. A-3. Typical heating and cooling system. This concept is used in many large office buildings.

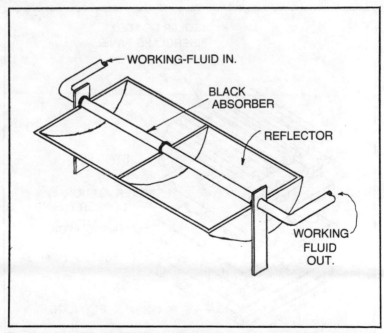

Fig. A-4. A typical concentrating collector with a parabolic reflector. Direct sun rays are focused on the black pipe (absorber), absorbed, and converted to heat.

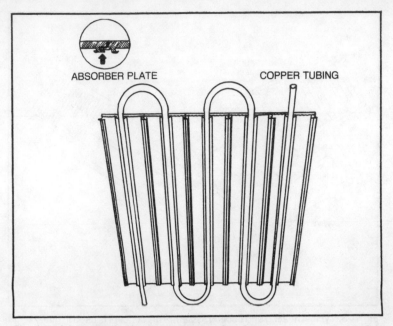

Fig. A-5. A homemade aluminum absorber flat-plate.

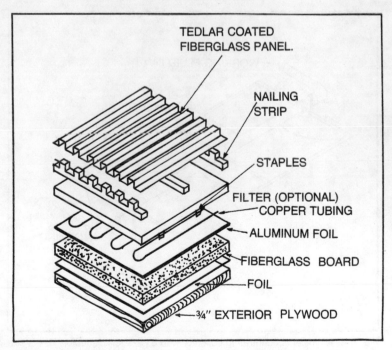

Fig. A-6. The integrated roof-type collector—exploded view.

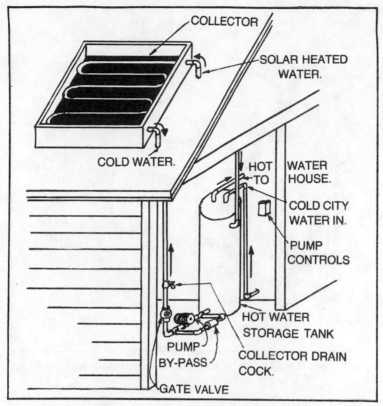

Fig. A-7. In a pump system, the collector can be located above the storage tank.

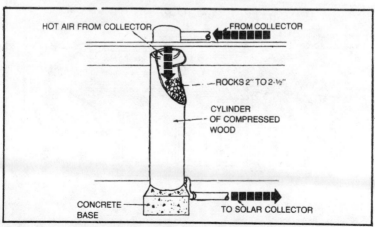

Fig. A-8. A vertical fiberboard cylinder used to contain a rock storage bed. Heat can flow to the room by natural convection as shown, or a fan can be used to circulate cool air through the rocks and back to the rooms.

135

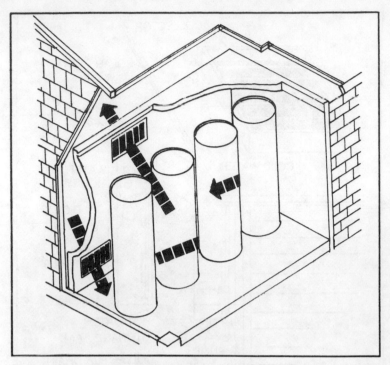

Fig. A-9. Water-filled Sun-Lite cylinders used for integrated collection and storage.

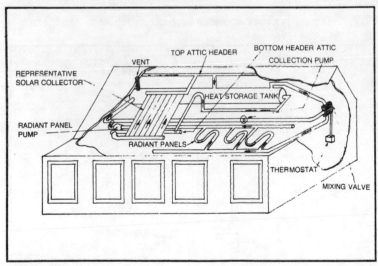

Fig. A-10. An in-attic storage system using water. The system storage capacity is 1200 gallons. The heat is distributed to the rooms by radiant panels. This is an indirect system.

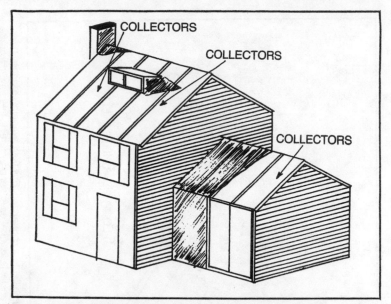

Fig. A-11. The shading of the collector by building elements. Chimneys, parapets, fire walls, dormers, and other building elements can cast shadows on adjacent roof-mounted solar collectors, as well as on vertical wall collectors. The drawing shows a house with a 45° collector facing south at latitude 40° North. By mid-afternoon, portions of the collector are shaded by the chimney, dormer, and the offset between the collector on the garage. Careful attention to the placement of building elements and to floor plan arrangement is required to assure that unwanted collector shading does not occur.

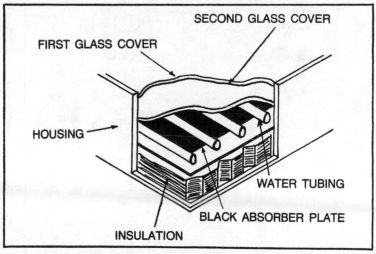

Fig. A-12. The flat-plate collector is used most often in solar applications that involve the home or other domestic uses. In this figure, the primary components are pointed out.

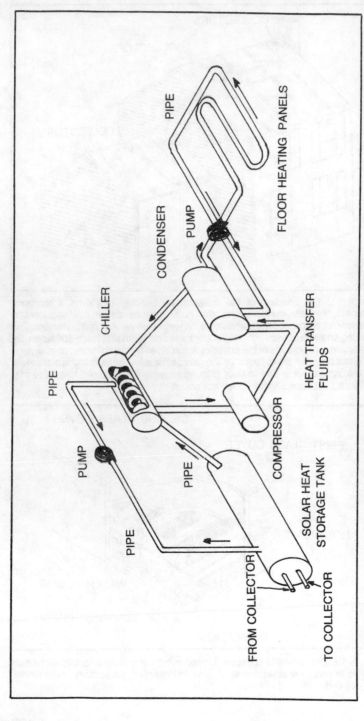

Fig. A-13. In a heat pump system, a compressor circulates a heat transfer fluid from a chiller to a condenser. This fluid evaporates in the chiller, absorbing heat from the water in it. This heat is deposited in the condenser, where the transfer fluid liquefies under pressure. In this way, low grade solar heat from the storage tank can still be used to heat the building, although indirectly.

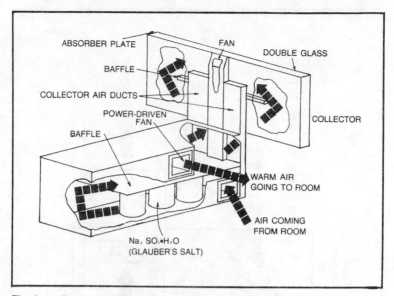

Fig. A-14. Typical heating system using glauber's salt as the storage medium.

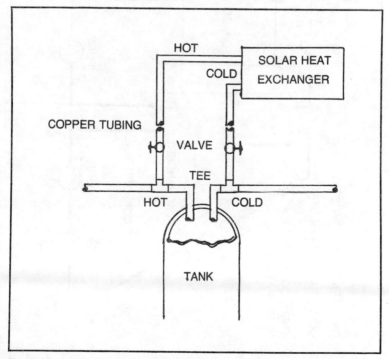

Fig. A-15. Piping diagram for a domestic hot water system that is solar pre-heated.

139

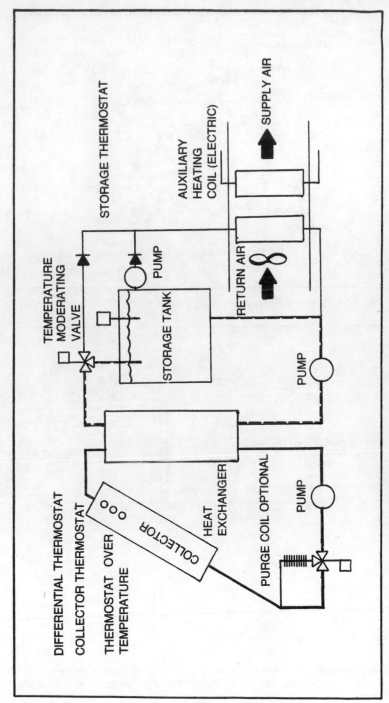

Fig. A-16. Solar hot water to warm air heating.

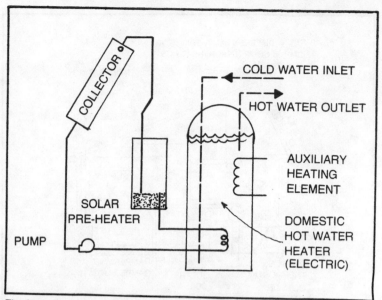

Fig. A-17. Solar water heater. In this figure, if the collector temperature is greater than the storage temperature, the pump is energized. The auxiliary heater adds heat if required.

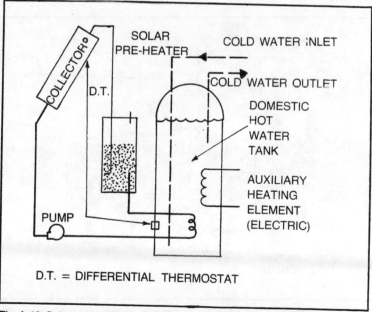

Fig. A-18. Solar water heater. In this figure, if the collector is not warm enough, or is not warmer than the storage tank, the pump shuts off, and the water drains down from the collector. Auxiliary heat is added if required.

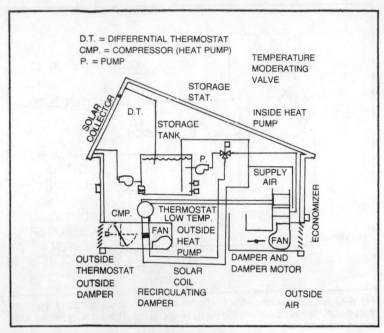

Fig. A-19. Solar assisted air-to-air heat pump.

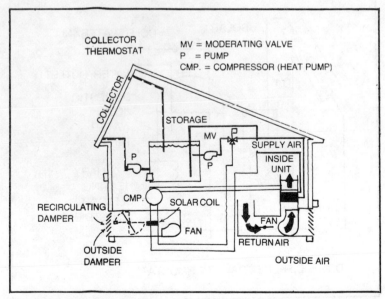

Fig. A-20. Solar assisted air-to-air heat pump. In this figure, whenever the collector temperature exceeds the storage temperature, the first pump will charge the storage facility. Air space requires heat. The storage facility temperature exceeds the control point. The second pump supplies heat to the indoor coil.

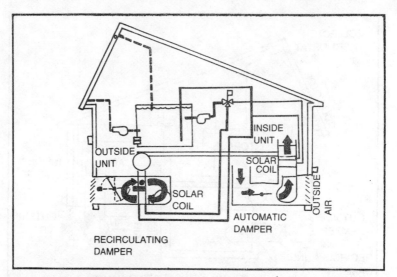

Fig. A-21. Space heat from solar preheat and heat pump. In this figure, whenever the collector temperature exceeds the storage temperature, the first pump will charge storage. The air space requires heat. Storage temperature is less than the control point but greater than the low temperature limit. Outside air temperature is lower than storage temperature. The outside damper is kept closed. The second pump supplies heat to the outdoor coil.

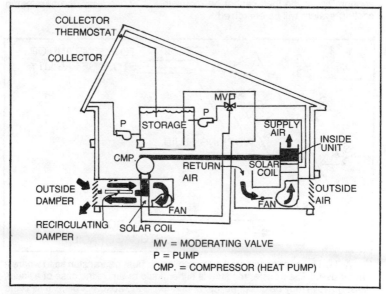

Fig. A-22. Space heat with a heat pump. In this figure, the collector temperature is the same or lower than the storage temperature. Air space requires heat. The storage temperature is below the low temperature limit. The outside temperature is higher than the storage temperature. The outside damper opens.

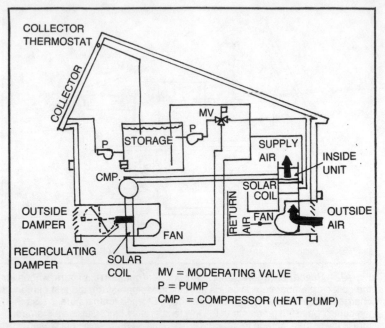

Fig. A-23. Space cooling with outside air. In this figure, the air space requires cooling. The outside conditions are satisfactory for providing cooling with an economizer. If the load cannot be met with the economizer, the heat pump cooling system will be energized.

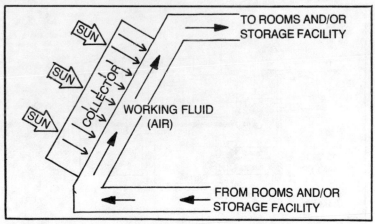

Fig. A-24. The energy gathered by the collector must be transferred to where it can be used. The transfer medium is either liquid or air. In the case of a liquid, passageways may be designed into or bonded to the absorber plate. If air is the medium, it is forced through the area behind and/or over the absorber plate. Normally, mising vanes of some type are added to improve heat transfer. A circulator, such as a pump or fan is generally used to move the transfer medium to where it will be used.

144

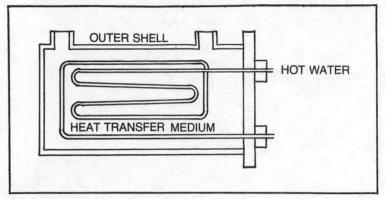

Fig. A-25. This type of heat exchanger is used to transfer heat from a circulating transfer medium to another medium used in storage or distribution. Shell and tube heat exchangers consist of another outer casing or shell surrounding a bundle of tubes. The water to be heated is normally circulated in the tubes, and the hot liquid is circulated in the shell. Tubes are usually metal, such as steel, copper, or stainless steel. A single shell and tube heat exchanger cannot be used for heat transfer from a toxic liquid to potable water because double separation is not provided and the toxic liquid may enter the potable water supply if a tube breaks.

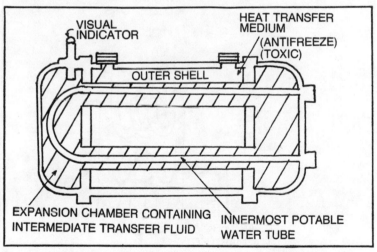

Fig. A-26. This type of heat exchanger is similar to the one in Fig. A-25 except that a secondary chamber is located within the shell to surround the potable water tube. The heated antifreeze then circulates inside the shell but around this second tube. An intermediary non-toxic heat transfer medium circulates through the shell, the intermediary liquid is heated, which in turn heats the potable water supply circulating through the innermost tube. This heat exchanger can be equipped with a sight-glass to detect leaks by a change in color because toxic liquids such as antifreeze often contain a dye. A change in the liquid level in the intermediary chamber would also indicate a failure in the outer shell or in the intermediary tube lining.

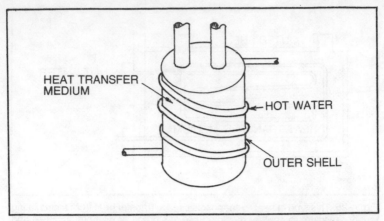

Fig. A-27. A double wall heat exchanger. Another method of providing a double separation between the transfer medium and the potable water supply consists of tubing or a plate coil wrapped around and bonded to a tank. The potable water is heated as it circulates through the coil or through the tank. When this method is used, the tubing coil must be adequately insulated to reduce heat loss.

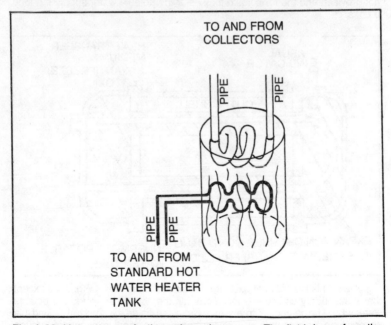

Fig. A-28. Hot water production using solar energy. The fluid drawn from the solar collectors is run through a coil in a tank of water and is heated. Water circulates through a second coil in the tank, heated, and drawn off for domestic uses. If you have a solar domestic hot water system, your system must be so constructed that any antifreeze solution used cannot leak into the hot water supply. This type of system is small and easily installed. It can be connected directly to your existing system.

146

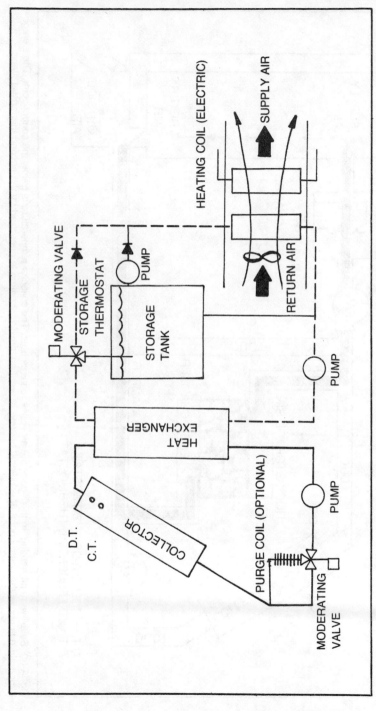

Fig. A-29. Solar hot water to warm air heating. Unlike Fig. A-15, the air space in this figure does require heat. In both figures, however, the collector temperature exceeds the control point.

147

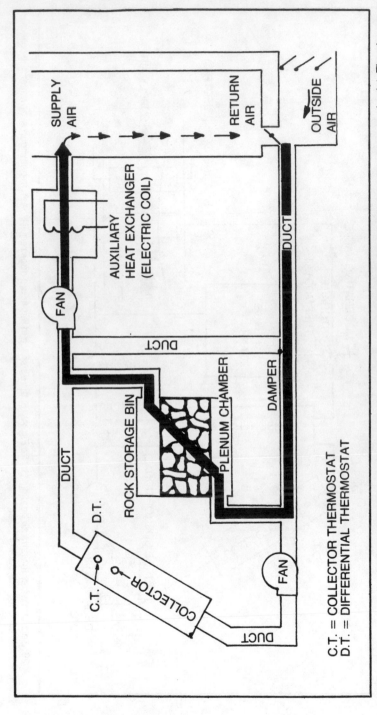

C.T. = COLLECTOR THERMOSTAT
D.T. = DIFFERENTIAL THERMOSTAT

Fig. A-30. Solar warm air heating. In this figure, the air space requires heat. The collector temperature is below the control point. The storage temperature is above the control point. If additional heating is required, auxiliary heating is energized by the second thermostat stage.

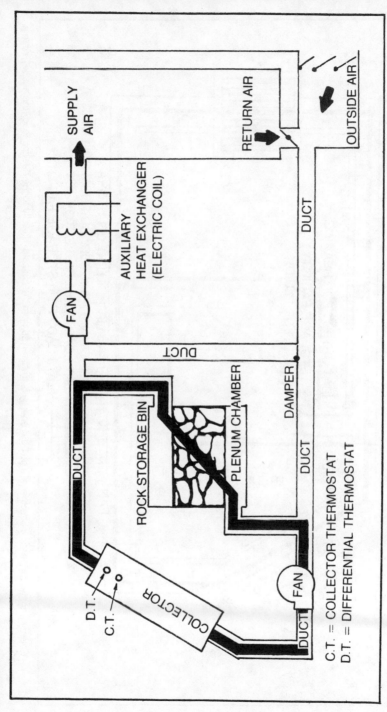

C.T. = COLLECTOR THERMOSTAT
D.T. = DIFFERENTIAL THERMOSTAT

Fig. A-31. Heat storage from the collector. In this figure, the air space requires no heat. The collector temperature exceeds the storage temperature.

149

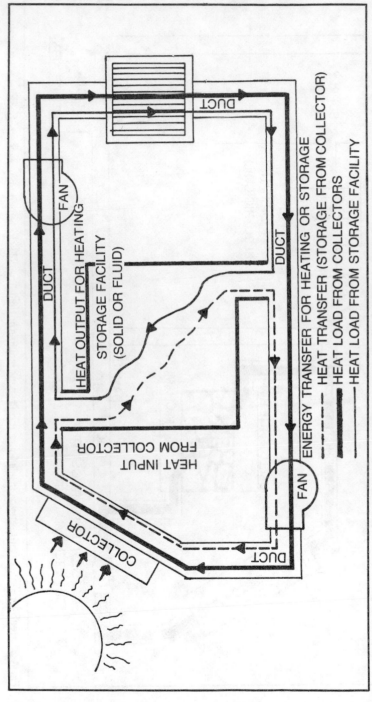

Fig. A-32. Energy transfer for heating or storage. The heat energy is transferred from the collector directly to the heating load (the house), or to a storage facility.

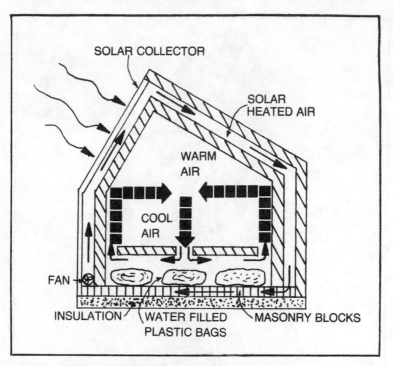

Fig. A-33. A system combining both passive and active systems. Waterbed-like plastic bags can be used for subfloor heat storage.

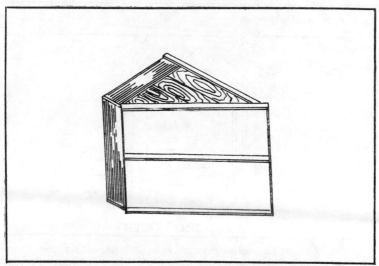

Fig. A-34. Ground mounting of a collector on a utility shed. Prefab supports can be used, or the solar collectors can be mounted against the south wall of a house with suitable attachments to prevent movement by the wind.

Fig. A-35. A windmill generator.

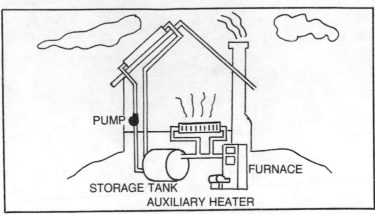

PUMP

FURNACE

STORAGE TANK

AUXILIARY HEATER

Fig. A-36. After the solar heat is exhausted, an auxiliary heater takes over. There should be enough heat in your storage medium to last one or more days. For your system to keep you warm much longer that that, it would have to be too large and expensive. Therefore, most systems are designed to provide 50 percent to 75 percent of your total heating needs.

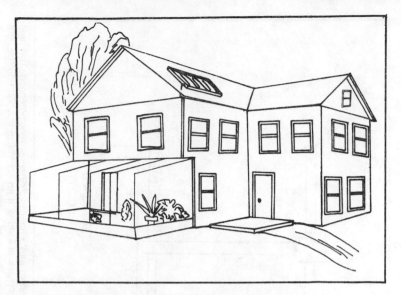

Fig. A-37. Retrofitted home with a solar greenhouse.

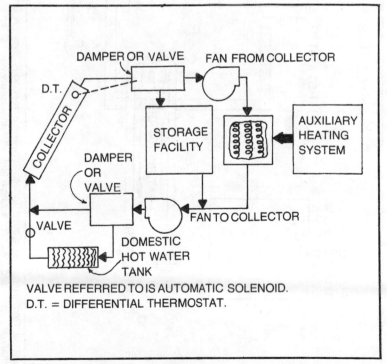

DAMPER OR VALVE

FAN FROM COLLECTOR

D.T.

COLLECTOR

STORAGE FACILITY

AUXILIARY HEATING SYSTEM

DAMPER OR VALVE

FAN TO COLLECTOR

VALVE

DOMESTIC HOT WATER TANK

VALVE REFERRED TO IS AUTOMATIC SOLENOID.
D.T. = DIFFERENTIAL THERMOSTAT.

Fig. A-38. A typical solar heating system.

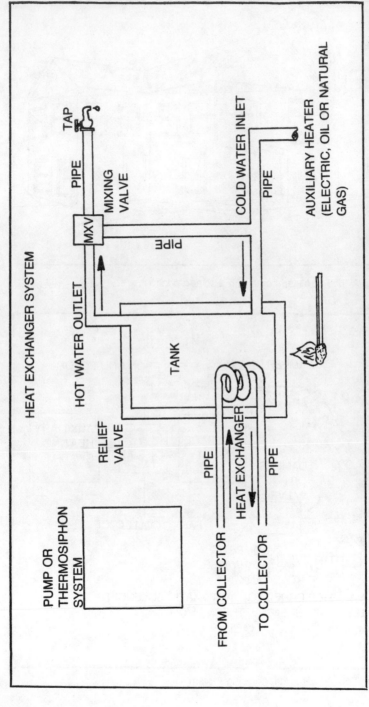

Fig. A-39. Heat exchanger system. In locations where freezing is common, a dual system with a heat exchanger is recommended. The heat exchanger system requires only a single tank with an auxiliary heater. The collector system is filled with an antifreeze solution and the heat exchanger is isolated from the hot water. The heat is transferred to the water through an immersed heating coil.

154

Fig. A-40. A night cooling system.

Fig. A-41. Sloped roof mounting of a collector or dormer mounting. Generally, solar collectors can be directly mounted on a 45° south-sloping roof, although some support might be required to provide an optimum tilt angle with respect to the sun's position.

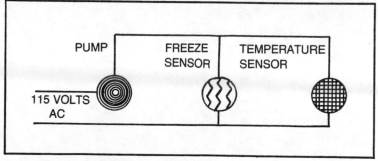

Fig. A-42. Control electrical diagram.

155

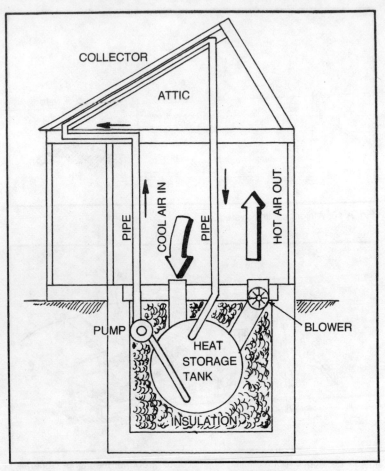

Fig. A-43. A solar space heating system using underground storage.

Appendix B
Facts About the Sun

Distance from the earth to the sun: 92,913,000 miles

Difference between January and June: 3,069,000 miles

Diameter of the sun: 864,000 miles

Total radiation of the sun: 3.86/10/33 ERG/Sec

Radiation received by the earth: 3.78/10/23 ERGS/Sec

The speed of light (1931): 186,284 miles/sec

Surface temperature of the sun: 6,000 degrees Celsius

Fuel burned in the sun: 140,000,000,000,000 tons/yr

WAVELENGTHS

Infrared	8000 Angstroms
Red	8000–6470 Angstroms
Orange	6470–5885 Angstroms
Yellow	5885–5500 Angstroms
Green	5500–4920 Angstroms
Blue	4920–4550 Angstroms
Indigo	4550–4300 Angstroms
Violet	4300–3600 Angstroms

Appendix C
Sun-Lite Solar Collector Cover Material

FEATURES:
**Solar Properties as Good as or Better Than Glass
**Light Stabilized
**Superior Impact and Shatter Resistance
**Inert to Chemical Atmosphere
**Self-Cleaning, Easy Maintenance and Repair
**Large Sheet Size Eliminates Joints
**Economical (Low Initial and Life Cycle Costs)
**Easily Cut with Hand Tools
**Low Thermal Expansion – Matches Aluminum
**Light Weight, Yet Rigid

PHYSICAL PROPERTIES [1]

	ASTM METHOD	UNITS	SUN-LITE REGULAR	SUN-LITE PREMIUM
Solar Energy Transmittance	E424 Method B	%	85–90	85–90
Estimated Solar Lifetime		Years	7 [2]	20 [3]
Thermal Sensitivity [4]		200°F	Excellent	Excellent
		300°F	Poor	Good
Heat Transmittance		5-20 microns		
Tensile Strength	D638	%	10	10
Tensile Strength	D638	PSI	16,000	16,000
Flexural Strength	D790	PSI	24,500	24,500
Flexural Modulus	D790	PSI × 10^6	1.0	1.0
Shear Strength	D732	PSI	14,000	14,000
Izod Impact	D256	Ft-lb./In.	18	18
Water Absorption	D570	%	0.20–0.33	0.20–0.33

Property	Test	Units		
Thermal Expansion	D696	in/in/°F×10^{-5}	1.4	1.4
Thermal Conductivity	C177	BTU–in/hr/ft.^{2}/°F	0.87	0.87
Specific Heat	D2766	BTU/lb/°F	0.35	0.35
Specific Gravity	D792		1.4	1.4
Weight	NBS P53–72	oz/ft.^{2}	2.8–4.7	2.8–4.7
Thickness	NBS P53–72	in	.025, .040	.025, .040
Sheet Size	NBS P53–72	ft	4' or 5' wide,	up to 1,200 long
Index of Refraction	D542	ratio	1.54	1.54

NOTE:

1. Modest deviations can be expected from these specifications due to the nature of the manufacturing process.
2. Tests indicate that Regular Sun-Lite will lose about 10 percent solar transmission in 7 years (estimate).
3. Tests indicate that Sun-Lite Premium should have no appreciable loss in solar transmission for 20 years (estimate).
4. Sun-Lite products are generally not affected by higher temperatures. The materials will not melt or cold flow since they are thermosetting and reinforced with glass fibers. The ignition temperature exceeds 900°F. However, continuous exposure at temperatures exceeding 200°F will cause a slight amber color to appear which will have only a modest effect (5 percent) on Sun-Lite's properties. Continuous exposure at 300°F, causes about a 10 percent decline in solar transmittance in Sun-Lite Premium and a severe decline in Sun-Lite Regular.
5. Special Sun-Lites are now under development to meet certain fire codes.
6. A special Sun-Lite is also under development for moist heat applications.

The above information is presented in good faith, but no warranty is expressed or implied.

Appendix D
Absorber Paints

3M Nextel Primer—911—T4 Light Grey.
3M Nextel Black Velvet Coating—101—C10 for spraying or 110—C10 for
use with a brush or roller.

Appendix E
Solar Data

The author wishes to thank C. A. Morrison, and E. A. Farber, coauthors of "Development and use of Solar Insolation Data in Northern Latitudes for South Facing Surfaces" in Symposium on *Solar Energy Applications*. New York ASHRAE, 1974. All material in this appendix is reprinted by permission.

Sources: ASHRAE, *Guide and Data Book*. 1970. ASHRAE, *Handbook of Fundamentals*, 1972. Reprinted by permission.

GLASS

The following is a chart designating the percentage of Solar Energy Transmittance through glass. All collector glazing glass should meet the following specifications: tempered, low iron.

1/8" glass	86% efficiency
3/16" glass	83% efficiency
1/4" glass	81% efficiency
Double Sheet Insulating Glass	70% efficiency

Table E-1 Percentage Heat Gains through various types and combinations of glass.

GLASS TYPE	SUMMER	WINTER
SINGLE GLAZING		
Clear	97	68
Heat-absorbing[1]	86	41
Reflective[2]	58	19
DOUBLE GLAZING		
Clear outside		
Clear inside	83	68
Clear outside		
Heat-absorbing inside	74	52
Clear outside		
Reflective inside	50	42
Heat-absorbing outside		
Clear inside	42	28
Reflective outside		
Heat-absorbing inside	31	17

1 Shading Coefficient = 0.50
2 Shading Coefficient = 0.35

The different types of glass that you can use may have a significant effect on the energy gains and losses. All glass, whether it is clear, heat absorbing, or reflecting, lose approximately the same amount of BTU through conduction. At the same time there is a great deal of difference in the energy in the form of solar heat which is transmitted through these three different types of glass. Table E-1 can give you some idea of the efficiency and heat gain or loss for the different types, and of different combinations of these types. The heat gain allows for a percentage of heat conduction through the glass. Plus the figures are for approximate gains under sunny conditions and don't allow for the different solar angles in summer and winter times of the solar year.

SUN PATH DIAGRAMS

In applications where strict accuracy is superfluous, solar angles can be quickly determined with sun path diagrams. In these diagrams, the sun's path across the sky vault is represented by a curve projected onto a horizontal plane (see diagram below). The horizon appears as a circle with the observation point at its center. Equally-spaced concentric circles represent the altitude angles, Θ, at 10° intervals, and equally-spaced radial lines represent the azimuth angles, ϕ, at the same intervals.

The elliptical curves running horizontally are the projection of the sun's path on the 21st day of each month; they are designated by two Roman numerals for the two months when the sun follows approximately this same path. A grid of vertical curves indicate the hours of the day in Arabic numerals.

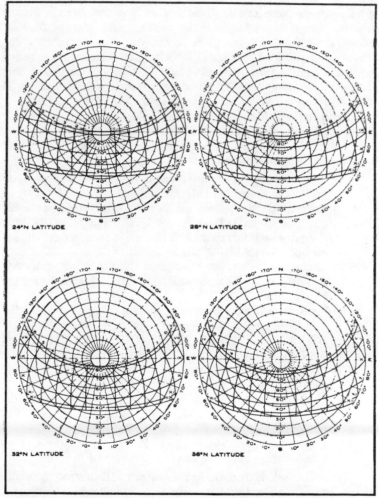

Fig. E-1. Percentage heat gains through various types and combinations of glass.

163

ASHRAE has developed tables that give the clear day insolation on tilted and south facing surfaces—such as those commonly used for solar collectors. For North latitudes L equal to 24°, 32°, 40°, 48°, and 56°, insolation values are given for south facing surfaces with tilt angles equal to L-10°, L, L+10°, L+20°, and 90° (vertical). Values are also given for the direct normal (perpendicular to the sun's rays) radiation and the insolation on a horizontal surface. The values listed in these tables are the sum of the direct solar and diffuse sky radiation hitting each surface on an average cloudless day. Data are given for the 21st day of each month; both hourly and daily total insolation are provided.

A brief examination of the 24°N table reveals that the insolation of south facing surfaces is symmetrical about solar noon. The values given for 8 a.m. are the same as those for 4 p.m., and they are listed concurrently. Moving from left to right on any fixed time line, you encounter values of: the solar altitude and azimuth (in degrees); the direct normal radiation and the insolation on a horizontal surface (in BTU/hr/ft²); and the insolation of the five south facing surfaces discussed above (in BTU/hr/ft²). Below these hourly data are values of the daily total insolation for each of these surfaces (in BTU/ft²). An example will help to illustrate the use of these tables.

Example: Determine the optimum tilt angle for a flat plate collector located in Atlanta, Georgia (32°N latitude). Select the tilt angles so as to maximize the surface insolation for the following three periods: a) heating season, b) cooling season, and c) the full year.

1) The heating season in Atlanta lasts from October through April; the cooling season from May to September.

2) Using the 32°N table, we sum the surface daily totals for the 22° tilt for the months October through April, and get 14,469 BTU/ft². We do the same for the 32°, 42°, 52°, and 90° tilts, and get totals of 15,142; 15,382; 15,172; and 10,588.

3) Comparing these totals, we conclude that the 42° tilt, or latitude plus 10°, is the best orientation for solar collection during the heating season.

4) A similar set of totals is generated for the cooling season, using the data for the months May through September. These are 11,987 BTU/ft² for 22°; 11,372 for 32°; 10,492 for 42°; 9,320 for 52°; and 3,260 for 90° tilt.

5) Comparing these totals, we conclude that the 22° tilt, or latitude minus 10°, is the best for summer cooling.

6) Using the data for the whole year, we get totals of 24,456 BTU/ft² for 22°; 26,514 for 32°; 25,874 for 42°; 24,492 for 52°; and 13,848 for 90° tilt.

7) Comparing these totals, we choose the 32° tilt, or latitude, as the best for year-round collection.

These conclusions are useful for the designer as they stand, but a little closer scrutiny is instructive. For example, the 42° tilt is best for heating, but the heating season totals for 32° and 52° are within 2 percent of the 42°

Table E-2. Solar position and insolation, 24° N latitude.

BTUH/SQ. FT. TOTAL INSOLATION ON SURFACES

DATE	SOLAR TIME AM	PM	SOLAR POSITION ALT	SOLAR POSITION AZM	NORMAL	HORIZ.	14	24	34	54	90
JAN 21	7	5	4.8	65.6	71	10	17	25	28	28	31
	8	4	16.9	58.3	239	83	110	126	137	145	127
	9	3	27.9	48.8	288	151	188	207	221	228	176
	10	2	37.2	36.1	308	204	246	268	282	287	207
	11	1	43.6	19.6	317	237	283	306	319	324	276
	12		46.0	0.0	320	249	296	319	332	336	232
	SURFACE DAILY TOTALS				2766	1622	1984	2174	2300	2360	1766
FEB 21	7	5	9.3	74.6	158	35	44	49	53	56	46
	8	4	22.3	67.2	263	116	135	145	150	151	102
	9	3	34.4	57.6	298	187	213	225	230	228	141
	10	2	45.1	44.2	314	241	273	286	291	287	168
	11	1	53.0	25.0	321	276	310	324	328	323	185
	12		56.0	0.0	324	288	323	337	341	335	191
	SURFACE DAILY TOTALS				3036	1998	2276	2396	2446	2424	1476
MAR 21	7	5	13.7	83.8	194	60	63	64	62	59	27
	8	4	27.2	76.8	267	141	150	152	149	142	64
	9	3	40.2	67.9	295	212	226	229	225	214	95
	10	2	52.3	54.8	309	266	285	288	283	270	120
	11	1	61.9	33.4	315	300	322	326	322	305	135
	12		66.0	0.0	317	312	334	339	333	317	140
	SURFACE DAILY TOTALS				3036	2270	2428	2456	2412	2298	1022
APR 21	6	6	4.7	100.6	40	7	5	4	3	3	2
	7	5	18.3	94.9	203	83	77	62	51	44	10
	8	4	32.0	89.0	256	160	157	137	122	106	16
	9	3	45.6	81.9	280	227	227	206	186	165	41
	10	2	59.0	71.8	292	278	282	261	237	211	61
	11	1	71.1	51.6	298	310	316	293	269	240	74
	12		77.6	0.0	299	321	328	305	280	250	79
	SURFACE DAILY TOTALS				3036	2454	2458	2374	2228	2016	488
MAY 21	6	6	8.0	108.4	86	22	15	10	10	9	5
	7	5	21.2	103.2	203	98	85	73	59	44	12
	8	4	34.6	98.5	248	171	159	145	127	106	15
	9	3	48.3	93.6	269	233	224	210	190	165	22
	10	2	62.0	87.7	280	281	275	261	239	211	34
	11	1	75.5	76.9	286	311	307	293	270	240	37
	12		86.0	0.0	288	322	317	304	281	250	37
	SURFACE DAILY TOTALS				3032	2556	2447	2286	2072	1800	246
JUN 21	6	6	9.3	111.6	97	29	20	12	12	11	7
	7	5	22.3	106.8	201	103	87	58	73	41	13
	8	4	35.5	102.6	242	173	158	122	142	99	16
	9	3	49.0	98.7	263	234	229	182	204	155	18
	10	2	62.6	95.0	274	280	269	229	253	199	18
	11	1	76.3	90.8	279	309	300	259	283	227	19
	12		89.4	0.0	281	319	310	269	294	236	22
	SURFACE DAILY TOTALS				2994	2574	2422	1992	2230	1700	204
JUL 21	6	6	8.2	109.0	81	23	16	11	11	10	6
	7	5	21.4	103.8	195	98	85	73	59	44	13
	8	4	34.8	99.2	239	169	157	143	125	105	16
	9	3	48.4	94.5	261	231	221	207	187	161	18
	10	2	62.1	89.0	272	278	272	256	235	206	21
	11	1	75.7	79.2	278	307	298	287	265	235	32
	12		86.6	0.0	280	317	312	298	275	245	36
	SURFACE DAILY TOTALS				2932	2526	2412	2250	2056	1766	246
AUG 21	6	6	5.0	101.3	35	7	5	4	3	2	2
	7	5	18.5	95.6	186	82	76	69	60	50	11
	8	4	32.2	89.7	241	158	154	146	134	118	16
	9	3	45.9	82.9	265	223	222	214	200	181	39
	10	2	59.3	73.0	278	273	275	268	252	230	58
	11	1	71.6	53.2	284	304	309	298	285	261	71
	12		78.3	0.0	286	315	320	313	296	272	75
	SURFACE DAILY TOTALS				2864	2408	2416	2316	2168	1958	470
SEP 21	7	5	13.7	83.8	173	57	59	60	59	56	26
	8	4	27.2	76.8	248	136	143	146	143	136	62
	9	3	40.2	67.9	278	205	217	218	217	206	93
	10	2	52.3	54.8	292	258	275	278	273	261	116
	11	1	61.9	33.4	299	291	311	315	309	295	131
	12		66.0	0.0	301	302	323	327	320	306	136
	SURFACE DAILY TOTALS				2878	2194	2342	2366	2322	2212	992
OCT 21	7	5	9.1	74.1	138	32	40	45	48	50	42
	8	4	22.0	66.7	247	111	129	139	144	145	99
	9	3	34.1	57.1	284	180	206	217	223	221	138
	10	2	44.7	43.8	301	234	265	277	282	279	165
	11	1	52.5	24.7	309	268	301	315	319	314	182
	12		55.5	0.0	311	279	314	328	332	327	188
	SURFACE DAILY TOTALS				2868	1928	2198	2314	2364	2346	1042
NOV 21	7	5	4.9	65.8	67	16	24	29	27	24	29
	8	4	17.0	58.4	232	82	108	123	135	142	124
	9	3	28.0	48.9	282	150	186	205	217	224	172
	10	2	37.3	36.3	303	203	244	265	278	283	204
	11	1	43.8	19.7	312	236	280	302	314	320	222
	12		46.2	0.0	315	247	293	315	328	332	228
	SURFACE DAILY TOTALS				2706	1610	1962	2146	2268	2324	1750

Table E-3. Solar position and insolation, 32° N latitude.

- SOLAR POSITION: ALT = altitude, AZM = azimuth
- BTU/SQ. FT. TOTAL INSOLATION ON SURFACES: NORMAL, HORIZ., then SOUTH FACING SURFACE ANGLE WITH HORIZ. at 22°, 32°, 42°, 52°, 90°

Months DEC 21 – MAY 21

DATE	SOLAR TIME AM	PM	ALT	AZM	NORMAL	HORIZ.	22	32	42	52	90
DEC 21	8	4	3.2	62.6	30	3	99	99	116	123	139
	9	3	14.9	55.3	225	71	176	198	206	212	214
	10	2	25.5	46.0	281	137	234	258	269	274	275
	11	1	34.3	33.7	304	189	270	295	308	312	312
	12		40.4	18.2	314	221	282	308	321	324	325
		12	42.6	0.0	317	232					
	SURFACE DAILY TOTALS				2624	1474	1852	2058	2204	2286	1808
JAN 21	7	5	1.4	65.2	1	0	1	1	1	1	1
	8	4	12.5	56.5	203	56	106	116	123	115	115
	9	3	22.5	46.0	269	118	193	206	212	214	181
	10	2	30.6	33.1	295	167	256	269	274	276	221
	11	1	36.1	17.5	306	198	295	308	312	315	245
	12		38.0	0.0	310	209	308	321	324	328	253
		12									
	SURFACE DAILY TOTALS				2458	1288	1839	2008	2118	2166	1779
FEB 21	7	5	7.1	73.5	121	34	37	40	40	38	38
	8	4	19.0	64.4	247	95	127	136	140	141	108
	9	3	29.9	53.4	288	161	206	217	222	220	158
	10	2	39.1	39.4	306	212	266	278	283	279	193
	11	1	45.6	21.4	315	244	304	317	321	315	214
	12		48.0	0.0	317	255	316	330	334	328	222
	SURFACE DAILY TOTALS				2872	1724	2188	2300	2345	2322	1644
MAR 21	7	5	12.7	81.9	185	54	60	60	59	56	32
	8	4	25.1	73.0	260	129	146	146	144	137	78
	9	3	36.8	62.1	290	194	222	224	220	209	119
	10	2	47.3	47.5	304	245	280	283	278	265	150
	11	1	55.0	26.8	311	277	317	321	315	300	170
	12		58.0	0.0	313	287	329	333	327	312	177
	SURFACE DAILY TOTALS				3012	2084	2378	2403	2356	2246	1276
APR 21	6	6	6.1	99.9	66	14	9	6	6	5	3
	7	5	18.8	92.2	206	86	78	71	62	51	10
	8	4	31.5	84.0	255	158	156	148	136	120	35
	9	3	43.9	74.2	278	225	225	217	203	183	68
	10	2	55.7	60.3	290	267	279	272	256	234	95
	11	1	65.4	37.5	295	292	313	306	290	265	112
	12		69.6	0.0	297	307	325	318	301	276	118
	SURFACE DAILY TOTALS				3076	2390	2444	2378	2206	1994	764
MAY 21	6	6	10.4	107.2	119	36	21	13	13	12	7
	7	5	22.8	100.1	211	107	88	75	60	44	13
	8	4	35.4	92.9	250	175	159	145	127	105	15
	9	3	48.1	84.7	269	233	223	209	188	163	33
	10	2	60.6	73.3	280	273	273	259	237	208	56
	11	1	72.0	51.9	285	305	305	290	268	237	72
	12		78.0	0.0	286	315	315	301	278	247	77
	SURFACE DAILY TOTALS				3112	2582	2454	2284	2064	1788	469

Months JUN 21 – NOV 21

DATE	SOLAR TIME AM	PM	ALT	AZM	NORMAL	HORIZ.	22	32	42	52	90
JUN 21	6	6	12.2	110.2	131	45	22	14	13	12	9
	7	5	24.3	103.4	210	115	91	76	59	41	14
	8	4	36.9	96.8	245	180	159	143	122	99	16
	9	3	49.6	89.4	264	236	221	204	181	153	19
	10	2	62.2	79.7	274	279	268	251	227	197	41
	11	1	74.2	60.9	279	306	299	282	257	224	56
	12		81.5	0.0	280	315	309	292	267	234	60
	SURFACE DAILY TOTALS				3084	2634	2436	2234	1990	1690	370
JUL 21	6	6	10.7	107.7	113	37	14	13	6	12	8
	7	5	23.1	100.6	203	107	75	60	60	44	14
	8	4	35.7	93.6	241	174	143	125	132	104	16
	9	3	48.4	85.5	261	231	205	185	197	159	31
	10	2	60.9	74.3	271	274	254	232	249	204	54
	11	1	72.4	53.3	277	302	285	262	281	232	69
	12		78.6	0.0	279	311	296	273	292	242	74
	SURFACE DAILY TOTALS				3012	2558	2250	2030	2144	1754	458
AUG 21	6	6	6.5	100.5	59	14	22	14	6	6	4
	7	5	19.1	92.8	190	85	87	75	60	50	12
	8	4	31.8	84.7	240	156	158	143	125	116	33
	9	3	44.3	75.0	263	216	220	205	185	178	65
	10	2	56.1	61.3	276	262	269	254	232	226	91
	11	1	66.0	38.4	282	292	300	285	262	257	107
	12		70.3	0.0	284	302	310	296	273	268	113
	SURFACE DAILY TOTALS				2902	2352	2388	2296	2144	1934	736
SEP 21	7	5	12.7	81.9	163	51	56	56	55	52	30
	8	4	25.1	73.0	240	124	140	141	138	131	75
	9	3	36.8	62.1	272	188	215	217	211	201	114
	10	2	47.3	47.5	287	237	273	273	268	255	145
	11	1	55.0	26.8	294	268	309	311	303	289	164
	12		58.0	0.0	296	278	321	324	315	300	171
	SURFACE DAILY TOTALS				2808	2014	2288	2264	2154	1934	1226
OCT 21	7	5	6.8	73.1	99	19	32	32	34	36	32
	8	4	18.7	64.0	229	90	128	133	133	134	104
	9	3	29.5	53.0	273	155	208	213	213	212	153
	10	2	38.7	39.1	293	204	269	273	273	270	188
	11	1	45.1	21.1	302	236	307	311	311	306	209
	12		47.5	0.0	304	247	320	324	324	318	217
	SURFACE DAILY TOTALS				2696	1654	2100	2208	2252	2232	1588
NOV 21	7	5	1.5	65.4	2	0	0	1	1	1	1
	8	4	12.7	56.6	196	55	91	104	113	119	111
	9	3	22.6	46.1	263	118	173	190	202	208	176
	10	2	30.8	33.2	289	166	233	252	265	270	217
	11	1	36.2	17.6	301	197	270	291	303	307	241
	12		38.2	0.0	304	207	282	304	316	320	249
	SURFACE DAILY TOTALS				2406	1280	1816	1980	2084	2130	1742

Table E-4. Solar position and insolation, 40° N latitude.

Units: BTUH/SQ. FT. TOTAL INSOLATION ON SURFACES. South-facing surface angle with horizontal: 30, 40, 50, 60, 90.

DATE	AM	PM	ALT	AZM	NORMAL	HORIZ	30	40	50	60	90
DEC 21	8	4	10.3	53.8	176	41	77	90	101	108	107
	9	3	19.8	43.1	257	102	161	180	195	204	183
	10	2	27.6	31.2	288	150	221	244	259	267	226
	11	1	32.7	16.4	301	180	258	282	298	305	251
		12	34.6	0.0	304	190	271	295	310	318	259
	SURFACE DAILY TOTALS				2348	1136	1704	1888	2016	2086	1794
JAN 21	8	4	8.1	55.3	142	28	65	74	81	85	84
	9	3	16.8	44.0	239	83	155	171	182	187	171
	10	2	23.8	30.9	274	127	218	237	249	254	223
	11	1	28.4	16.0	289	154	257	277	290	293	253
		12	30.0	0.0	294	164	270	291	303	306	263
	SURFACE DAILY TOTALS				2182	948	1660	1810	1944	1906	1726
FEB 21	7	5	4.8	72.7	69	10	19	21	23	24	22
	8	4	15.4	62.2	224	73	114	122	126	127	107
	9	3	25.0	50.2	274	132	195	205	209	208	167
	10	2	32.8	35.9	295	178	256	267	271	267	210
	11	1	38.1	18.9	305	206	293	306	310	304	236
		12	40.0	0.0	308	216	306	319	323	317	245
	SURFACE DAILY TOTALS				2640	1414	2060	2162	2202	2176	1730
MAR 21	7	5	11.4	80.2	171	46	55	55	54	51	35
	8	4	22.5	69.6	250	114	140	141	138	131	89
	9	3	32.8	57.3	282	173	215	217	213	209	138
	10	2	41.6	41.9	297	218	273	276	271	258	176
	11	1	47.7	22.6	305	247	310	313	307	293	200
		12	50.0	0.0	307	257	322	326	320	305	208
	SURFACE DAILY TOTALS				2916	1852	2308	2330	2284	2174	1484
APR 21	6	6	7.4	98.9	89	20	11	8	7	7	4
	7	5	18.9	89.5	206	87	77	70	61	50	12
	8	4	30.3	79.3	252	152	153	145	133	117	53
	9	3	41.3	67.2	274	207	221	213	199	179	93
	10	2	51.2	51.4	286	250	275	267	252	229	126
	11	1	58.7	29.2	292	277	308	301	285	260	147
		12	61.6	0.0	293	287	320	312	296	271	154
	SURFACE DAILY TOTALS				3092	2274	2412	2320	2158	1956	1022
MAY 21	5	7	1.9	114.7	1	0	0	0	0	0	0
	6	6	12.7	105.6	144	49	25	15	14	13	9
	7	5	24.0	96.6	216	114	89	76	60	44	13
	8	4	35.4	87.2	250	175	158	144	125	104	44
	9	3	46.8	76.0	267	221	206	186	160	134	59
	10	2	57.5	60.9	277	267	270	255	233	205	72
	11	1	66.2	37.1	283	293	301	287	264	234	79
		12	70.0	0.0	284	301	312	297	274	243	81
	SURFACE DAILY TOTALS				3160	2552	2442	2264	2040	1760	724

DATE	AM	PM	ALT	AZM	NORMAL	HORIZ	30	40	50	60	90
JUN 21	5	7	4.2	117.3	22	4	4	3	2	2	1
	6	6	14.8	108.4	155	60	30	18	17	16	10
	7	5	26.0	99.7	216	123	92	77	59	41	14
	8	4	37.4	90.7	246	182	159	142	121	97	16
	9	3	48.8	80.2	263	233	219	202	179	151	47
	10	2	59.8	65.8	272	272	266	248	224	194	74
	11	1	69.2	41.9	277	296	296	278	253	221	89
		12	73.5	0.0	279	304	306	289	263	230	98
	SURFACE DAILY TOTALS				3180	2648	2224	2004	1728	1472	610
JUL 21	5	7	2.3	115.2	2	0	0	0	0	0	0
	6	6	13.1	106.1	138	50	26	17	15	14	9
	7	5	24.3	97.2	208	114	87	75	60	44	14
	8	4	35.8	87.8	241	174	157	142	124	102	44
	9	3	47.2	76.7	259	225	218	203	182	157	75
	10	2	57.9	61.7	269	265	266	251	229	200	102
	11	1	66.7	37.9	275	290	292	281	258	228	113
		12	70.6	0.0	276	298	303	292	269	238	121
	SURFACE DAILY TOTALS				3062	2534	2409	2230	2006	1728	769
AUG 21	6	6	7.9	99.5	81	21	12	9	8	7	5
	7	5	19.3	90.0	191	87	76	69	60	49	12
	8	4	30.7	79.9	237	150	150	141	129	113	50
	9	3	41.8	67.9	260	205	216	207	193	173	89
	10	2	51.7	52.1	272	246	267	259	244	221	120
	11	1	59.3	29.7	278	273	292	285	270	247	140
		12	62.3	0.0	280	282	303	296	281	257	147
	SURFACE DAILY TOTALS				2916	2354	2258	2176	2006	1728	978
SEP 21	7	5	11.4	80.2	149	43	51	51	49	47	32
	8	4	22.5	69.6	230	109	133	134	131	124	84
	9	3	32.8	57.3	263	167	206	208	203	193	132
	10	2	41.6	41.9	280	211	262	265	260	247	168
	11	1	47.7	22.6	287	239	298	301	295	281	192
		12	50.0	0.0	290	249	310	313	307	292	200
	SURFACE DAILY TOTALS				2708	1788	2210	2228	2182	2074	1416
OCT 21	7	5	4.5	72.3	48	7	14	15	17	17	16
	8	4	15.0	61.9	204	68	106	113	117	118	100
	9	3	24.5	49.8	257	126	185	195	198	193	160
	10	2	32.4	35.6	280	170	245	257	261	257	203
	11	1	37.6	18.7	291	199	283	295	299	294	229
		12	39.5	0.0	294	208	295	308	312	306	238
	SURFACE DAILY TOTALS				2454	1348	1962	2060	2098	2074	1654
NOV 21	8	4	8.2	55.4	136	28	63	72	78	82	81
	9	3	17.0	44.1	232	82	152	167	178	183	167
	10	2	24.0	31.0	268	126	215	233	245	249	219
	11	1	29.6	16.1	283	153	254	273	285	288	248
		12	30.2	0.0	288	163	267	287	298	301	258
	SURFACE DAILY TOTALS				2128	942	1636	1778	1870	1908	1688

Table E-5. Solar position and insolation, 48° N latitude.

DATE	SOLAR TIME AM	SOLAR TIME PM	SOLAR POSITION ALT	SOLAR POSITION AZM	BTUH/SQ. FT. TOTAL INSOLATION ON SURFACES NORMAL	HORIZ.	SOUTH FACING SURFACE ANGLE WITH HORIZ. 38	48	58	68	90
DEC	8	4	5.5	53.0	89	14	39	45	50	54	56
	9	3	14.0	41.9	217	65	135	157	164	171	163
	10	2	20.7	29.4	261	107	200	221	235	242	221
	11	1	25.0	15.2	280	134	239	262	276	283	252
	12		26.6	0.0	285	143	253	275	290	296	263
	SURFACE DAILY TOTALS				1978	782	1480	1634	1740	1796	1646
JAN 21	8	4	3.5	54.6	37	4	17	19	21	22	22
	9	3	11.0	42.6	185	46	120	132	140	145	139
	10	2	16.9	29.4	239	83	190	206	216	220	206
	11	1	20.7	15.1	261	107	231	249	260	263	243
	12		22.0	0.0	267	115	245	264	275	278	255
	SURFACE DAILY TOTALS				1710	596	1360	1478	1550	1578	1478
FEB 21	7	5	2.4	72.2	12	1	3	4	4	4	4
	8	4	11.6	60.5	188	49	95	102	105	106	96
	9	3	19.7	47.7	251	100	178	187	191	190	167
	10	2	26.2	33.3	278	139	240	251	255	251	217
	11	1	30.5	17.2	290	165	278	290	294	288	247
	12		32.0	0.0	293	173	291	304	307	301	258
	SURFACE DAILY TOTALS				2330	1080	1880	1972	2024	1978	1720
MAR 21	7	5	10.0	78.7	153	37	49	49	47	45	35
	8	4	19.5	66.8	236	96	131	132	129	122	96
	9	3	28.2	53.4	270	147	205	207	203	193	152
	10	2	35.4	37.8	287	187	263	266	261	248	195
	11	1	40.3	19.8	295	212	300	303	297	283	223
	12		42.0	0.0	298	220	312	315	309	294	232
	SURFACE DAILY TOTALS				2780	1578	2208	2228	2182	2074	1632
APR 21	6	6	8.6	97.8	108	27	13	9	8	7	5
	7	5	18.6	86.7	205	85	76	69	59	48	21
	8	4	28.5	74.9	247	142	149	141	129	113	69
	9	3	37.8	61.2	268	191	216	208	194	174	115
	10	2	45.8	44.6	280	228	268	260	245	223	152
	11	1	51.5	24.0	286	252	301	294	278	254	177
	12		53.6	0.0	288	260	313	305	289	264	185
	SURFACE DAILY TOTALS				3076	2106	2358	2266	2114	1902	1262
MAY 21	5	7	5.2	114.3	41	9	4	4	4	3	2
	6	6	14.7	103.7	162	61	27	16	15	13	10
	7	5	24.6	93.0	219	118	89	75	60	43	13
	8	4	34.7	81.6	248	171	156	142	123	101	45
	9	3	44.3	68.3	264	217	217	202	182	156	86
	10	2	53.0	51.3	274	252	265	251	229	200	120
	11	1	59.5	28.6	279	274	296	281	258	228	141
	12		62.0	0.0	280	281	306	292	269	238	149
	SURFACE DAILY TOTALS				3254	2482	2418	2234	2010	1728	982
JUN 21	5	7	7.9	116.5	77	21	9	9	8	7	5
	6	6	17.2	106.2	172	74	33	19	18	16	12
	7	5	27.0	95.8	220	129	93	77	59	39	15
	8	4	37.1	84.6	246	181	157	140	119	95	35
	9	3	46.9	71.6	261	225	216	198	175	147	74
	10	2	55.8	54.8	269	259	262	244	220	189	105
	11	1	62.7	31.2	274	280	291	273	248	216	126
	12		65.5	0.0	275	287	301	283	258	225	133
	SURFACE DAILY TOTALS				3312	2626	2420	2204	1950	1644	874
JUL 21	5	7	5.7	114.7	43	10	5	5	4	4	3
	6	6	15.2	104.1	156	62	28	18	16	15	11
	7	5	25.1	93.5	211	118	89	75	59	42	14
	8	4	35.1	82.1	240	171	154	140	121	99	43
	9	3	44.8	68.8	256	215	214	199	178	153	83
	10	2	53.5	51.9	266	250	261	246	224	195	116
	11	1	60.1	29.0	271	272	291	276	253	223	137
	12		62.6	0.0	272	279	301	286	263	232	144
	SURFACE DAILY TOTALS				3158	2474	2386	2200	1974	1694	956
AUG 21	6	6	9.1	98.3	99	28	14	10	9	8	6
	7	5	19.1	87.2	190	85	75	67	58	47	20
	8	4	29.0	75.4	232	141	145	137	125	109	65
	9	3	38.4	61.8	254	189	210	201	187	168	110
	10	2	46.4	45.1	266	225	260	252	237	214	146
	11	1	52.2	24.3	272	248	293	285	268	244	169
	12		54.3	0.0	274	256	304	296	279	255	177
	SURFACE DAILY TOTALS				2898	2086	2300	2200	2046	1836	1208
SEP 21	7	5	10.0	78.7	131	35	44	44	43	40	31
	8	4	19.5	66.8	215	92	124	124	121	115	90
	9	3	28.2	53.4	251	142	196	197	193	183	143
	10	2	35.4	37.8	269	181	251	254	248	236	185
	11	1	40.3	19.8	278	205	287	289	284	269	212
	12		42.0	0.0	280	213	299	302	296	281	221
	SURFACE DAILY TOTALS				2568	1522	2102	2118	2070	1966	1546
OCT 21	7	5	2.0	71.9	4	0	1	1	1	1	1
	8	4	11.2	60.2	165	44	86	91	95	95	87
	9	3	19.3	47.4	233	94	167	176	180	178	157
	10	2	25.7	33.1	262	133	228	239	242	239	207
	11	1	30.0	17.1	274	157	266	277	281	276	237
	12		31.5	0.0	278	166	279	291	294	288	247
	SURFACE DAILY TOTALS				2154	1022	1774	1860	1890	1866	1626
NOV 21	8	4	3.6	54.7	36	5	17	19	21	22	22
	9	3	11.2	42.7	179	46	117	129	137	141	135
	10	2	17.1	29.5	233	83	186	202	212	215	201
	11	1	20.9	15.1	255	107	227	245	255	258	238

Table E-6. Solar position and insolation, 56° N latitude.

BTUH/SQ. FT. TOTAL INSOLATION ON SURFACE — JUN 21 through DEC 21

DATE	AM	PM	ALT	AZM	NORMAL	HORIZ.	46	56	66	76	90
JUN 21	5	7	4.2	127.2	21	2	2	2	2	2	8
	6	6	11.4	115.3	122	40	14	11	17	15	12
	7	5	19.3	103.6	185	86	54	30	17	17	15
	8	4	27.6	91.7	222	132	92	74	58	41	61
	9	3	35.9	78.8	243	175	154	136	116	96	106
	10	2	43.8	64.1	257	212	211	193	170	147	142
	11	1	50.7	46.4	265	240	255	238	214	189	165
	12		55.6	24.9	269	258	284	267	242	216	173
			57.5	0.0	271	264	294	276	251	225	173
			SURFACE DAILY TOTALS		3438	2562	2388	2166	1910	1508	1120
JUL 21	4	8	1.7	125.8	0	0	0	0	0	0	0
	5	7	9.0	113.7	91	27	11	10	11	9	7
	6	6	17.0	101.9	169	72	30	18	65	45	28
	7	5	25.3	89.7	212	119	88	74	119	104	78
	8	4	33.6	76.7	237	163	151	136	179	160	126
	9	3	41.4	62.0	252	201	208	193	232	206	166
	10	2	48.2	44.6	261	230	254	239	267	227	191
	11	1	52.9	23.7	265	248	283	278	258	265	200
	12		54.6	0.0	267	254	293	285	285	245	233
			SURFACE DAILY TOTALS		3240	2372	2342	2152	1926	1760	1392
AUG 21	5	7	2.0	109.2	0	0	0	0	0	0	0
	6	6	10.2	97.0	112	34	16	10	10	9	7
	7	5	18.5	84.5	187	82	73	56	56	45	28
	8	4	26.7	71.3	225	128	140	131	119	104	78
	9	3	34.3	56.7	246	168	202	195	179	160	126
	10	2	40.5	40.7	258	199	251	242	232	206	166
	11	1	44.8	20.9	264	218	282	273	267	227	191
	12		46.3	0.0	266	225	293	285	285	245	200
			SURFACE DAILY TOTALS		2850	1884	2218	2118	1966	1760	1392
SEP 21	7	5	8.3	77.5	107	25	36	32	34	28	28
	8	4	16.2	64.4	194	72	111	102	108	89	89
	9	3	23.3	50.3	233	114	182	168	178	147	147
	10	2	29.0	34.9	253	146	237	221	232	193	193
	11	1	32.7	17.9	263	166	273	254	267	223	223
	12		34.0	0.0	266	173	285	265	279	233	233
			SURFACE DAILY TOTALS		2368	1220	1950	1962	1918	1820	1588
OCT 21	8	4	7.1	59.1	104	26	66	99	99	95	57
	9	3	13.8	45.7	193	60	138	147	148	154	138
	10	2	19.0	31.3	231	92	201	201	213	210	195
	11	1	22.3	16.0	248	112	240	240	253	266	230
	12		23.5	0.0	253	119	253	255	266	248	241
			SURFACE DAILY TOTALS		1804	688	1511	1586	1612	1598	1480
NOV 21	9	3	5.2	41.9	76	12	39	99	99	95	58
	10	2	9.5	28.5	165	39	172	147	149	152	148
	11	1	13.1	14.5	201	58	201	193	193	203	196
	12		14.1	0.0	211	65	194	209	217	219	211
			SURFACE DAILY TOTALS		1094	284	914	981	1046	1016	722
DEC 21	9	3	5.2	40.5	5	0	3	95	101	104	103
	10	2	9.5	27.5	113	37	142	154	163	167	164
	11	1	13.9	13.9	166	59	159	173	182	186	182
	12		10.6	0.0	180	—	—	—	—	—	—
			SURFACE DAILY TOTALS		748	—	628	—	—	—	722

BTUH/SQ. FT. TOTAL INSOLATION ON SURFACES — DEC 21 through MAY 21

DATE	AM	PM	ALT	AZM	NORMAL	HORIZ.	27	46	56	66	76	90
DEC 21	9	3	8.0	40.9	140					105	106	106
	10	2	13.4	28.2	214	63	180	164	182	193	197	193
	11	1	17.3	14.4	242	86	226	207	226	239	244	240
	12		18.6	0.0	250	94	241	222	241	254	260	255
			SURFACE DAILY TOTALS		1404	446		1136	1250	1326	1364	1044
JAN 21	9	3	5.0	41.8	78	11		50	55	59	60	66
	10	2	9.9	28.5	170	39		135	146	154	156	153
	11	1	12.9	14.5	207	58		183	197	206	208	201
	12		14.0	0.0	217	65		198	214	222	225	217
			SURFACE DAILY TOTALS		1126	282		1058	1310	1074	1074	1044
FEB 21	8	4	7.6	59.4	129	25	65	65	69	72	72	69
	9	3	14.2	45.9	214	65	151	151	159	162	161	151
	10	2	19.4	31.5	250	98	215	215	225	228	224	208
	11	1	22.8	16.1	266	119	254	254	265	268	263	243
	12		24.0	0.0	270	126	268	268	279	282	276	255
			SURFACE DAILY TOTALS		1986	740	1640	1640	2084	2040	1716	1598
MAR 21	7	5	8.3	77.5	128	28	40	40	40	39	37	28
	8	4	16.2	64.4	215	75	119	119	120	116	111	97
	9	3	23.3	50.3	253	118	192	192	193	189	180	154
	10	2	29.0	34.9	272	151	249	249	251	245	234	205
	11	1	32.7	17.9	282	172	285	285	288	282	268	236
	12		34.0	0.0	284	179	297	297	300	294	280	246
			SURFACE DAILY TOTALS		2586	1268	2066	2066	2084	2040	1830	1598
APR 21	5	7	1.4	108.8	0	0	0	0	0	0	0	0
	6	6	9.6	96.5	122	32	25	14	17	8	7	6
	7	5	18.0	84.1	201	81	72	74	66	57	46	29
	8	4	26.1	70.9	239	129	143	143	135	119	108	82
	9	3	33.6	56.3	260	169	208	208	200	186	167	133
	10	2	39.9	39.7	272	201	259	259	251	236	214	174
	11	1	44.1	20.7	278	220	292	292	284	268	245	200
	12		45.6	0.0	280	227	303	303	295	279	255	209
			SURFACE DAILY TOTALS		3024	1892	2282	2282	2186	2038	1830	1458
MAY 21	4	8	1.2	125.5	0	0	0	0	0	0	0	0
	5	7	8.5	113.4	93	25	14	17	17	8	7	6
	6	6	16.5	101.5	175	71	28	74	74	58	41	11
	7	5	24.8	89.3	219	119	88	138	138	119	98	63
	8	4	33.1	76.3	244	165	153	197	197	176	151	109
	9	3	40.9	61.6	259	201	212	251	251	222	194	146
	10	2	47.6	44.2	268	231	259	288	274	251	222	170
	11	1	52.3	23.4	273	249	288	299	295	261	251	178
	12		54.0	0.0	275	255	299	299	295	266	255	178
			SURFACE DAILY TOTALS		3340	2374	2374	2374	2188	1962	1682	1218

total. Thus, other design considerations (such as building layout, structural framing, height restrictions) can enter the decision process without seriously affecting the final collector efficiency.

The Clear Day Insolation Data are an extremely valuable design tool, but their limitations should be kept in mind. For instance, there is no ground reflection included in the listed values. This can lead one to underestimate the clear day insolation on a vertical surface. In the example the heating season total for a 90° surface is about 30 percent below the 42° maximum. In reality, the insolation on a vertical surface is only 10 to 20 percent lower than this maximum during the heating season because of the contribution of ground reflection—especially at higher latitudes. Another limitation of these data is their assumption of an "average" clear day. Many locations are clearer than this (high altitudes and deserts), and many are less clear (industrial and dusty areas). To correct for this assumption, the numbers in these tables should be multiplied by the area-wide clearness factors given on page 394 of the 1972 ASHRAE *Handbook of Fundamentals*. Finally, the Clear Day Insolation Data do not account for cloudy weather conditions, which become quite important for long term predictions. There are ways to account for cloudiness. As always, judgement is needed for the use of these extremely valuable tables.

SOLAR RADIATION MAPS

The quantity of solar radiation actually available for use in heating is difficult to calculate exactly. Most of this difficulty is due to the many highly variable factors that influence the radiation available at a collector location. But most of these factors can be treated by statistical methods using long-term averages of recorded weather data.

The least modified and therefore most usable solar radiation data is available from the U.S. Weather Bureau. Some of these data, averaged over a period of many years, have been published in the *Climate Atlas of the United States* in the form of tables or maps. A selection of these average data is reprinted here for your convenience. They are taken to be a good indicator of future weather trends. More recent and complete information may be obtained from the National Weather Records Center in Asheville, North Carolina.

As one example, daily insolation has been recorded at more than 80 weather stations across the United States. The available data have been averaged over a period of more than 30 years; these averages are summarized in the first 12 (one for each month) contour maps—"Mean Daily Solar Radiation." Values are given in langleys, or calories per square centimeter; multiply by 3.69 to convert to BTU per square foot. These figures represent the monthly average of the daily total of direct, diffuse, and reflected radiation on a horizontal surface. Trigonometric conversions (as explained later in this Appendix) must be applied to these data to convert them to the insolation on vertical or tilted surfaces.

Other useful information include the Weather Bureau records of the amount of sunshine, which is listed as the "hours of sunshine" or the

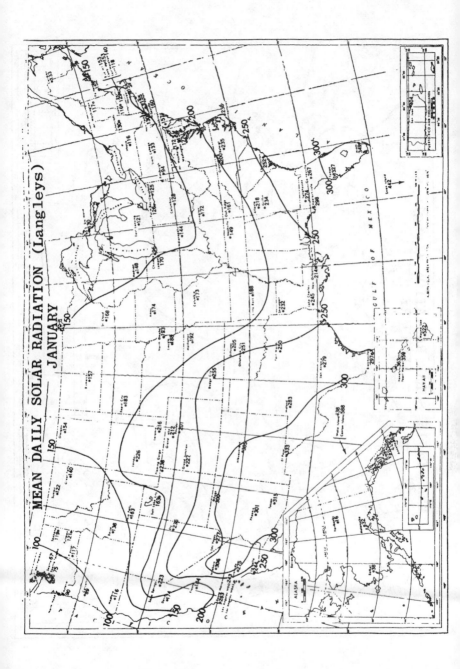

MEAN DAILY SOLAR RADIATION (Langleys)
JANUARY

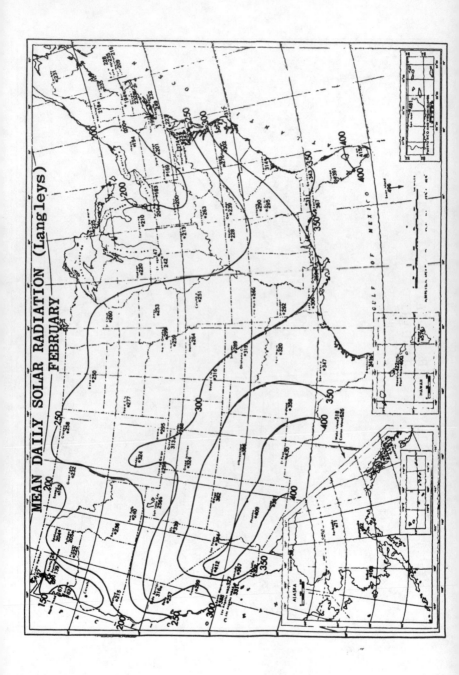

MEAN DAILY SOLAR RADIATION (Langleys)
FEBRUARY

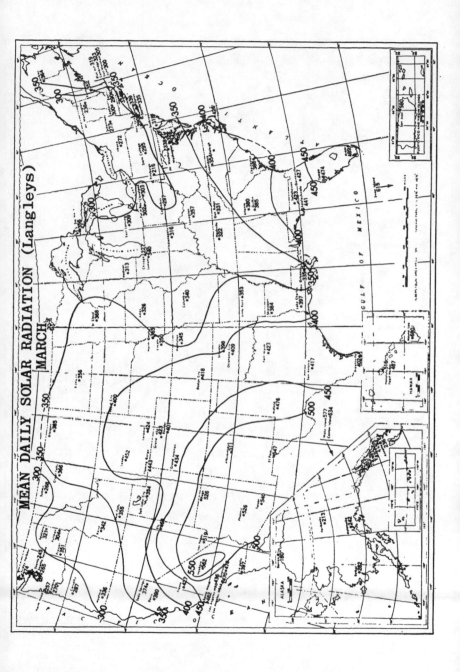

MEAN DAILY SOLAR RADIATION (Langleys)
MARCH

173

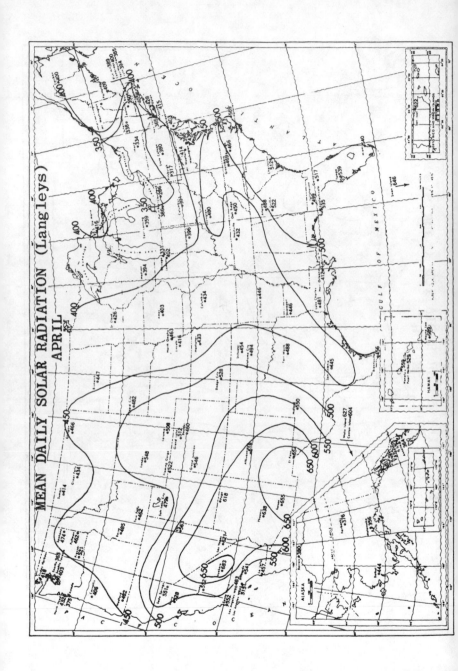

MEAN DAILY SOLAR RADIATION (Langleys)
APRIL

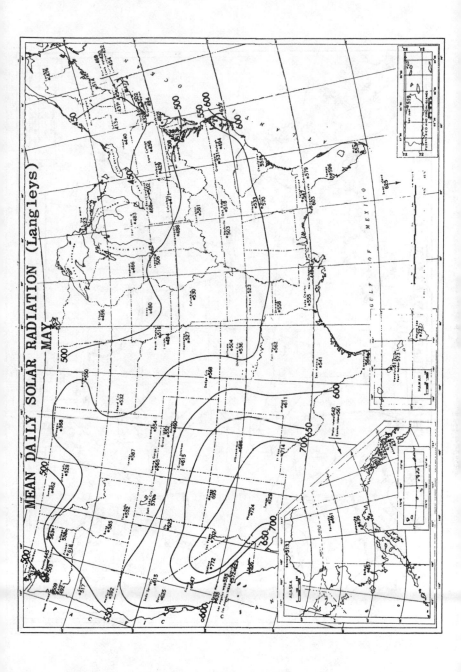

MEAN DAILY SOLAR RADIATION (Langleys)
MAY

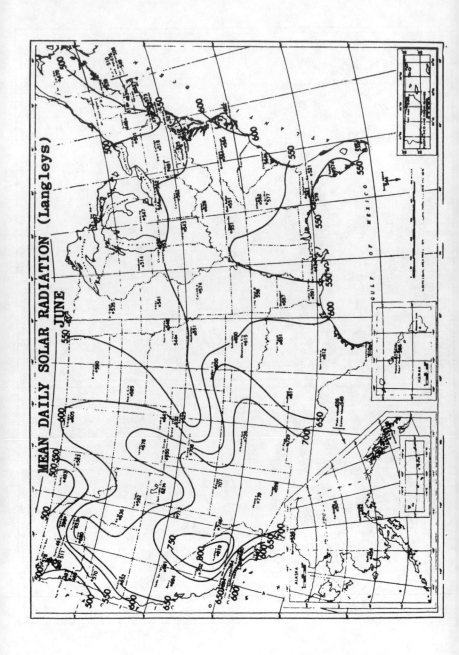

MEAN DAILY SOLAR RADIATION (Langleys)
JUNE

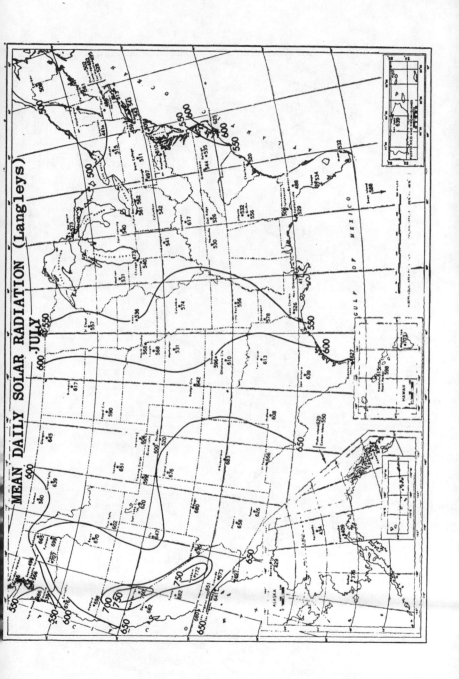

MEAN DAILY SOLAR RADIATION (Langleys)
JULY

177

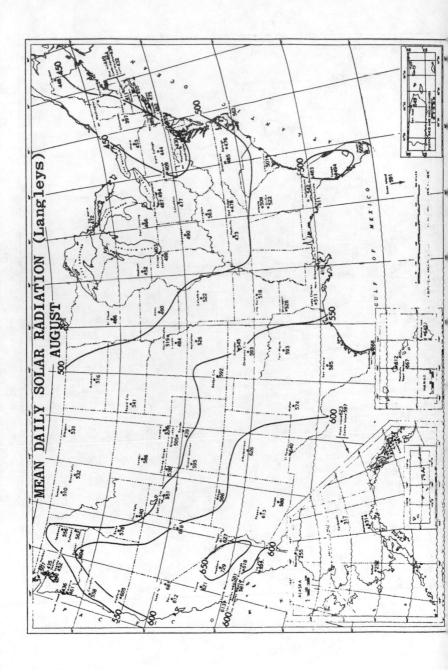

MEAN DAILY SOLAR RADIATION (Langleys)
AUGUST

178

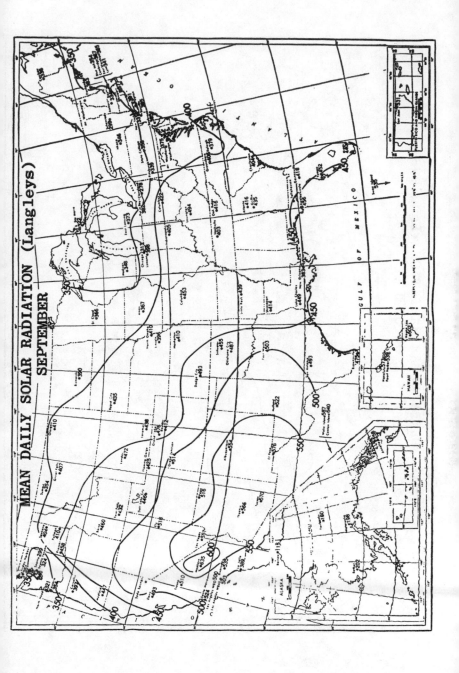

MEAN DAILY SOLAR RADIATION (Langleys)
SEPTEMBER

179

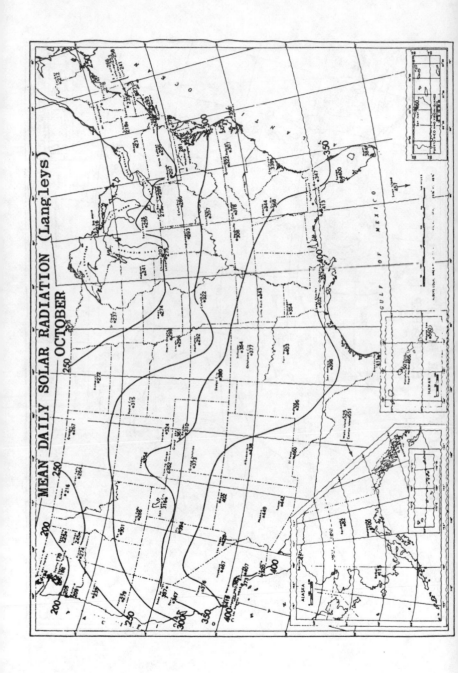

MEAN DAILY SOLAR RADIATION (Langleys)
OCTOBER

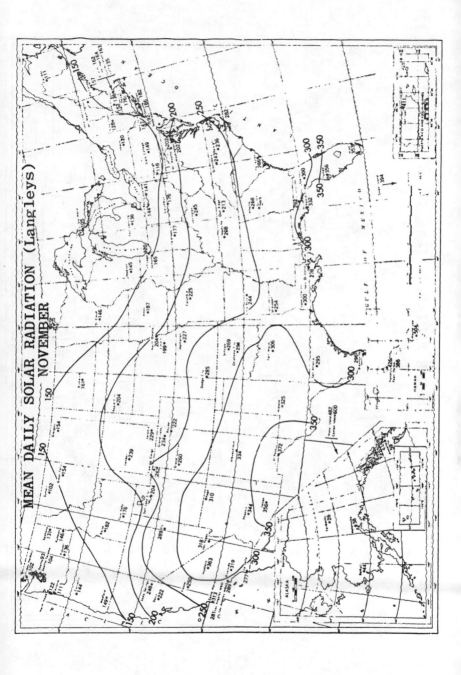

MEAN DAILY SOLAR RADIATION (Langleys)
NOVEMBER

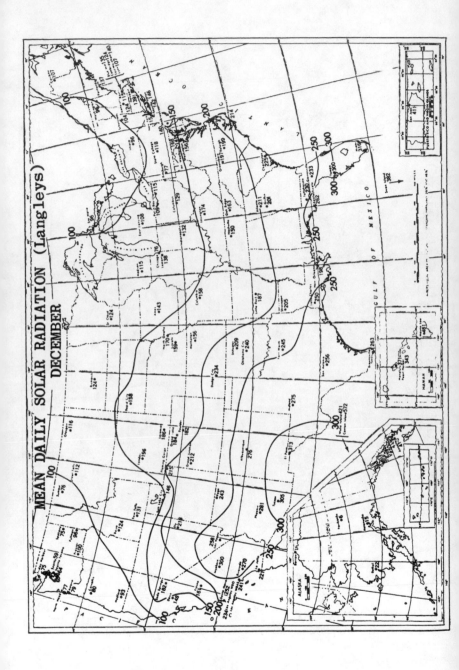

MEAN DAILY SOLAR RADIATION (Langleys)
DECEMBER

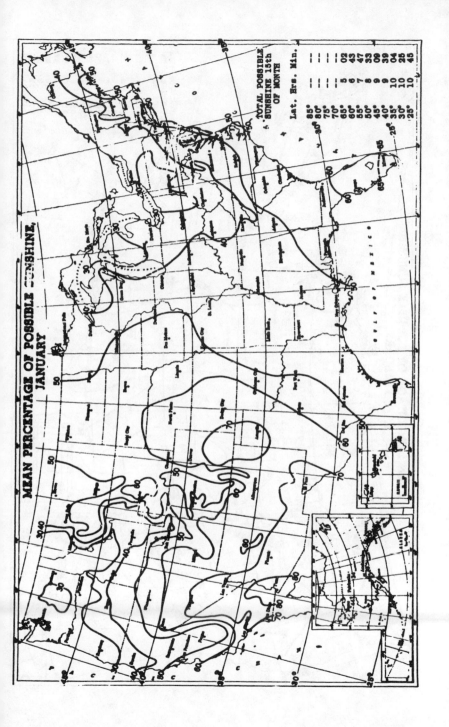

MEAN PERCENTAGE OF POSSIBLE SUNSHINE,
JANUARY

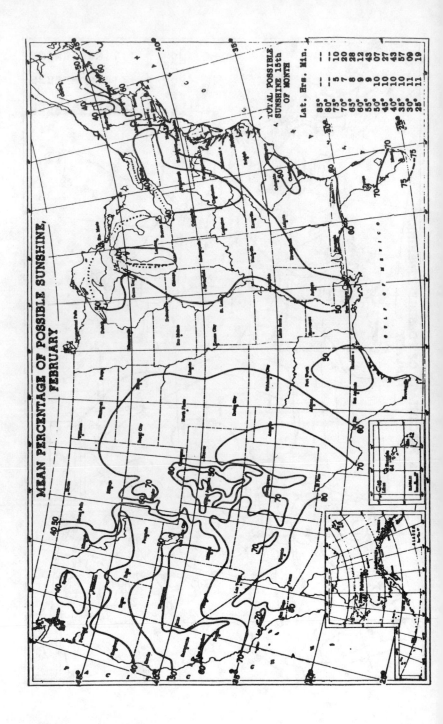

MEAN PERCENTAGE OF POSSIBLE SUNSHINE, FEBRUARY

Lat.	Hrs.	Min.
85°	—	—
80°	—	10
75°	5	20
70°	7	28
65°	8	12
60°	9	43
55°	9	07
50°	10	27
45°	10	43
40°	10	57
35°	11	09
30°	11	19
25°	11	

TOTAL POSSIBLE SUNSHINE 15th OF MONTH

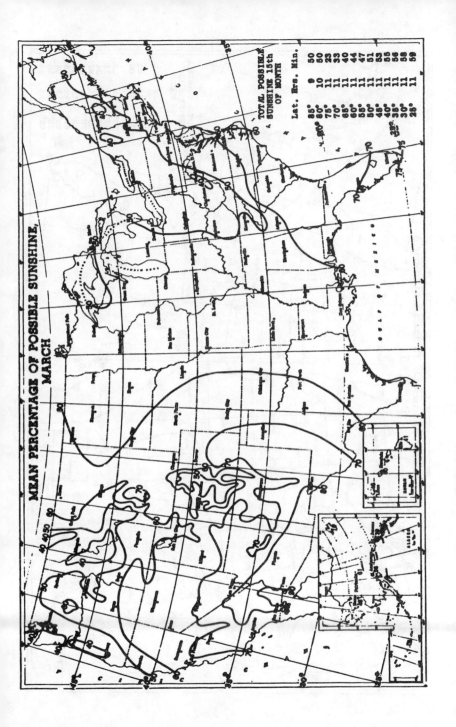

MEAN PERCENTAGE OF POSSIBLE SUNSHINE, MARCH

	TOTAL POSSIBLE SUNSHINE 15th OF MONTH	
Lat.	Hrs.	Min.
85°	9	50
80°	10	50
75°	11	23
70°	11	33
65°	11	40
60°	11	44
55°	11	47
50°	11	51
45°	11	53
40°	11	55
35°	11	56
30°	11	58
25°	11	59

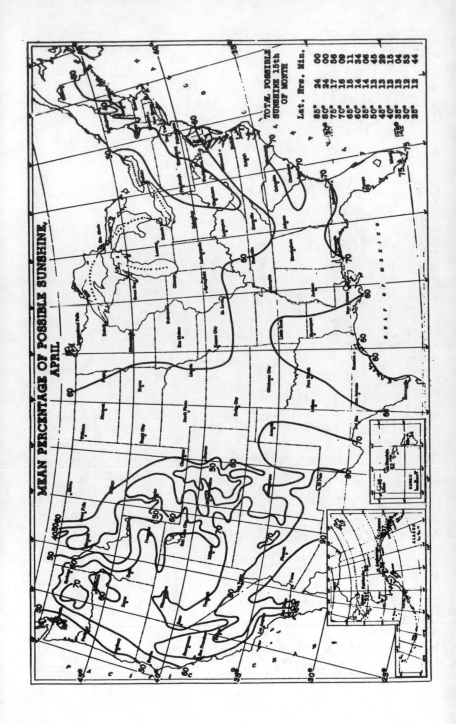

MEAN PERCENTAGE OF POSSIBLE SUNSHINE,
APRIL

TOTAL POSSIBLE
SUNSHINE 15th
OF MONTH

Lat.	Hrs.	Min.
85°	24	00
80°	24	00
75°	17	56
70°	16	09
65°	15	11
60°	14	34
55°	14	08
50°	13	45
45°	13	29
40°	13	15
35°	13	04
30°	12	53
25°	12	44

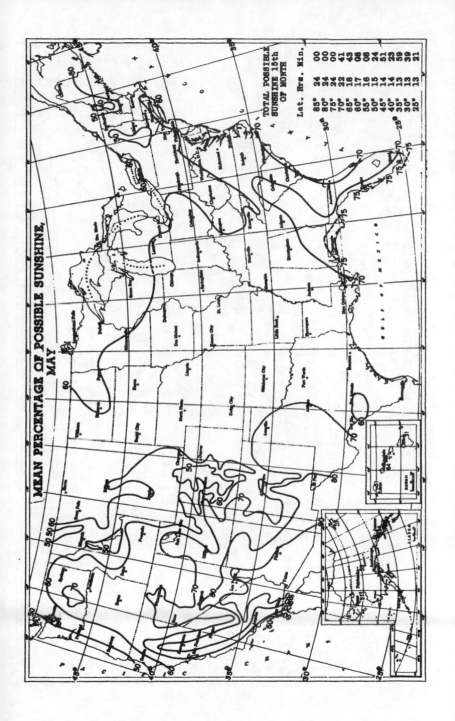

MEAN PERCENTAGE OF POSSIBLE SUNSHINE, MAY

Lat.	Hrs.	Min.
85°	24	00
80°	24	00
75°	24	41
70°	22	43
65°	18	08
60°	17	08
55°	16	24
50°	15	51
45°	14	23
40°	14	59
35°	13	39
30°	13	21
25°	13	

TOTAL POSSIBLE SUNSHINE 15th OF MONTH

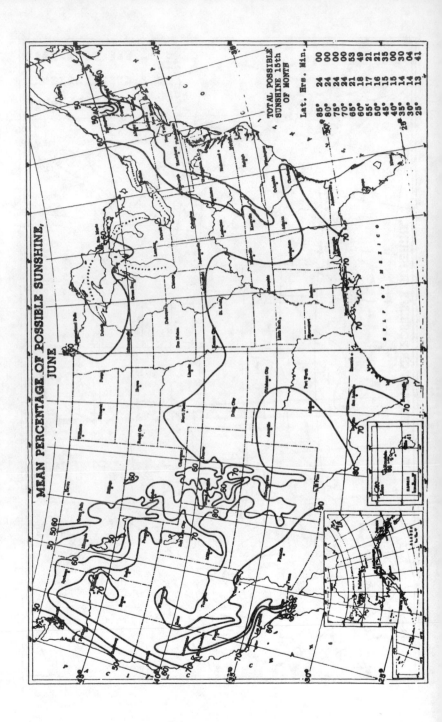

MEAN PERCENTAGE OF POSSIBLE SUNSHINE, JUNE

	TOTAL POSSIBLE SUNSHINE 15th OF MONTH	
Lat.	Hrs.	Min.
85°	24	00
80°	24	00
75°	24	00
70°	24	00
65°	21	53
60°	18	49
55°	17	21
50°	16	21
45°	15	35
40°	15	00
35°	14	30
30°	14	04
25°	13	41

188

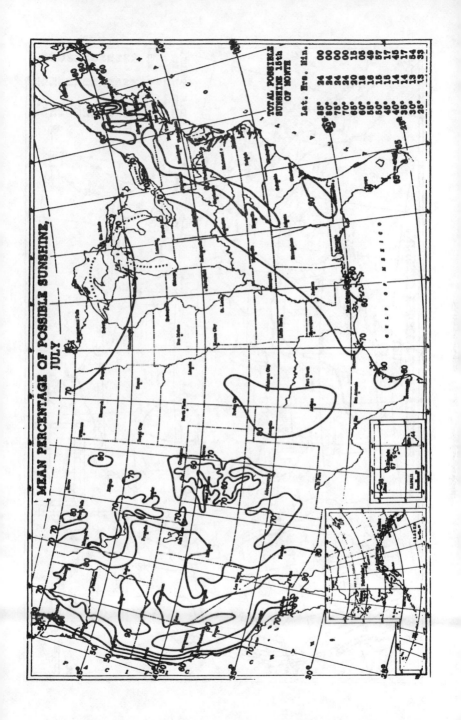

MEAN PERCENTAGE OF POSSIBLE SUNSHINE, JULY

TOTAL POSSIBLE SUNSHINE 15th OF MONTH		
Lat.	Hrs.	Min.
85°	24	00
80°	24	00
75°	24	00
70°	20	15
65°	18	49
60°	16	57
55°	16	17
45°	14	45
40°	14	17
30°	13	54
25°	13	33

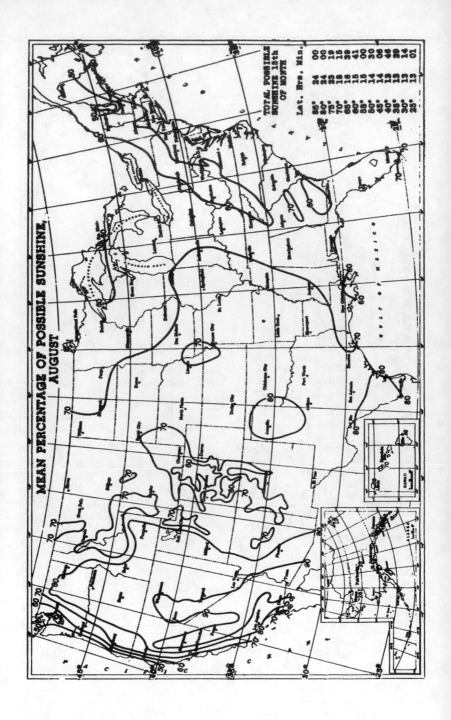

MEAN PERCENTAGE OF POSSIBLE SUNSHINE, AUGUST

TOTAL POSSIBLE SUNSHINE 15th OF MONTH		
Lat.	Hrs.	Min.
65°	24	00
60°	24	00
70°	22	15
65°	16	30
60°	15	00
55°	14	30
45°	14	00
40°	13	44
35°	13	22
30°	13	14
25°	13	01

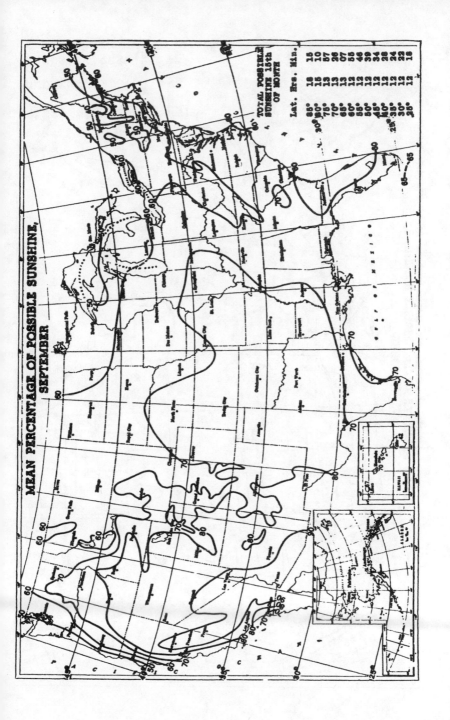

MEAN PERCENTAGE OF POSSIBLE SUNSHINE, SEPTEMBER

Lat.	Eve.	Min.
85°	13	13
80°	13	10
75°	13	57
70°	13	28
65°	13	07
60°	13	55
55°	13	46
50°	13	39
45°	13	34
40°	13	28
35°	12	24
30°	12	22
25°	12	19

TOTAL POSSIBLE SUNSHINE 15th OF MONTH

191

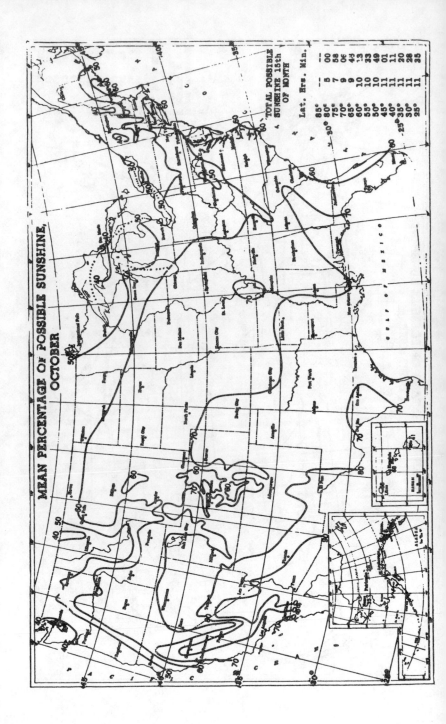

MEAN PERCENTAGE OF POSSIBLE SUNSHINE, OCTOBER

TOTAL POSSIBLE SUNSHINE 15th OF MONTH		
Lat.	Hrs.	Min.
85°	—	00
80°	5	58
75°	7	06
70°	9	13
65°	10	33
60°	10	49
55°	11	01
50°	11	11
45°	11	11
40°	11	20
35°	11	28
30°	11	35
25°	11	

192

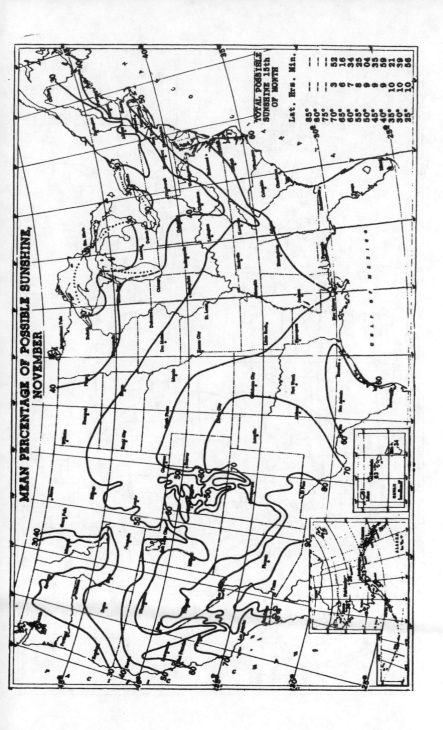

MEAN PERCENTAGE OF POSSIBLE SUNSHINE, NOVEMBER

TOTAL POSSIBLE SUNSHINE 15th OF MONTH		
Lat.	Hrs.	Min.
85°	—	—
80°	—	—
75°	—	—
70°	3	52
65°	6	16
60°	7	25
55°	8	34
50°	9	04
45°	9	35
40°	9	59
35°	10	21
30°	10	39
25°	10	56

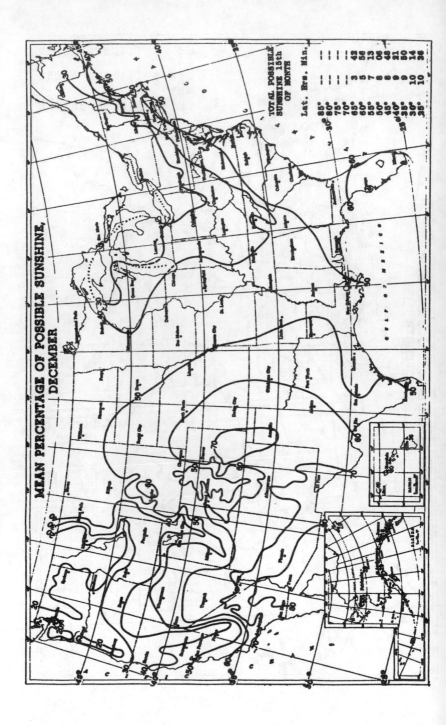

MEAN PERCENTAGE OF POSSIBLE SUNSHINE,
DECEMBER

TOTAL POSSIBLE
SUNSHINE 15th
OF MONTH

Lat.	Hrs.	Min.
85°	—	42
80°	—	56
75°	—	13
70°	—	08
65°	—	48
60°	5	21
55°	7	50
50°	8	14
45°	9	38
40°	9	
35°	10	
30°	10	

194

"percentage of possible sunshine." A device records the cumulative total hours each day when there is enough direct solar radiation to "cast a shadow." This number of hours is then divided by the total hours from sunrise to sunset to get the percentage of possible sunshine. Monthly averages of this percentage are provided in the next 12 contour maps—"Mean Percentage of Possible Sunshine." These values can be taken as the average portion of the daytime hours each month when the sun is not obscured by clouds.

Also included in each of these 12 maps is a table of the average number of hours between sunrise and sunset for that month. You can multiply this number by the mean percentage of possible sunshine to obtain the mean number of hours of sunshine for a particular month and location. A table at the end of this section lists the mean number of hours of sunshine for selected locations across the United States.

These national maps are useful for getting an overview or approximation of the available solar radiation at a particular spot. For many locations, they may be the only way of finding a particular value. As a rule, however, they should be used only when other more local data are unavailable. Many local factors can have significant effect, so care and judgement are important when using interpolated data from these national weather maps.

The total solar radiation is the sum of direct, diffuse, and reflected radiation. At present, a statistical approach is the only reliable method of separating out the diffuse component of horizontal insolation. The full detail of this method is contained in an article by Liu and Jordan; we only summarize their results here. First we ascertain the ratio of the daily insolation on a horizontal surface (measured at a particular weather station) to the extraterrestrial radiation on another horizontal surface (outside the atmosphere). This ratio (usually called the *percent of Extraterrestial radiation*, or % ETR) can be determined from the National Weather Records Center; it is also given in the article by Liu and Jordan. With a knowledge of the % ETR, you can use the accompanying graph to determine the percentage of diffuse radiation of a horizontal surface. For example, 50% ETR corresponds to 38% diffuse radiation and 62% direct radiation.

You are now prepared to convert the direct and diffuse components of the horizontal insolation into the daily total insolation on south-facing tilted or vertical surfaces. The conversion factor for the direct component F_D, depends on the latitude, L, the tilt angle of the surface, β, and the *sunset hour angles*, ω and ω', of the horizontal and tilted surfaces:

$$\text{horizontal surface: } \cos \omega = -\tan L \tan \delta$$
$$\text{tilted surface: } \cos \omega = -\tan (L-\beta)\tan \delta$$

Depending on the value of these two angles ω and ω' the calculation of F_D is slightly different. If ω is less than ω; then

SOURCE: Environmental Science Services Administration, *Climatic Atlas of the United States*. Washington, U.S. Department of Commerce, 1968.

Table E-7. Mean number of hours of sunshine.

STATE AND STATION	YEARS	JAN.	FEB.	MAR.	APR.	MAY	JUNE	JULY	AUG.	SEPT.	OCT.	NOV.	DEC.	ANNUAL
ALA. BIRMINGHAM	30	138	152	207	248	293	294	269	265	244	234	182	136	2662
MOBILE	22	157	158	212	253	301	289	249	259	235	254	195	146	2708
MONTGOMERY	30	160	168	227	267	317	311	288	290	260	250	200	156	2894
ALASKA ANCHORAGE	19	78	114	210	254	268	288	255	184	128	96	68	49	1992
FAIRBANKS	20	54	120	224	302	319	334	274	164	122	85	71	36	2105
JUNEAU	29	71	102	171	200	230	251	193	161	123	67	60	51	1680
NOME	27	72	109	193	226	285	297	204	146	142	101	67	42	1884
ARIZ. PHOENIX	30	248	244	314	346	404	404	377	351	334	307	267	236	3832
PRESCOTT	14	222	230	293	323	378	392	323	305	315	286	254	228	3549
TUCSON	13	255	266	317	350	399	394	329	329	335	317	280	258	3829
YUMA	30	258	266	337	365	419	420	404	380	351	330	285	262	4077
ARK. FT. SMITH	30	146	156	202	234	268	303	321	305	261	230	174	147	2747
LITTLE ROCK	30	143	158	213	243	291	316	321	316	265	251	181	142	2840
CALIF. EUREKA	30	120	138	180	209	247	261	244	205	195	164	127	108	2198
FRESNO	29	153	192	283	330	389	418	435	406	355	306	221	144	3632
LOS ANGELES	30	224	217	273	264	292	299	352	336	295	263	249	220	3284
RED BLUFF	15	156	186	246	302	366	396	438	407	341	277	199	154	3468
SACRAMENTO	30	134	169	255	300	367	405	437	406	347	283	197	122	3422
SAN DIEGO	30	216	212	262	242	261	253	293	277	255	234	236	217	2958
SAN FRANCISCO	30	165	182	251	281	314	330	300	272	267	243	198	156	2959
COLO. DENVER	30	207	205	247	252	281	311	321	297	274	246	200	192	3033
GRAND JUNCTION	30	169	182	243	265	314	350	349	311	291	255	198	168	3095
PUEBLO	30	224	217	261	271	299	340	349	318	290	265	225	211	3270
CONN. HARTFORD	30	141	166	206	223	267	285	299	268	220	193	137	136	2541
NEW HAVEN	30	155	178	215	234	274	291	309	284	238	215	157	154	2704
D. C. WASHINGTON	30	138	160	205	226	267	288	291	264	233	207	162	135	2576
FLA. APALACHICOLA	26	193	195	233	274	328	296	273	259	236	263	216	175	2941
JACKSONVILLE	30	192	189	241	267	296	260	255	248	199	205	191	170	2713
KEY WEST	30	229	238	285	296	307	273	277	269	236	237	226	225	3098
LAKELAND	7	204	186	222	251	285	268	252	242	203	209	212	198	2732
MIAMI	30	222	227	266	275	280	251	267	263	216	215	212	209	2903
PENSACOLA	30	175	180	232	270	311	302	278	284	249	265	206	166	2918
TAMPA	30	223	220	260	283	320	275	257	252	232	243	227	209	3001
GA. ATLANTA	25	154	165	218	266	309	304	284	285	247	241	188	160	2821
MACON	30	177	178	235	279	321	314	292	295	253	236	202	168	2950
SAVANNAH	30	175	173	229	274	307	279	267	256	212	216	197	167	2752
HAWAII HILO	7	153	135	161	112	106	158	184	134	137	153	106	131	1670
HONOLULU	30	227	202	250	255	276	280	293	290	279	257	221	211	3041
LIHUE	10	171	162	176	176	211	246	246	236	246	210	170	161	2411
IDAHO BOISE	30	116	144	218	274	322	352	412	378	311	232	143	104	3006
POCATELLO	30	111	143	211	255	300	338	380	347	296	230	145	108	2864
ILL. CAIRO	15	124	140	218	254	298	324	345	336	279	254	181	145	2918
CHICAGO	30	126	142	199	221	274	300	333	299	247	216	136	118	2611
MOLINE	18	132	139	189	214	255	279	337	300	251	214	130	123	2563
PEORIA	30	134	149	198	229	273	303	336	299	259	222	149	122	2673
SPRINGFIELD	30	127	149	193	224	282	304	346	312	266	225	152	122	2702
IND. EVANSVILLE	30	123	145	199	237	294	322	342	318	274	236	156	120	2766
FT. WAYNE	30	113	136	191	217	281	310	342	306	242	210	120	102	2570
INDIANAPOLIS	30	118	140	193	227	278	313	342	313	265	222	139	118	2668
TERRE HAUTE	24	125	148	189	231	274	302	341	305	253	235	150	122	2675
IOWA BURLINGTON	19	148	165	217	241	284	315	353	327	270	243	175	147	2885
CHARLES CITY	22	137	157	190	226	258	285	336	290	241	207	130	115	2572
DES MOINES	30	155	170	203	236	276	303	346	299	263	227	156	136	2770
SIOUX CITY	30	164	177	216	254	300	320	363	320	270	236	160	146	2926
KAN. CONCORDIA	30	180	172	214	243	281	315	348	308	249	245	189	172	2916
DODGE CITY	30	205	191	249	268	305	335	359	335	290	266	218	198	3219
TOPEKA	18	159	160	193	215	260	287	310	304	263	229	173	149	2702
WICHITA	30	187	186	223	254	291	321	350	325	277	245	206	182	3057
KY. LOUISVILLE	30	115	135	188	221	283	303	324	295	256	219	148	114	2601
LA. NEW ORLEANS	30	160	158	213	247	292	287	260	269	241	260	200	157	2744
SHREVEPORT	19	151	172	214	240	298	332	339	322	289	273	208	177	3015
MAINE EASTPORT	22	133	151	196	201	245	248	275	260	205	175	105	115	2309
PORTLAND	30	155	174	213	226	268	286	312	294	229	202	146	148	2653
MD. BALTIMORE	30	148	170	211	229	270	295	299	272	238	212	164	145	2653
MASS. BLUE HILL OBS.	10	125	136	165	182	233	248	266	241	211	181	134	135	2257
BOSTON	30	148	168	212	222	263	283	300	280	232	207	152	148	2615
NANTUCKET	22	128	156	214	227	278	284	291	279	242	208	149	129	2585
MICH. ALPENA	24	86	124	198	228	261	303	339	285	204	159	70	67	2324
DETROIT	30	90	128	180	212	263	295	321	284	226	189	98	89	2375
LANSING	30	84	119	175	215	272	305	344	294	228	182	87	73	2378
ESCANABA	30	112	148	204	226	266	283	316	267	198	162	90	94	2366
GRAND RAPIDS	30	74	117	178	218	277	306	349	304	231	188	92	70	2406
MARQUETTE	30	78	113	172	207	248	268	305	251	186	142	68	66	2104
SAULT STE. MARIE	30	83	123	187	217	252	269	309	256	165	133	61	62	2117
MINN. DULUTH	30	125	163	221	235	268	282	328	277	203	166	100	107	2475
MINNEAPOLIS	30	140	166	200	231	272	302	343	296	237	193	115	112	2607
MISS. JACKSON	12	130	147	199	244	280	287	279	287	235	223	185	150	2646
VICKSBURG	30	136	141	199	232	284	304	291	297	254	244	183	140	2705
MO. COLUMBIA	30	147	164	207	232	281	296	341	298	262	225	166	138	2757
KANSAS CITY	30	154	170	211	235	278	313	347	308	266	235	178	151	2846
ST. JOSEPH	23	154	165	211	231	274	301	347	287	260	224	168	144	2766
ST. LOUIS	30	137	152	202	235	283	301	325	289	256	223	166	125	2694
SPRINGFIELD	30	155	164	213	238	278	305	342	310	269	233	183	140	2820
MONT. BILLINGS	21	140	154	208	236	283	301	372	332	258	213	136	129	2762
GREAT FALLS	19	154	176	245	261	299	299	381	342	256	206	132	133	2884
HAVRE	30	136	174	234	268	311	312	384	339	260	202	132	122	2874
HELENA	30	138	168	215	241	292	292	342	336	258	202	137	121	2742
MISSOULA	25	85	109	167	209	261	260	378	328	246	178	90	66	2377

196

STATE AND STATION	YEARS	JAN.	FEB.	MAR.	APR.	MAY	JUNE	JULY	AUG.	SEPT.	OCT.	NOV.	DEC.	ANNUAL
NEBR. LINCOLN	30	173	172	213	244	287	316	356	309	266	237	174	160	2907
NORTH PLATTE	30	181	179	221	246	282	310	343	304	264	242	184	169	2925
OMAHA	30	172	188	222	259	305	332	379	311	270	248	166	145	2997
VALENTINE	30	185	194	229	252	296	323	369	326	275	242	174	172	3037
NEV. ELY	22	186	197	262	260	300	354	359	344	303	255	204	187	3211
LAS VEGAS	8	239	251	314	336	386	411	383	364	345	301	258	250	3838
RENO	30	185	199	267	306	354	376	414	391	336	273	212	170	3483
WINNEMUCCA	30	142	155	207	255	312	346	395	375	316	242	177	139	3061
N. H. CONCORD	23	136	153	192	196	229	261	286	260	214	179	122	126	2354
MT. WASHINGTON OBS.	18	94	98	133	141	162	145	150	143	139	159	89	87	1540
N. J. ATLANTIC CITY	30	151	173	210	233	273	287	298	271	239	218	177	153	2683
TRENTON	30	145	168	203	235	277	294	309	273	239	208	160	142	2653
N. MEX. ALBUQUERQUE	30	221	218	273	299	343	365	340	317	299	279	245	219	3418
ROSWELL	21	218	223	286	306	330	333	341	313	266	266	242	216	3340
N. Y. ALBANY	30	125	151	194	213	266	301	317	286	224	192	115	112	2496
BINGHAMTON	30	94	119	151	170	226	256	266	230	184	158	92	79	2025
BUFFALO	30	110	125	180	212	274	319	338	297	239	183	97	84	2458
NEW YORK	30	154	171	213	237	268	289	302	271	235	213	169	155	2677
ROCHESTER	30	93	123	172	209	274	314	333	294	224	173	97	86	2392
SYRACUSE	30	87	115	165	197	261	295	316	276	211	163	81	74	2241
N. C. ASHEVILLE	30	146	161	211	247	289	292	268	250	235	222	179	146	2646
CAPE HATTERAS	9	152	168	206	259	293	301	286	265	214	202	169	154	2669
CHARLOTTE	30	165	177	230	267	313	316	291	277	247	243	198	167	2891
GREENSBORO	30	157	171	217	231	298	302	287	272	243	236	190	163	2767
RALEIGH	29	154	168	220	255	290	284	277	253	224	215	184	156	2680
WILMINGTON	30	179	180	237	279	314	312	286	273	237	238	206	178	2919
N. DAK. BISMARCK	30	141	170	205	236	279	294	358	307	243	198	130	125	2686
DEVILS LAKE	30	150	177	220	250	291	297	352	302	230	198	123	124	2714
FARGO	30	132	170	210	232	283	288	343	293	222	187	112	114	2586
WILLISTON	29	141	168	215	260	305	312	377	328	247	206	131	129	2819
OHIO CINCINNATI (ABBE)	30	115	137	186	222	273	309	323	295	253	205	138	118	2574
CLEVELAND	30	79	111	167	209	274	301	325	288	235	187	99	77	2352
COLUMBUS	30	112	132	177	215	270	296	323	291	250	210	131	101	2506
DAYTON	10	114	136	195	222	281	313	323	307	268	229	152	124	2664
SANDUSKY	30	100	128	183	229	285	312	343	302	248	201	111	91	2533
TOLEDO	30	93	120	170	203	263	296	331	298	241	196	106	92	2409
OKLA. OKLAHOMA CITY	29	175	182	235	253	290	329	352	331	282	243	201	175	3048
TULSA	18	152	164	200	213	244	287	314	308	281	241	207	172	2783
OREG. BAKER	22	118	143	198	251	302	313	406	368	289	215	132	100	2835
PORTLAND	30	77	97	142	203	246	249	329	275	218	134	87	65	2122
ROSEBURG	30	69	96	148	205	257	278	369	329	255	146	81	50	2283
PA. HARRISBURG	30	132	160	203	230	277	297	319	282	233	200	140	131	2604
PHILADELPHIA	30	142	166	203	231	270	281	288	253	225	205	158	142	2564
PITTSBURGH	25	89	114	163	200	239	260	283	250	234	180	114	76	2202
READING	30	133	151	195	220	259	275	293	259	219	198	144	127	2473
SCRANTON	30	108	138	178	199	251	269	290	249	213	183	120	105	2303
R. I. PROVIDENCE	30	145	168	211	221	271	285	292	267	226	207	153	143	2589
S. C. CHARLESTON	30	188	189	243	284	323	308	297	281	244	239	210	187	2993
COLUMBIA	30	173	183	233	274	312	312	291	283	243	242	202	166	2914
GREENVILLE	26	166	176	227	274	307	300	278	274	239	232	192	157	2822
S. DAK. HURON	30	153	177	213	250	295	321	367	320	260	212	142	134	2844
RAPID CITY	30	164	182	222	245	278	300	348	317	266	228	164	144	2858
TENN. CHATTANOOGA	30	126	146	187	239	290	295	278	266	247	220	169	128	2591
KNOXVILLE	30	124	144	189	237	281	288	277	248	237	213	157	120	2515
MEMPHIS	30	135	152	204	244	296	321	319	314	261	243	180	139	2808
NASHVILLE	30	123	142	196	241	285	308	292	279	250	224	168	126	2634
TEX. ABILENE	13	190	199	250	259	290	347	335	322	276	245	223	201	3137
AMARILLO	30	207	199	258	276	305	338	350	328	288	260	229	205	3243
AUSTIN	30	148	152	207	221	266	302	331	320	261	242	180	160	2790
BROWNSVILLE	30	147	152	187	210	272	297	326	311	246	252	165	151	2716
CORPUS CHRISTI	24	160	165	212	237	295	329	366	341	276	264	194	164	3003
DALLAS	30	155	159	220	238	279	326	341	325	274	240	191	163	2911
DEL RIO	27	173	173	230	237	259	279	331	319	252	240	195	178	2866
EL PASO	30	234	236	299	329	373	369	336	327	300	287	257	236	3583
GALVESTON	30	155	149	203	230	288	322	305	292	257	264	199	151	2811
HOUSTON	30	144	141	193	212	266	298	294	281	238	239	181	146	2633
PORT ARTHUR	30	153	149	209	235	292	317	285	281	252	256	191	148	2768
SAN ANTONIO	30	148	153	213	224	258	292	325	307	261	241	183	160	2765
UTAH SALT LAKE CITY	30	137	155	227	269	329	358	377	346	306	249	171	135	3059
VT. BURLINGTON	30	103	127	184	185	244	270	291	266	199	152	77	80	2178
VA. LYNCHBURG	26	153	169	216	243	288	297	288	264	235	217	177	158	2705
NORFOLK	30	156	174	223	257	304	311	296	282	237	220	182	161	2803
RICHMOND	30	144	166	211	248	280	296	286	263	230	211	176	152	2663
WASH. NORTH HEAD	22	76	97	135	182	221	214	226	186	170	123	87	66	1783
SEATTLE	30	74	99	154	201	247	234	304	248	197	122	77	62	2019
SPOKANE	30	78	120	197	262	308	309	397	350	264	177	86	57	2605
TATOOSH ISLAND	30	70	100	135	182	229	217	235	190	175	129	71	69	1793
WALLA WALLA	30	72	106	194	262	317	335	411	367	280	198	92	51	2685
W. VA. ELKINS	24	110	119	158	198	227	256	225	236	211	186	131	103	2160
PARKERSBURG	30	91	111	155	200	252	277	286	264	230	189	117	93	2265
WIS. GREEN BAY	30	121	148	194	210	251	279	314	266	213	176	110	106	2388
MADISON	30	126	147	196	214	258	285	336	288	230	198	116	108	2502
MILWAUKEE	30	116	134	191	218	267	293	340	292	235	193	125	106	2510
WYO. CHEYENNE	30	191	197	243	237	259	304	318	286	265	242	188	170	2900
LANDER	30	200	208	260	264	301	340	361	326	280	233	186	185	3144
SHERIDAN	30	160	179	226	245	286	303	367	333	266	221	153	145	2884
P. R. SAN JUAN	30	231	229	273	252	240	245	264	257	219	229	217	222	2878

$$F_D = \frac{\cos(L-\beta)}{\cos L} \times \frac{\sin \omega - \omega \cos \omega'}{\sin \omega - \omega \cos \omega}$$

If ω' is smaller than ω, then

$$F_D = \frac{\cos(L-\beta)}{\cos L} \times \frac{\sin \omega' - \omega' \cos \omega'}{\sin \omega - \omega \cos \omega}$$

The direct component of the radiation on a tilted or vertical surface is $I'_D = F_D \times I_D$, where I_D is the direct horizontal insolation.

The treatment of diffuse and reflected radiation is a bit different. The diffuse rdiation is assumed to come uniformly from all corners of the sky, so one need only determine the fraction of the sky exposed to a tilted surface and reduce the horizontal diffuse radiation accordingly. The diffuse radiation on a surface tilted at an angle β is

$$I'_d = \frac{1 + \cos \beta}{2} \times I_d$$

where I_d is the daily horizontal diffuse radiation. The reflected radiation on a tilted surface is

$$I'_r = p \times \frac{1 - \cos \beta}{2} \times (I_D + I_d)$$

where p is the reflectance of the horizontal surface.

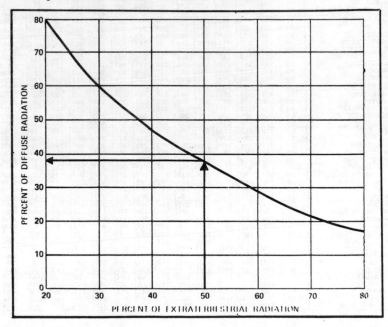

The hourly, monthly, and yearly heat loss from a house depends on the temperature difference between the indoor and outdoor air. To aid in the calculation of these heat losses, ASHRAE publishes the expected winter *design temperatures* and the monthly and yearly total *degree days* for many cities and towns in the United States.

The maximum heat loss rate occurs when the temperature is lowest, and you need some idea of the lowest likely temperature in your locale in order to size a conventional heating unit. The ASHRAE *Handbook of Fundamentals* provides three choices—the "median of annual extremes" and the "99%" and "97½%" design temperatures. The median of annual extremes is the average of the lowest winter temperatures recorded in each of the past 30 to 40 years. The 99% and 97½% design temperatures are the temperatures which are normally *exceeded* during those percentages of the time in December, January and February. We list the 97½% temperatures here together with the average winter temperatures. For example, the temperature will fall below 19°F for 2½% of the time (about 2 days) during a typical Birmingham winter. Consult the ASHRAE *Handbook of Fundamentals* for more detailed listings.

Degree days gauge heating requirements over the long run. One degree day accrues for every day the average outdoor temperature is 1°F below 65°F, which is the base for degree day calculations because most houses don't require any heating until outdoor temperatures fall below this level. For example, if the outdoor air temperature remained constant at 30°F for the entire month of January, then $31 \times (65 - 30) = 1085$ degree days would result. Both monthly and yearly total degree days are listed in these tables, but only the months from September to May are included here because very little heating is needed in the summer. The yearly total degree days are the sum over *all 12 months*. More complete listings of monthly and yearly degree days can be found in the ASHRAE *Guide and Data Book*.

The conduction heat flow through a wall, window, door, roof, ceiling, or floor decreases as more *resistance* is placed in the path of the flow. All materials have some resistance to conduction heat flow. Those that have high resistance are called insulators; those with low resistance are called conductors.

Insulators are compared to one another according to their R-values, which are a measure of their resistance. The R-value of material increases with its thickness—a two-inch thick sheet of styrofoam has twice the resistance of a one-inch sheet. And two similar building materials that differ in dentisy will also differ in R-value. Generally, though not always, the lighter material will have a higher rx/value because it has more pockets or air trapped in it. Finally, the average temperature of a material also affects its R-value. The colder it gets, the better most materials retard the flow of heat.

SOURCE: Liu, B.Y.H. and R.C. Jordan, "Availability of Solar Energy for Flat-Plate Solar Heat Collectors." in *Low Temperature Engineering Applications of Solar Energy*, edited by Richard C. Jordan, New York: ASHRAE, 1967.

Table E-8. Degree days and design temperatures. continued on page 201 and 202.

State	City	Avg. Winter Temp	Design Temp	Sep	Oct	Nov	Dec	Jan	Feb	Mar	Apr	May	Yearly Total
Ala	Birmingham	54 2	19	6	93	363	555	592	462	363	108	9	2551
	Huntsville	51 3	13	12	127	426	663	694	557	434	138	19	3070
	Mobile	59 9	26	0	22	213	357	415	300	211	42	0	1560
	Montgomery	55 4	22	0	68	330	527	543	417	316	90	0	2291
Alaska	Anchorage	23 0	−25	516	930	1284	1572	1631	1316	1293	879	592	10864
	Fairbanks	6.7	−53	642	1203	1833	2254	2359	1901	1739	1068	555	14279
	Juneau	32 1	− 7	483	725	921	1135	1237	1070	1073	810	601	9075
	Nome	13 1	−32	693	1094	1455	1820	1879	1666	1770	1314	930	14171
Ariz	Flagstaff	35.6	0	201	558	867	1073	1169	991	911	651	437	7152
	Phoenix	58 5	31	0	22	234	415	474	328	217	75	0	1765
	Tucson	58 1	29	0	25	231	406	471	344	242	75	6	1800
	Winslow	43 0	9	6	245	711	1008	1054	770	601	291	96	4782
	Yuma	64 2	37	0	0	108	264	307	190	90	15	0	974
Ark	Fort Smith	50 3	9	12	127	450	704	781	596	456	144	22	3292
	Little Rock	50 5	19	9	127	465	716	756	577	434	126	9	3219
	Texarkana	54 2	22	0	78	345	561	626	468	350	105	0	2533
Calif	Bakersfield	55 4	31	0	37	282	502	546	364	267	105	19	2122
	Burbank	58.6	36	6	43	177	301	366	277	239	138	81	1646
	Eureka	49 9	32	258	329	414	499	546	470	505	438	372	4643
	Fresno	53 3	28	0	84	354	577	605	426	335	162	62	2611
	Long Beach	57 8	36	9	47	171	316	397	311	264	171	93	1803
	Los Angeles	57 4	41	42	78	180	291	372	302	288	219	158	2061
	Oakland	53 5	35	45	127	309	481	527	400	353	255	180	2870
	Sacramento	53.9	30	0	56	321	546	583	414	332	178	72	2502
	San Diego	59 5	42	21	43	135	236	298	235	214	135	90	1458
	San Francisco	55 1	42	102	118	231	388	443	336	319	279	239	3001
	Santa Maria	54 3	32	96	146	270	391	459	370	363	282	233	2967
Colo	Alamosa	29 7	−17	279	639	1065	1420	1476	1162	1020	696	440	8529
	Colorado Springs	37 3	− 1	132	456	825	1032	1128	938	893	582	319	6423
	Denver	37 6	− 2	117	428	819	1035	1132	938	887	558	288	6283
	Grand Junction	39 3	8	30	313	786	1113	1209	907	729	387	146	5641
	Pueblo	40 4	− 5	54	326	750	986	1085	871	772	429	174	5462
Conn	Bridgeport	39 9	4	66	307	615	986	1079	966	853	510	208	5617
	Hartford	37 3	1	117	394	714	1101	1190	1042	908	519	205	6235
	New Haven	39 0	5	87	347	648	1011	1097	991	871	543	245	5897
Del	Wilmington	42 5	12	51	270	588	927	980	874	735	387	112	4930
D C	Washington	45 7	16	33	217	519	834	871	762	626	288	74	4224
Fla	Daytona Beach	64 5	32	0	0	75	211	248	190	140	15	0	879
	Fort Myers	68.6	38	0	0	24	109	146	101	62	0	0	442
	Jacksonville	61 9	29	0	12	144	310	332	246	174	21	0	1239
	Key West	73 1	55	0	0	0	28	40	31	9	0	0	108
	Lakeland	66 7	35	0	0	57	164	195	146	99	0	0	661
	Miami	71 1	44	0	0	0	65	74	56	19	0	0	214
	Miami Beach	72 5	45	0	0	0	40	56	36	9	0	0	141
	Orlando	65 7	33	0	0	72	198	220	165	105	6	0	766
	Pensacola	60 4	29	0	19	195	353	400	277	183	36	0	1463
	Tallahassee	60 1	25	0	28	198	360	375	286	202	36	0	1485

SOURCES: ASHRAE, *Guide and Data Book*, 1970. Reprinted by permission.
ASHRAE, *Handbook of Fundamentals*, 1972. Reprinted by permission.

Right table (top)

State	City	Avg. Winter Temp	Design Temp	Sep	Oct	Nov	Dec	Jan	Feb	Mar	Apr	May	Yearly Total
Mich.	Alpena	29.7	-5	273	580	912	1268	1404	1299	1218	777	446	8506
	Detroit	37.2	4	87	360	738	1088	1181	1058	936	522	220	6232
	Escanaba	29.6	-7	243	539	924	1293	1445	1296	1203	777	456	8481
	Flint	33.1	-1	159	465	843	1212	1330	1198	1066	639	319	7377
	Grand Rapids	34.9	5	135	434	804	1147	1259	1134	1011	579	279	6894
	Lansing	34.8	2	138	431	813	1163	1262	1142	1011	579	273	6909
	Marquette	30.2	-8	240	527	936	1268	1411	1268	1187	771	468	8393
	Muskegon	36.0	4	120	400	762	1088	1209	1100	995	594	310	6696
	Sault Ste. Marie	27.7	-12	279	580	951	1367	1525	1380	1277	810	477	9048
Minn.	Duluth	23.4	-19	330	632	1131	1581	1745	1518	1355	840	490	10000
	Minneapolis	28.3	-14	189	505	1014	1454	1631	1380	1166	621	288	8382
	Rochester	28.8	-17	186	474	1005	1438	1593	1366	1150	630	301	8295
Miss.	Jackson	55.7	21	0	65	315	502	540	414	310	87	0	2239
	Meridian	55.4	20	0	81	339	518	543	417	310	81	0	2289
	Vicksburg	56.9	23	0	53	279	462	512	384	282	69	0	2041
Mo.	Columbia	42.3	2	54	251	651	967	1076	874	716	324	121	5046
	Kansas City	43.9	4	39	220	612	905	1032	818	682	294	109	5711
	St Joseph	40.3	1	60	285	708	1039	1172	949	769	267	133	5484
	St Louis	43.1	4	60	251	627	936	1026	848	704	312	121	4900
	Springfield	44.5	5	45	223	680	877	973	781	680	291	105	4900
Mont.	Billings	34.5	-10	186	487	897	1135	1296	1100	970	570	285	7049
	Glasgow	26.4	-25	270	608	1104	1466	1711	1400	1187	648	335	8996
	Great Falls	32.8	-20	258	543	921	1169	1349	1154	1063	642	384	7750
	Havre	28.1	-22	306	595	1065	1367	1584	1364	1181	657	338	8700
	Helena	31.1	-17	294	601	1042	1265	1438	1170	1042	651	381	8129
	Kalispell	31.4	-7	321	654	1020	1240	1401	1134	1029	639	397	8191
	Miles City	31.2	-19	174	502	972	1296	1504	1252	1057	579	276	7723
	Missoula	31.5	-7	303	651	1035	1287	1420	1120	970	621	391	8125
Neb.	Grand Island	36.0	-6	108	381	834	1172	1314	1089	908	462	211	6530
	Lincoln	38.8	-4	75	301	726	1066	1237	1016	834	402	171	5864
	Norfolk	34.0	-11	111	397	873	1234	1414	1170	983	498	233	6979
	North Platte	35.5	-6	123	440	885	1166	1271	1039	930	519	248	6684
	Omaha	35.6	-5	105	357	828	1175	1355	1126	939	465	208	6612
	Scottsbluff	35.9	-8	138	459	876	1128	1231	1008	921	552	285	6673
Nev.	Elko	34.0	-13	225	561	924	1197	1314	1036	911	621	409	7433
	Ely	33.1	-6	234	592	939	1184	1308	1075	977	672	456	7733
	Las Vegas	53.5	23	0	78	387	617	688	487	335	111	6	2709
	Reno	39.3	2	204	490	801	1026	1073	916	837	573	357	6332
	Winnemucca	36.7	1	210	536	876	1091	1172	1006	911	510	363	6761
N H	Concord	33.0	-11	177	505	822	1240	1358	1184	1032	636	298	7383
N J	Atlantic City	43.2	14	39	251	549	880	936	848	741	420	133	4812
	Newark	42.8	11	30	248	573	921	983	876	729	430	118	4589
	Trenton	42.4	12	57	264	576	924	985	885	753	399	121	4980
N M	Albuquerque	45.0	14	12	229	642	868	930	703	595	288	81	4348
	Raton	38.1	-2	126	431	825	1048	1116	904	834	543	301	6228
	Roswell	47.5	16	18	202	573	806	840	641	481	201	31	3793
	Silver City	48.0	14	6	183	525	729	791	605	518	261	87	3705

Left table (bottom)

State	City	Avg. Winter Temp	Design Temp	Sep	Oct	Nov	Dec	Jan	Feb	Mar	Apr	May	Yearly Total
	Tampa	66.4	36	0	0	60	171	202	148	102	0	0	683
	West Palm Beach	68.4	40	0	0	0	65	87	64	31	0	0	253
Ga.	Athens	51.8	17	12	115	405	632	642	529	431	141	22	2929
	Atlanta	51.7	18	18	124	417	648	636	518	428	147	25	2961
	Augusta	54.5	20	0	78	333	552	549	445	350	90	0	2397
	Columbus	54.8	23	0	87	333	543	552	434	338	90	0	2383
	Macon	56.2	23	0	71	297	502	505	403	295	63	0	2136
	Rome	49.9	16	24	161	474	701	710	577	468	177	34	3326
	Savannah	57.8	24	0	47	246	437	437	353	254	45	0	1819
Hawaii	Hilo	71.9	59	0	0	0	0	0	0	0	0	0	0
	Honolulu	74.2	60	0	0	0	0	0	0	0	0	0	0
Idaho	Boise	39.7	4	132	415	792	1017	1113	854	722	438	245	5809
	Lewiston	41.0	6	123	403	756	933	1063	815	694	426	219	5542
	Pocatello	34.8	-8	172	493	900	1166	1324	1058	905	555	319	7033
Ill.	Chicago	37.5	-4	81	326	753	1113	1209	1044	890	480	211	6155
	Moline	36.4	-7	99	335	774	1181	1314	1100	918	450	189	6408
	Peoria	38.1	-2	87	326	759	1113	1218	1025	921	426	183	6025
	Rockford	34.8	-7	114	400	837	1221	1333	1137	961	516	236	6830
	Springfield	40.6	-1	72	291	696	1023	1135	955	904	354	135	5429
Ind.	Evansville	45.0	6	66	220	606	896	955	767	620	237	68	4435
	Fort Wayne	37.3	0	105	378	783	1135	1178	1028	890	471	189	6205
	Indianapolis	39.6	0	90	316	723	1051	1113	949	834	432	177	5699
	South Bend	36.6	-3	111	372	777	1125	1221	1070	933	525	239	6439
Iowa	Burlington	37.6	-7	93	322	768	1135	1259	1044	859	426	177	6114
	Des Moines	35.5	-10	96	363	828	1225	1370	1137	915	438	180	6588
	Dubuque	32.7	-12	156	450	906	1304	1445	1210	1023	540	260	7376
	Sioux City	34.0	-11	108	369	867	1240	1435	1198	989	483	214	6951
	Waterloo	32.6	-12	138	428	909	1296	1460	1221	1023	531	229	7320
Kans.	Dodge City	42.5	3	33	251	666	939	1051	840	719	354	124	4986
	Goodland	37.8	-2	81	381	810	1073	1166	955	884	507	236	6141
	Topeka	41.7	3	57	270	672	980	1122	893	722	330	124	5182
	Wichita	44.2	5	33	229	618	905	1023	804	645	270	87	4620
Ky.	Covington	41.4	3	75	291	669	983	1035	893	756	390	149	5265
	Lexington	43.8	6	54	239	660	983	946	818	685	325	105	4683
	Louisville	44.0	8	54	248	609	890	930	818	682	315	105	4660
La.	Alexandria	57.5	25	0	56	273	431	471	361	260	69	0	1921
	Baton Rouge	59.8	25	0	31	216	369	409	294	208	33	0	1560
	Lake Charles	60.5	29	0	19	210	341	381	274	195	39	0	1459
	New Orleans	61.0	32	0	19	192	322	363	258	192	39	0	1385
	Shreveport	56.2	22	0	47	297	477	552	426	304	81	0	2184
Me.	Caribou	24.4	-18	336	682	1044	1535	1690	1470	1308	858	468	9767
	Portland	33.0	-5	195	508	807	1215	1339	1182	1042	675	372	7511
Md.	Baltimore	43.7	12	48	264	585	905	936	820	679	327	90	4654
	Frederick	42.0	7	66	307	624	955	989	876	741	384	127	5087
Mass.	Boston	40.0	6	60	316	603	983	1088	972	846	513	208	5634
	Pittsfield	32.6	-5	219	524	831	1231	1339	1196	1063	660	326	7578
	Worcester	34.7	3	147	450	774	1172	1271	1123	998	612	304	6969

Table E-8. continued from page 201.

State	City	Avg Winter Temp	Design Temp	Sep	Oct	Nov	Dec	Jan	Feb	Mar	Apr	May	Yearly Total
N Y	Albany	34.6	5	138	440	777	1194	1311	1156	992	564	239	6875
	Binghamton	34.5	1	141	471	732	1107	1262	1081	949	543	229	6451
	Buffalo	34.5	3	141	440	777	1156	1256	1145	1039	645	329	7062
	New York	42.8	11	30	233	540	902	986	885	760	408	118	4871
	Rochester	35.4	2	126	415	747	1125	1234	1123	1014	597	279	6748
	Schenectady	35.4	-5	123	431	756	1159	1283	1131	1008	531	229	6650
	Syracuse	35.2	2	132	415	744	1153	1271	1140	1004	570	248	6756
N C	Asheville	46.7	13	48	245	555	775	784	683	592	273	87	4042
	Charlotte	50.4	18	6	124	438	691	691	582	481	156	22	3191
	Greensboro	47.5	14	33	192	513	778	784	672	552	234	47	3805
	Raleigh	49.4	16	21	164	450	716	725	616	487	180	34	3393
	Wilmington	54.0	23	0	74	291	521	524	462	357	96	0	2347
	Winston Salem	48.4	14	21	171	483	747	753	652	524	207	37	3595
N D	Bismarck	26.6	-24	222	577	1083	1463	1708	1442	1203	645	329	8851
	Devils Lake	22.4	-23	273	642	1191	1634	1872	1579	1345	753	381	9901
	Fargo	24.8	-22	219	574	1107	1569	1789	1520	1262	690	357	9226
	Williston	25.2	-21	261	601	1122	1513	1758	1473	1262	681	357	9243
Ohio	Akron Canton	38.1	1	96	381	726	1070	1016	871	489	202	39	6037
	Cincinnati	45.1	8	39	208	558	862	915	790	642	294	90	4410
	Cleveland	37.2	2	105	384	738	1088	1159	1047	918	552	260	6351
	Columbus	39.7	2	84	347	714	1039	1088	949	809	426	171	5660
	Dayton	39.8	0	78	360	696	1045	1097	955	809	429	167	5622
	Mansfield	36.4	1	114	397	768	1110	1169	1042	924	543	245	6403
	Toledo	36.4	1	117	406	792	1110	1169	1042	921	540	248	6494
	Youngstown	36.8	1	120	412	771	1108	1169	1047	921	540	248	6417
Okla	Oklahoma City	48.3	11	15	164	498	768	868	664	527	189	34	3725
	Tulsa	47.7	12	18	158	522	787	893	683	539	213	47	3860
Ore	Astoria	45.6	27	229	493	591	753	834	622	636	480	363	5186
	Eugene	45.6	22	219	460	585	803	825	627	589	426	279	4726
	Medford	43.2	21	78	372	678	871	918	697	642	432	242	5008
	Pendleton	42.6	3	111	350	711	884	1017	773	617	396	205	5127
	Portland	45.6	21	114	335	597	735	825	644	586	396	245	4635
	Roseburg	46.3	25	105	329	567	713	766	608	570	405	267	4491
	Salem	45.4	21	111	338	594	729	822	641	611	417	273	4754
Pa	Allentown	38.9	3	90	353	693	1045	1116	1002	849	471	167	5810
	Erie	36.8	7	102	391	714	1063	1169	1081	971	585	288	6451
	Harrisburg	41.2	9	63	298	648	992	1045	907	766	396	124	5251
	Philadelphia	41.8	10	60	267	620	965	1016	889	747	392	118	5144
	Pittsburgh	38.4	5	105	375	726	1063	1119	1002	874	480	195	5987
	Reading	42.4	6	54	257	597	930	983	885	735	372	105	4945
	Scranton	37.2	2	132	434	762	1104	1156	1028	893	498	195	6254
	Williamsport	38.5	1	111	375	717	1074	1122	1002	856	468	177	5934
R I	Providence	38.8	0	96	372	660	1023	1110	988	868	534	236	5954
S C	Charleston	57.9	26	0	34	210	425	443	307	273	42	0	1794
	Columbia	54.0	20	0	84	345	577	570	470	357	81	0	2484
	Florence	54.5	21	0	78	315	552	552	459	355	90	0	2387
	Greenville Spartanburg	51.6	18	6	121	399	651	660	546	446	132	19	2980
S D	Huron	28.8	-16	165	508	1014	1432	1628	1355	1125	600	288	8223
S D	Rapid City	33.4	-9	165	481	897	1172	1333	1145	1051	615	326	7345
	Sioux Falls	30.6	-14	168	462	972	1361	1544	1285	1082	573	290	7839
Tenn	Bristol	46.2	11	51	236	573	828	828	700	598	261	48	4143
	Chattanooga	50.3	15	18	143	468	698	782	577	453	150	25	3254
	Knoxville	49.2	13	30	171	489	725	791	613	493	198	43	3494
	Memphis	50.5	17	18	130	447	698	729	585	456	147	22	3232
	Nashville	48.9	12	30	158	495	732	778	644	512	189	40	3578
Tex	Abilene	53.9	17	0	99	366	586	642	470	347	114	0	2624
	Amarillo	47.0	8	18	205	570	797	877	546	540	252	56	3985
	Austin	59.1	25	0	31	225	388	468	325	223	51	0	1711
	Corpus Christi	64.6	32	0	0	120	220	291	174	109	0	0	914
	Dallas	55.3	19	0	62	321	524	601	440	319	90	6	2363
	El Paso	52.9	21	0	84	414	648	685	445	399	105	0	2700
	Houston	62.0	28	0	6	183	307	384	288	192	36	0	1274
	Laredo	66.0	32	0	0	105	217	267	134	74	0	0	797
	Lubbock	48.8	11	18	174	513	744	800	613	484	201	31	3578
	Port Arthur	60.5	29	0	22	207	329	384	274	192	39	0	1447
	San Antonio	60.1	25	0	31	204	363	428	286	195	39	0	1546
	Waco	57.2	21	0	43	270	456	536	389	270	66	0	2030
	Wichita Falls	53.0	15	0	99	381	632	698	518	378	120	6	2832
Utah	Milford	38.4	5	99	443	867	1141	1252	948	822	519	279	6497
	Salt Lake City	38.4	3	81	419	849	1082	1172	910	763	459	233	6052
Vt	Burlington	29.4	-12	207	539	891	1349	1513	1333	1187	714	353	8269
Va	Lynchburg	46.0	15	51	223	540	822	849	731	605	267	78	4166
	Norfolk	49.2	20	0	136	408	698	738	655	533	216	37	3421
	Richmond	47.3	14	36	214	495	815	793	675	546	219	53	3865
	Roanoke	46.1	15	51	229	549	825	834	714	614	261	65	4150
Wash	Olympia	44.2	21	198	422	732	834	834	675	645	450	307	5236
	Seattle	46.9	28	129	329	543	657	738	599	577	396	242	4424
	Spokane	36.5	-2	168	493	879	1082	1231	980	834	531	288	6655
	Walla Walla	43.8	12	85	350	711	884	1045	868	713	435	177	4805
	Yakima	39.1	6	144	450	828	1039	1163	868	713	453	220	5941
W Va	Charleston	44.8	9	63	254	591	865	880	770	648	300	78	4470
	Elkins	40.1	1	135	400	729	992	1008	896	791	444	198	5675
	Huntington	45.0	10	63	257	585	856	880	764	636	294	99	4446
	Parkersburg	43.5	8	60	264	600	905	942	826	691	339	115	4754
Wis	Green Bay	30.3	-12	174	484	924	1333	1494	1313	1141	654	335	8029
	La Crosse	31.5	-12	165	450	918	1339	1504	1277	1070	540	245	7589
	Madison	30.9	-9	174	474	930	1330	1473	1274	1113	618	310	7863
	Milwaukee	32.6	-6	174	471	876	1252	1376	1193	1054	642	372	7635
Wyo	Casper	33.4	-11	192	524	942	1169	1290	1084	1020	657	381	7410
	Cheyenne	34.2	-6	219	543	909	1085	1212	1042	1026	702	428	7381
	Lander	34.5	-16	204	555	1020	1299	1417	1145	1017	654	381	7870
	Sheridan	33.1	-12	210	539	948	1200	1355	1154	1051	642	366	7680

Knowledge of the R-values of insulators and other components permits us to calculate the heat transmission through a wall or other building surface. Toward this end, we list the R-values of many common building materials in the first table. R-values are given per inch of thickness and for standard thicknesses. If you have some odd size not listed in the table, use the R-value per inch thickness and multiply by its thickness. Unless otherwise noted, the R-values are quoted for a temperature of 75°F.

Further tables list R-values for surface air films and for air spaces, both of which have insulating value. These R-values vary markedly with the reflectance of the surfaces facing the air film or space. Radiation heat flow is very slow across an air space with aluminum foil on one side, for example, and the R-value of such an air space is correspondingly high. This is why fiberglass batt insulation is often coated with an aluminized surface. In the tables we have used three categories of surface: non-reflective (such as painted wood or metal), fairly reflective (such as aluminum-coated paper), and highly reflective (such as metallic foil). The R-value of an air film or air space also depends on the orientation of the surface and the direction of heat flow that we are trying to retard. These differences are reflected in the tables.

The total resistance R_t of a wall or other building surface is just the sum of the R-values of all its components—including air films and spaces. The coefficient of heat transmission, or U-value, is the inverse of the total resistance $U = 1/R_t$. To get the rate of heat loss through a wall, for example, you multiply its U-value by the total surface area of the wall and by the temperature difference between the indoor and outdoor air. The next table in this section lists U-values for windows and skylights. Here again, the U-value depends upon the surface orientation, the direction of heat flow, and the season of the year. The U-values in these tables apply only to the glazing surfaces; to include the effects of a wood sash, multiply these U-values by about 80 to 90 percent, depending upon the area of the wood.

Different materials absorb different amounts of heat while undergoing the same temperature rise. Ten pounds of water will absorb 100 BTU during a 10°F temperature rise, but 10 pounds of cast iron will absorb only 12 BTU over the same range. There are two common measures of the ability of a material to absorb and store heat—its specific heat and its heat capacity.

The *specific heat* of a material is the number of BTU absorbed by a pound of that material as its temperature rises 1°F. All specific heats vary with temperature and a distinction must be made between the *true* and the *mean* specific heat. The true specific heat is the number of BTU absorbed per pound per °F temperature rise at a fixed temperature. Over a wider temperature range, the mean specific heat is the average number of BTU absorbed per pound per °F temperature rise. In the following table, only true specific heats are given—for room temperature unless otherwise noted.

The *heat capacity* of a material is the amount of heat absorbed by one cubic foot of that material during a 1°F temperature rise. The heat capacity

Table E-9. R-values of building materials.

Material and Description		Density (lb/ft^3)	R-value* per inch thickness	R-value* for listed thickness
Building Boards, Panels, Flooring				
Asbestos-cement board		120	0.25	–
Asbestos-cement board	1/8"	120	–	0.03
Gypsum or plaster board	3/8"	50	–	0.32
Gypsum or plaster board	1/2"	50	–	0.45
Plywood (see Siding Materials)		34	1.25	–
Sheathing, wood fiber (impregnated or coated)	25/32"	20	–	2.06
Wood fiber board (laminated or homogenous)		26	2.38	–
Wood fiber, hardboard type		65	0.72	–
Wood fiber, hardboard type	1/4"	65	–	0.18
Wood subfloor	25/32"	–	–	0.98
Wood, hardwood finish	3/4"	–	–	0.68
Building Paper				
Vapor-permeable felt		–	–	0.06
Vapor-seal, 2 layers of mopped 15 lb felt		–	–	0.12
Vapor-seal plastic film		–	–	negl.
Finish Materials				
Carpet and fibrous pad		–	–	2.08
Carpet and rubber pad		–	–	1.23
Cork tile	1/8"	–	–	0.28
Terrazzo	1"	–	–	0.08
Tile (asphalt, linoleum, vinyl, rubber)		–	–	0.05
Gypsumboard	1/2"	–	–	0.45
Gypsumboard	5/8"	–	–	0.56
Hardwood flooring	25/32"	–	–	0.68
Insulating Materials				
Blankets and Batts:				
Mineral wool, fibrous form (from rock, slag or glass)		0.5	3.12	–
		1.5-4.0	3.70	–
Wood fiber		3.2-3.6	4.00	–
Boards and Slabs:				
Cellular glass	90°F	9	2.44	
	60°F		2.56	–
	30°F		2.70	–
	0°F		2.86	–
Corkboard	90°F	6.5-8.0	3.57	–
	60°F		3.70	–
	30°F		3.85	–
	0°F		4.00	–
	90°F	12	3.22	–
	60°F		3.33	–
	30°F		3.45	–
	0°F		3.57	–

Table E-9. R-Values of Building Materials (continued on page 206).

Material and Description		Density (lb/ft³)	R-value* per inch thickness	R-value* for listed thickness
Glass fiber	90°F	4.0-9.0	3.85	–
	60°F		4.17	–
	30°F		4.55	–
	0°F		4.76	–
Expanded rubber (rigid)	75°F	4.5	4.55	–
Expanded polyurethane (R-11 blown;	100°F	1.5-2.5	5.56	–
1" thickness or more)	75°F		5.88	–
	50°F		6.25	–
	25°F		5.88	–
	0°F		5.88	–
Expanded polystyrene, extruded	75°F	1.9	3.85	–
	60°F		4.00	–
	30°F		4.17	–
	0°F		4.55	–
Expanded polystyrene, molded beads	75°F	1.0	3.57	–
	30°F		3.85	–
	0°F		4.17	–
Mineral fiberboard, felted core or roof insulation		16-17	2.94	–
acoustical tile[1]		18	2.86	–
acoustical tile[1]		21	2.73	–
Mineral fiberboard, molded acoustical tile[1]		23	2.38	–
Wood or cane fiberboard acoustical tile	1/2"	-	-	1.19
acoustical tile	3/4"	-	-	1.78
interior finish		15	2.86	
Insulating roof deck[2]	1"	--	–	2.78
	2"	–	–	5.56
	3"	–	–	8.33
Shredded wood (cemented, preformed slabs)		22	1.67	–
Loose Fills:				
Macerated paper or pulp		2.5-3.5	3.57	–
Mineral wool	90°F	2.0-5.0	3.33	–
	60°F		3.70	–
	30°F		4.00	–
	0°F		4.35	–
Perlite (expanded)	90°F	5.0-8.0	2.63	–
	60°F		2.78	–
	30°F		2.94	–
	0°F		3.12	–
Vermiculite (expanded)	90°F	7.0-8.2	2.08	–
	60°F		2.18	–
	30°F		2.27	–
	0°F		2.38	–
Sawdust or shavings		0.8-15	2.22	–

Material and Description		Density (lb/ft^3)	R-value* per inch thickness	for listed thickness
Masonry Materials—Concretes				
Cement mortar		116	0.20	–
Gypsum-fiber concrete (87½% gypsum, 12½% concrete)		51	0.60	–
Lightweight aggregates		120	0.19	–
(expanded shale, clay or slate;		100	0.28	–
expanded slags, or cinders;		80	0.40	–
pumice; perlite or vermiculite;		60	0.59	–
cellular concretes)		40	0.86	–
		20	1.43	–
Sand and gravel or stone aggregate (oven dried)		140	0.11	–
Sand and gravel or stone aggregate (not dried)		140	0.08	–
Stucco		116	0.20	–
Masonry Units				
Brick, common[3]		120	0.20	–
Brick, face[3]		130	0.11	–
Clay tile, hollow				
1 cell deep	3″	–	–	0.80
1 cell deep	4″	–	–	1.11
2 cells deep	6″	–	–	1.52
2 cells deep	8″	–	–	1.85
3 cells deep	10″	–	–	2.22
3 cells deep	12″	–	–	2.50
Concrete block, 3 oval core				
Sand and gravel aggregate	4″	–	–	0.71
	8″	–	–	1.11
	12″	–	–	1.28
Cinder aggregate	3″	–	–	0.86
	4″	–	–	1.11
	8″	–	–	1.72
	12″	–	–	1.89
Lightweight aggregate	3″	–	–	1.27
(expanded shale, clay	4″	–	–	1.50
slate or slag; pumice)	8″	–	–	2.00
	12″	–	–	2.72
Concrete blocks, rectangular core				
Sand and gravel aggregate				
2 core, 36 lb[4]	8″	–	–	1.04
same, filled cores[5]		–	–	1.93
Lightweight aggregates				
3 core, 19 lb[4]	6″	–	–	1.65
same, filled cores[5]		–	–	2.99
2 core, 24 lb[4]	8″	–	–	2.18
same, filled cores[5]		–	–	5.03
3 core, 38 lb[4]	12″	–	–	2.48
same, filled cores[5]		–	–	5.82
Stone, lime or sand		–	0.08	–
Granite, marble		150-175	0.05	–

Table E-9. R-Values of Building Materials (continued on page 208).

Material and Description		Density (lb/ft^3)	R-value* per inch thickness	R-value* for listed thickness
Plastering Materials				
Cement plaster, sand aggregate		116	0.20	–
Gypsum plaster				
Lightweight aggregate	1/2"	45	–	0.32
Lightweight aggregate	3/8"	45	–	0.39
Same, on metal lath	3/4"	–	–	0.47
Perlite aggregate		45	0.67	–
Sand aggregate		105	0.18	–
Same, on metal lath	3/4"	–	–	0.10
Same, on wood lath	3/4"	–	–	0.40
Vermiculite aggregate		45	0.59	–
Roofing Materials				
Asbestos-cement shingles		120	–	0.21
Asphalt roll roofing		70	–	0.15
Built-up roofing	3/8"	70	–	0.44
Slate roofing	1/2"	–	–	0.05
Wood shingles		–	–	0.94
Siding Materials				
Shingles				
Asbestos-cement		120	–	0.21
Wood, 16" with 7½" exposure		–	–	0.80
Wood, double 16" with 12" exposure		–	–	1.19
Wood, plus insulating backer board	5/16"	–	–	1.40
Siding				
Asbestos-cement lapped	1/4"	–	–	0.21
Asphalt roll siding		–	–	0.15
Asphalt insulating siding	1/2"	–	–	1.46
Wood, drop (1" × 8")		–	–	0.79
Wood, drop (½" × 8" lapped)		–	–	0.81
Wood, bevel (¾" × 10", lapped)		–	–	1.05
Plywood, lapped	3/8"	–	–	0.59
Plywood	1/4"	–	–	0.31
	3/8"	–	–	0.47
	1/2"	–	–	0.62
	5/8"	–	–	0.78
	3/4"	–	–	0.94
Stucco		116	0.20	–
Sheathing, insulating board	1/2"	–	–	1.32
(regular density)	25/32"	–	–	2.04
Woods				
Hardwoods (maple, oak)		45	0.91	–
Softwoods (fir, pine)		32	1.25	–

Material and Description		Density (lb/ft^3)	R-value*	
			per inch thickness	for listed thickness
	25/32"	32	—	0.98
	1−5/8"	32	—	2.03
	2−5/8"	32	—	3.28
	3−5/8"	32	—	4.55
Wood Doors				
Solid core	1"	—	—	1.56
	1−1/4"	—	—	1.82
	1−1/2"	—	—	2.04
	2"	—	—	2.33

*Representative values intended for use as design values of dry building materials in normal use.
[1] R-values of acoustical tile depend upon the board and the type, size and depth of perforations; these are average values.
[2] Roof deck insulation is made in thicknesses to meet these standards; thickness may vary somewhat with manufacturer.
[3] Face brick and common brick do not always have these densities and R-values.
[4] Weights of blocks approximately 7−5/8" high by 15−3/8" long.
[5] Vermiculite, perlite, or mineral wool insulation.
SOURCE: ASHRAE *Handbook of Fundamentals.* 1967. Reprinted by permission

Table E-10. R-values of air films.

Type and Orientation of Air Film	Direction of Heat Flow	R-value for Air Film On:		
		Non-reflective surface	Fairly reflective surface	Highly reflective surface
Still air:				
Horizontal	up	0.61	1.10	1.32
Horizontal	down	0.92	2.70	4.55
45° slope	up	0.62	1.14	1.37
45° slope	down	0.76	1.67	2.22
Vertical	across	0.68	1.35	1.70
Moving air:				
15 mph wind	any*	0.17	—	—
7½ mph wind	any[†]	0.25	—	—

*Winter conditions.
[†]Summer conditions.
SOURCE: ASHRAE, *Handbook of Fundamentals*, 1972. Reprinted by permission

Table E-11. R-values of air spaces.

Orientation & Thickness of Air Space		Direction of Heat Flow	R-value for Air Space Facing:‡		
			Non-reflective surface	Fairly reflective surface	Highly reflective surface
Horizontal	¾″	up*	0.87	1.71	2.23
	4″		0.94	1.99	2.73
	¾″	up†	0.76	1.63	2.26
	4″		0.80	1.87	2.75
	¾″	down*	1.02	2.39	3.55
	1½″		1.14	3.21	5.74
	4″		1.23	4.02	8.94
	¾	down†	0.84	2.08	3.25
	1½″		0.93	2.76	5.24
	4″		0.99	3.38	8.03
45° slope	¾″	up*	0.94	2.02	2.78
	4″		0.96	2.13	3.00
	¾″	up†	0.81	1.90	2.81
	4″		0.82	1.98	3.00
	¾″	down*	1.02	2.40	3.57
	4″		1.08	2.75	4.41
	¾″	down†	0.84	2.09	3.34
	4″		0.90	2.50	4.36
Vertical	¾″	across*	1.01	2.36	3.48
	4″		1.01	2.34	3.45
	¾″	across†	0.84	2.10	3.28
	4″		0.91	2.16	3.44

‡One side of the air space is a non-reflective surface.
*Winter conditions.
†Summer conditions.
SOURCE: ASHRAE, *Handbook of Fundamentals*, 1972. Reprinted by permission.

Description	U-values[1]	
	Winter	Summer
Vertical panels:		
Single pane flat glass	1.13	1.06
Insulating glass—double[2]		
3/16″ air space	0.69	0.64
1/4″ air space	0.65	0.61
1/2″ air space	0.58	0.56
Insulating glass—triple[2]		
1/4″ air spaces	0.47	0.45
1/2″ air spaces	0.36	0.35
Storm windows		
1-4″ air space	0.56	0.54
Glass blocks[3]		
6 × 6 × 4″ thick	0.60	0.57
8 × 8 × 4″ thick	0.56	0.54
same, with cavity divider	0.48	0.46
Single plastic sheet	1.09	1.00
Horizontal panels:[4]		
Single pane flat glass	1.22	0.83
Insulating glass—double[2]		
3/16″ air space	0.75	0.49
1/4″ air space	0.70	0.46
1/2″ air space	0.66	0.44
Glass blocks[3]		
11 × 11 × 3″ thick, with cavity divider	0.53	0.35
12 × 12 × 4″ thick, with cavity divider	0.51	0.34
Plastic bubbles[5]		
single-walled	1.15	0.80
double-walled	0.70	0.46

[1] in units of Btu/hr/ft^2/°F

[2] double and triple refer to the number of lights of glass.

[3] nominal dimensions.

[4] U-values for horizontal panels are for heat flow *up* in winter and *down* in summer.

[5] based on area of opening, not surface.

SOURCE: ASHRAE, *Handbook of Fundamentals*, 1972. Reprinted by permission.

Table E-13. Class 1 substances: absorptance to emittance ratios (α/ϵ) less than 1.0

Substance	α	ϵ	α/ϵ
White plaster	0.07	0.91	0.08
Snow, fine particles, fresh	0.13	0.82	0.16
White paint on aluminum	0.20	0.91	0.22
Whitewash on galvanized iron	0.22	0.90	0.24
White paper	0.25-0.28	0.95	0.26-0.29
White enamel on iron	0.25-0.45	0.90	0.28-0.50
Ice, with sparse snow cover	0.31	0.96-0.97	0.32
Snow, ice granules	0.33	0.89	0.37
Aluminum oil base paint	0.45	0.90	0.50
Asbestos felt	0.25	0.50	0.50
White powdered sand	0.45	0.84	0.54
Green oil base paint	0.50	0.90	0.56
Bricks, red	0.55	0.92	0.60
Asbestos cement board, white	0.59	0.96	0.61
Marble, polished	0.5-0.6	0.90	0.61
Rough concrete	0.60	0.97	0.62
Concrete	0.60	0.88	0.68
Grass, wet	0.67	0.98	0.68
Grass, dry	0.67-0.69	0.90	0.76
Vegetable fields and shrubs, wilted	0.70	0.90	0.78
Oak leaves	0.71-0.78	0.91-0.95	0.78-0.82
Grey paint	0.75	0.95	0.79
Desert surface	0.75	0.90	0.83
Common vegetable fields and shrubs	0.72-0.76	0.90	0.82
Red oil base paint	0.74	0.90	0.82
Asbestos, slate	0.81	0.96	0.84
Ground, dry plowed	0.75-0.80	0.70-0.96	0.83-0.89
Linoleum, red-brown	0.84	0.92	0.91
Dry sand	0.82	0.90	0.91
Green roll roofing	0.88	0.91-0.97	0.93
Slate, dark grey	0.89	—	—
Bare moist ground	0.90	0.95	0.95
Wet sand	0.91	0.95	0.96
Water	0.94	0.95-0.96	0.98
Black tar paper	0.93	0.93	1.0
Black gloss paint	0.90	0.90	1.0
Small hole in large box, furnace or enclosure	0.99	0.99	1.0
"Hohlraum," theoretically perfect black body	1.00	1.0	1.0

Table E-14. Class 2 Substances:
Absorptance to Emittance Ratios (α/ϵ) Greater Than 1.0.

Substance	α	ϵ	α/ϵ
Black silk velvet	0.99	0.97	1.02
Alfalfa, dark green	0.97	0.95	1.02
Lamp black	0.98	0.95	1.03
Black paint on aluminum	0.94-0.98	0.88	1.07-1.11
Granite	0.55	0.44	1.25
Dull brass, copper, lead	0.2-0.4	0.4-0.65	1.63-2.0
Graphite	0.78	0.41	1.90
Stainless steel wire mesh	0.63-0.86	0.23-0.28	2.70-3.0
Galvanized sheet iron, oxidized	0.80	0.28	2.86
Galvanized iron, clean, new	0.65	0.13	5.00
Aluminum foil	0.15	0.05	3.00
Cobalt oxide on polished nickel*	0.93-0.94	0.2+0.40	3.9
Magnesium	0.30	0.07	4.3
Chromium	0.49	0.08	6.13
Nickel black on galvanized iron*	0.89	0.12	7.42
Cupric oxide on sheet aluminum*	0.85	0.11	7.73
Nickel black on polished nickel*	0.91-0.94	0.11	8.27-8.55
Polished zinc	0.46	0.02	23.0

*Selective surfaces

SOURCES: ASHRAE, *Handbook of Fundamentals.* 1972.
Bowden, *Alternative Sources of Energy.* July 1973.
Duffie and Beckman, *Solar Energy Thermal Processes.* 1974.
McAdams, *Heat Transmission.* 1954.
Severns and Fellows, *Air Conditioning and Refrigeration.* 1966.
Sounders, *The Engineer's Companion.* 1966.

is just the product of the density of the material (in lb/ft^3) times its specific heat. Specific heats, heat capacities, and densities of common building materials and other substances are given in the following table.

Table E-15. Specific heats and heat capacities of materials.

Material	Specific Heat (Btu/lb/°F)	Density (lb/ft³)	Heat Capacity (Btu/ft³/°F)
Air (at 1 atmosphere)	0.24 [75]	0 075	0.018
Aluminum (alloy 1100)	0.214	171	36.6
Asbestos fiber	0.25	150	37.5
Asbestos insulation	0.20	36	7.2
Ashes, wood	0.20	40	8.0
Asphalt	0.22	132	29.0
Bakelite	0.35	81	28.4
Brick, building	0.2	123	24.6
Brass, red (85% Cu, 15% Zn)	0.09	548	49.3
Brass, yellow (65% Cu, 35% Zn)	0.09	519	46.7
Bronze	0.104	530	55.1
Cellulose	0.32	3.4	1.1
Cement (Portland clinker)	0.16	120	19.2
Chalk	0.215	143	30.8
Charcoal (wood)	0.20	15	3.0
Clay	0.22	63	13.9
Coal	0.3	90	27.0
Concrete (stone)	0.22	144	31.7
Copper (electrolytic)	0.092	556	51.2
Cork (granulated)	0.485	5.4	2.6
Cotton (fiber)	0.319	95	30.3
Ethyl alcohol	0.68	49.3	33.5
Fireclay brick	0.198 [212]	112	22.2
Glass, crown (soda-lime)	0.18	154	27.7
Glass, flint (lead)	0.117	267	31.2
Glass, pyrex	0.20	139	27.8
Glass, "wool"	0.157	3.25	0.5
Gypsum	0.259	78	20.2
Hemp (fiber)	0.323	93	30.0
Ice	0.487 [32]	57.5	28.0
Iron, cast	0.12 [212]	450	54.0
Lead	0.031	707	21.8
Limestone	0.217	103	22.4
Magnesium	0.241	108	26.0
Marble	0.21	162	34.0
Nickel	0.105	555	58.3
Octane	0.51	43.9	22.4
Paper	0.32	58	18.6
Paraffin	0.69	56	38.6
Porcelain	0.18	162	29.2
Rock salt	0.219	136	29.8
Salt water	0.75	72	54.0
Sand	0.191	94.6	18.1
Silica	0.316	140	44.2
Silver	0.056	654	36.6
Steel (mild)	0.12	489	58.7
Stone (quarried)	0.2	95	19.0
Tin	0.056	455	25.5
Tungsten	0.032	1210	38.7
Water	1.0 [39]	62.4	62.4
Wood, white oak	0.570	47	26.8
Wood, white fir	0.65	27	17.6
Wood, white pine	0.67	27	18.1
Zinc	0.092	445	40.9

*Values are for room temperature unless otherwise noted in brackets.

Table E-16. Conversion factors.

Multiply:	By:	To obtain:	Multiply:	By:	To obtain:
Acres	43,560	Square feet	Horsepower	0.7457	Kilowatts
Acre-feet	1,233.5	Cubic meters	Inches of mercury at 32°F	0.4912	Pounds per square inch
Barrels, oil (crude)	5.8×10^6	Btu	Kilowatts	56.90	Btu per minute
Barrels, oil	5.615	Cubic feet	Kilowatts	1.341	Horsepower
Btu	777.48	Foot-pounds	Kilowatt-hours	3,413	Btu
Btu	1,055	Joules	Kilowatt-hours	2.66×10^6	Foot-pounds
Btu	0.29305	Watt-hours	Langleys (cal/cm^2)	3.69	Btu per square foot
Btu/hr/ft^2/°F	5.682×10^4	Watts/cm^2/°C	Langleys per minute	0.0698	Watts per square centimeter
Btu per square foot	0.271	Langleys (cal/cm^2)	Microns	1×10^{-4}	Centimeters
Calories	3.9685×10^{-3}	Btu	Months (mean calendar)	730.1	Hours
Calories	4.184	Joules	Newtons	0.22481	Pounds (force)
Cords	128	Cubic feet	Pounds of water	0.1198	Gallons
Cubic feet	0.037037	Cubic yards	Pounds per square inch	0.068046	Standard atmospheres
Cubic feet	7.48	Gallons	Pounds per square inch	51.715	Millimeters of mercury at 0°C
Cubic feet per second	448.83	Gallons per minute	Standard atmospheres	14.696	Pounds per square inch
Feet of water (39.2°F)	0.4335	Pounds per square inch	Tons (short)	2,000	Pounds
Feet of water	0.88265	Inches of mercury at 32°F	Tons (short)	0.907185	Metric tons
Gallons	0.1337	Cubic feet	Tons (metric)	2,204.62	Pounds
Gallons of water at 60°F	8.3453	Pounds	Tons of refrigeration	12,000	Btu per hour
Horsepower	33,000	Foot-pounds per minute	Therms	1×10^5	Btu
Horsepower	42.42	Btu per minute	Watts	3.413	Btu per hour
Horsepower	2,546	Btu per hour	Watts	0.00134	Horsepower
Horsepower	1.014	Metric horsepower			

Table E-17. Metric/English equivalents.

English Measure	Metric Equivalent	Metric Measure	English Equivalent
inch	2.54 centimeters	millimeter	0.04 inch
foot	30.50 centimeters	centimeter	0.39 inch
yard	0.91 meter	meter	3.28 feet
mile (statute)	1.60 kilometers	meter	1.09 yards
		kilometer	0.62 miles
square inch	6.45 square centimeters	square centimeter	0.16 square inch
square foot	929.00 square centimeters	square meter	1.19 square yards
square yard	0.84 square meter	square kilometer	0.38 square mile
square mile	2.60 square kilometers		
ounce	28.30 grams	gram	0.035 ounces
pound (mass)	0.45 kilogram	kilogram	2.20 pounds
short ton	907.00 kilograms	ton (1,000 kg)	1.10 short tons
fluid ounce	29.60 milliliters	milliliters	0.03 fluid ounce
pint	0.47 liter	liter	1.06 quarts
quart	0.95 liter	liter	0.26 gallon
gallon	3.78 liters	cubic meter	35.3 cubic feet
cubic foot	0.03 cubic meter	cubic meter	1.3 cubic yards
cubic yard	0.76 cubic meter		
Btu	251.98 calories	calorie	0.004 Btu
pound (force)	4.45 newtons	newton	0.225 pound (force)

Table E-18. Metric/English Temperature Equivalents.

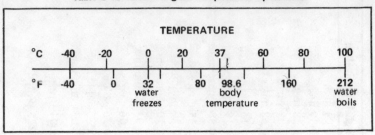

Buyer's Index

SWIMMING POOL COLLECTORS

Alten Corporation
2594 Leghorn Street
Mountain View, CA 94043
Telephone 415/969-6474

Aluminum Company of America
1501 Alcoa Building
Pittsburgh, PA 15219
Telephone 412/553-3185

American Solar Manufacturing
P.O.Box 194
Byron, CA 94514
Telephone 415/634-2426

American Sun Industries
996 Lawrence Drive
Newbury Park, CA 91320
Telephone 805/498-9700

Aqua Blanket, Inc.
1900 Old Middlefield Way
Mountain View, CA 94043
Telephone 415/969-1372

Aquasolar, Inc.
1232 Zacchini Avenue
Sarasota, FL 33577
Telephone 813/366-7080

Bio-Energy Systems, Inc.
Mountainside Road·
Spring Glen, NY 12483
Telephone 914/434-7858

Burke Industries, Inc.
2250 South 10th Street
San Jose, CA 95112
Telephone 408/297-3500

Calmac Manufacturing Corporation
150 South Van Brunt Street
Englewood, NJ 07631
Telephone 201/569-0420

Chancellor Industries
13138 Poway Road
Poway, CA 92064
Telephone 714/748-8313

Cole Solar Systems, Inc.
440 East Stant Elmo Road
Austin, TX 78745
Telephone 512/444-2565

Colt Inc.
71590 San Jacinto
Rancho Mirage, CA 92270
Telephone 714/346-8033

Conserdyne Corporation
4437 San Fernando Road
Glendale, CA 91204
Telephone 213/246-8408

Ecosol Materials Inc.
1006 Brown Street
Peekskill, NY 10566
Telephone 914/739-7002

Electrasol Labs Inc.
2326 Fieldingwood Road
Maitland, FL 32751
Telephone 305/831-4481

Energex Manufacturing Corporation
4227 S. 36th Place
Phoenix, AZ 85040
Telephone 602/267-9474

Energy Systems Inc.
4570 Alvarado Canyon Road
San Diego, CA 92120
Telephone 714/280-6660

Free Heat Division, Atlas Vinyl Products
7002 Beaver Dam Road
Levittown, PA 19057
Telephone 215/946-3620

Grumman Energy Systems Inc.
4175 Veterans Memorial Highway
Ronkonkoma, NY 11779
Telephone 516/575-7291

Hansberger Refrigeration Electric Company
2450 West 8th Street
Yuma, AZ 85364
Telephone 602/783-3331

Hyperion
7209 Valtec Court
Boulder, CO 80301
Telephone 303/449-9544

ISLC
7010 Convoy Court
San Diego, CA 92111
Telephone 714/560-9173

Lab Sciences, Division of National Plastics, Inc.
604 Park Drive
Boca Raton, FL 33341
Telephone 305/994-1833

Natural Heating Systems
2417 Front Street
West Sacramento, CA 95691
Telephone 916/372-2993

Powell Brothers, Inc.
5903 Firestone Blvd.
Southgate, CA 90280
Telephone 213/869-3307

RA Energy Systems
8630 Production Avenue, Suite A
San Diego, CA 92121
Telephone 714/578-2260

RAN Solar Energy Products
50-P Brook Avenue
Deer Park, NY 71729
Telephone 516/586-5008

R.D. Herbert & Sons Company
601 Harrison Street
Nashville, TN 37219
Telephone 615/242-3501

R-M Products
5010 Cook
Denver, CO 80216
Telephone 303/825-0203

Robert Mitchell Solar System Design
RD-3, Box 147
Selkirk, NY 12158
Telephone 518/767-3100

Solar Applications, Inc.
7926 Convoy Court
San Diego, CA 92111
Telephone 714/292-1857

Solar Central
7213 Ridge Road
Mechanicsburg, OH 43044
Telephone 513/828-1350

Solarcoa, Inc.
2115 East Spring Street
Long Beach, CA 90806
Telephone 213/426-7655

Solar Comfort Systems
4853 Cordell Avenue, Suite 606
Bethesda, MD 20014
Telephone 301/951-0095 or
301/652-8941

Solar Development, Inc.
4180 Westroads Drive
West Palm Beach, FL 33407
Telephone 305/842-8935

Solar Energy Applications, Inc.
1103 East Washington
Phoenix, AZ 85034
Telephone 602/244-1822

Solar Energy Systems, Inc.
2345 Santa Fe Avenue
Los Angeles, CA 90058
Telephone 213/583-5808

Solar-Eye Products, Inc.
1300 Northwest McNab Road, Building G-H
Fort Lauderdale, FL 33309
Telephone 305/974-2500

Solar Heating of New Jersey
811 Wyetta Place
Paramus, NJ 07652
Telephone 201/652-3819

Solar Industries, Inc.
Monmouth Airport Industrial Park
Farmingdale, NJ 07727
Telephone 201/938-7000

Solarmaster
722-D West Betteravia Road
Santa Maria, CA 93454
Telephone 805/922-0205

Solar Power West
709 Spruce Street
Aspen, CO 81611
Telephone 303/925-4698

Solar Products
Box 36
Spencertown, NY 12165
Telephone 518/392-5573

Solar Products Manufacturing Corporation
151 John Downey Drive
New Britain, CT 06051
Telephone 203/224-2164

Solar Sun, Inc.
235 West 12th Street
Cincinnati, OH 45210
Telephone 513/241-4200

Solar Systems
26046 Eden Landing Road, Suite 41
Hayward, CA 94545
Telephone 415/785-0711

Solar Systems by Sundance, Inc.
13939 Northwest 60th Avenue
Miami Lake, FL 33014
Telephone 305/557-2882

Solar Systems International
6065 Northwest 82nd Avenue
Miami, FL 33166
Telephone 800/327-7066

Solartec, Inc.
250 Pennsylvania Avenue
Salem, OH 44460
Telephone 216/332-9100

Sol-Ray, Inc.
204-B Carleton
Oranga, CA 92667
Telephone 714/997-9431

Southeastern Solar Systems, Inc.
2812 New Spring Road, Suite 150
Atlanta, GA 30339
Telephone 404/434-4447

Spectra Energy Systems, Inc.
P/O Box 6036
Santa Barbara, CA 93111
Telephone 805/967-1053

Sun Bank, Inc.
924 North Main, Box 4149
Wichita, KS 67204
Telephone 316/265-0866

Sunblazer Energy Systems, Inc.
P/O Box 1992
Charlotte, NC 28233
Telephone 704/333-2551

Sunburst Solar Energy, Inc.
P/O Box 2799
Menlo Park, CA 94025
Telephone 415/327-8022

Sun Century Systems
Box 2036
Florence, AL 35630
Telephone 205/764-0795

Sundee Company
3319 Keys Lane
Anaheim, CA 92804
Telephone 714/828-2873

Sunergy Power, Ltd.
400 West Main Street
Babylon, NY 11702
Telephone 516/587-0611

Sun Power Corporation
P/O Box 16963
Orlando, FL 32811
Telephone 305/876-2237

Sunray Solar Heat, Inc.
202 Classon Avenue
Brooklyn, NY 11205
Telephone 212/857-0193

Sunsav, Inc.
890 East Street
Tewksburg, MA 01876
Telephone 617/851-5913

Sun Systems
1825 West Indian School Road
Phoenix, AZ 85015
Telephone 602/263-0699

Sun-wall, Inc.
P/O Box 9723
Pittsburgh, PA 15229
Telephone 412/364-5349

Sunwater Energy Products
1488 Pioneer Way, #17
El Cajon, CA 92020
Telephone 714/579-0771

United States Solar Systems, Inc.
P/O Box 48695
Los Angeles, CA 90048
Telphone 213/654-1926

The Solar Store Corporation
Box 841
Peoria, IL 61652
Telephone 309/673-0458

Wallace Company
831 Dorsey Street, P/O Box 511
Gainsville, GA 30501
Telephone 404/534-5971

Wojick Industries, Inc.
527 North Main Street
Fallbrook, CA 92028
Telephone 714/728-5593

NON-FOCUSING LIQUID COLLECTORS

Ace Solar Systems
Route #1 Box 50
Mission, TX 78572
Telephone 512/582-6353

Acorn Structures, Inc.
Box 250
Concord, MA 01720
Telephone 617/369-4111

Advance Cooler Manufacturing Corp.
ACM Solar Group
Clifton Park, NY 12065
Telephone 518/371-2140

Airloc, Inc.
337 Elm St.
Struthers, OH 44471
Telephone 216/755-9851

Air Temp Corp.
Woodbridge Ave.
Edison, NJ 08817
Telephone 201/549-7200

Aldrich Roofing Company
142 Cannon St.
Poughkeepsie, NY 12601
Telephone 914/454-1210

AllSun Power, Inc.
10400 S.W. 187th St.
Miami, FL 33157
Telephone 305/233-2224

Alpha Solarco
Suite 2230 Kroger Building
Cincinnati, OH 45202
Telephone 513/621-1243

Alten Corp.
2594 Leghorn St.
Mountain View, CA 94043
Telephone 415/969-6474

Alternative Energy Resources
1155 Larry Mahon Dr.
El Paso, TX 79925
Telephone 915/593-1927

Alternative Heating Systems, Inc.
1975 31st St.
Boulder, CO 80301
Telephone 303/443-2881

Aluminum Company of America
1501 Alcoa Building
Pittsburgh, PA 15219
Telephone 412/553-3185

American Heliothermal Corp.
2625 S. Santa Fe Dr.
Denver, CO 80223
Telephone 303/778-0650

American Home Solar Energy Systems
868 Catalina
Laguna Beach, CA 92651
Telephone 715/831-9794

American Solar Energy Corp.
55 South Colorado Blvd.
Denver, CO 80206
Telephone 303/377-6527

American Solar Heat Corp.
7 National Place
Danburg, CT 06810
Telephone 203/792-0077

American Solar King Corp.
6801 New McGregor Highway
Waco, TX 76710
Telephone 817/776-3860

American Solar Manufacturing
P/O Box 194
Bryon, CA 94514
Telephone 415/634-2426

American Solar Power
715 Swann Ave.
Tampa, FL 33606
Telephone 805/254-4461

American Solar Systems
415 E. Branch St.
Arroya Grande, CA 93420
Telephone 805/481-1010

American Sun Industries
996 Lawrence Dr.
Newburg Park, CA 91320
Telephone 805/498-9700

American Sun Power and Light Company
10005 McKalla
Austin, TX 78758
Telephone 512/837-2627

Ametek Inc.
One Spring Ave.
Hatfield, PA 19446
Telephone 215/822-2971

Arizona Engineering and Refrigeration
635 W. Commerce Ave.
Gilbert, AZ 85234
Telephone 602/892-9050

Aston Solar Industries, Inc.
465 McCormick St.
San Leando, CA 94577
Telephone 415/632-5400

Astro Solar Corp.
457 Santa Anna Dr.
Palm Springs, FL 33461
Telephone 305/965-0606

Attwood Corp.
1016 N. Monroe
Lowell, MI 49331
Telephone 616/897-9241

Aztec Solar Company
P.O. Box 272
Maitland, FL 33166
Telephone 305/628-5004

Beutals Solar Heater Company
7161 N.W. 74th St.
Miami, FL 33166
Telephone 305/885-0122

Brown Manufacturing Company
P/O Box 14546
Oklahoma City, OK 73114
Telephone 405/751-1323

Business and Technology, Inc.
2800 Upton Street
N.W. Washington, D.C. 20008
Telephone 202/362-5991

Butler Ventamatics
P/O Box 728
Mineral Wells, TX 76067
Telephone 817/325-7887

Calmac Manufacturing Corp.
150 South Van Brunt St.
Englewood, NJ 07631
Telephone 201/569-0420

Capital Solar Heating
376 N.W. 25th St.
Miami, FL 33127
Telephone 305/576-2380

Carolina Solar Comfort Inc.
P/O Box 2068
Salisbury, NC 28144
Telephone 704/637-1243

Catalano & Sons, Inc.
301 Stagg St.
Brooklyn, NY 11206
Telephone 212/821-6100

CBM Manufacturing Inc.
621 N.W. Sixth Ave.
Fort Lauderdale, FL 33311
Telephone 305/463-5810

CF Roark Welding and Engineering Company, Inc.
136 N. Green St.
Brownburg, IN 46112
Telephone 317/852-3163

Chamberlain Manufacturing Corp.
845 Larch Ave.
Elmhurst, IL 60126
Telephone 312/279-3600

Chemical Processors Inc.
P/O Box 10636
St. Petersburg, FL 33733
Telephone 813/822-3689

Climatrol Corp.
Woodbridge Ave.
Edison, NJ 08817
Telephone 201/549-7200

Cole Solar Systems Inc.
440A East Saint Elmo Road
Austin, TX 78745
Telephone 512/444-2565

Colorado Sunworks
P.O. Box 455
Boulder, CO 80306
Telephone 303/443-9199

Colt Inc.
71590 San Jacinto
Rancho Mirage, CA 92270
Telephone 714/346-8033

Columbia Chase Solar Energy Division
55 High Street
Holdbrook, MA 02343
Telephone 617/767-0513

Conserdyne Corporation
4437 San Fernando Road
Glendale, CA 91204
Telephone 213/246-8408

Consolar Inc.
800 West Panorama Road
Tucson, AZ 85704
Telephone 602/297-3556

Consumer Energy Corporation
4234 S.W. 75th Avenue
Miami, FL 33155
Telephone 305/266-0124

Continental Solar Systems Inc.
1901 Avenue of The Stars, Suite 600,
Century City
Los Angeles, CA 90067
Telephone 213/552-0003

C.S.I. Solar Systems Division Inc.
12400 49th Street
Clearwater, FL 33520
Telephone 813/577-4228

Daystar Corporation
90 Cambridge Street
Burlington, MA 01803
Telephone 617/272-8460

Dixon Energy Systems Inc.
47 East Street
Hadley, MA 01035
Telephone 413/584-8831

Dumont Industries
Box 117, Main Street
Monmouth, ME 04259
Telephone 207/933-4281

Dura-Plex Industries Inc.
720 East Herrin Street
Herrin, IL 62948
Telephone 618/942-7302

D.W. Browning Contracting Company
475 Carswell Avenue
Holly Hill, FL 32017
Telephone 904/252-1528

EK Service Company
16824 74th N.E.
Bothell, WA 98011
Telephone 206/486-6660

E.C.M. Associates
1928 6th Street
Boulder, CO 80302
Telephone 303/443-7970

El Cam Inc.
5330 Debbie Lane
Santa Barbara, CA 93111
Telephone 805/964-8676

Electric Motor Repair & Service
Box 763
Lake Leelanau, MI 49653
Telephone 616/256-9558

Energex Manufacturing Corporation
4227 S. 36th Place
Phoenix, AZ 85040
Telephone 602/267-9474

Energy Converters Inc.
2501 N. Orchard Knob Avenue
Chattanooga, TN 37406
Telephone 615/624-2608

Energy Design Inc.
1925 Curry Road
Schenectady, NY 12303
Telephone 518/355-3322

Energy Dynamics Inc.
4077 Woodcock Drive
Jacksonville, FL 32207
Telephone 904/398-1144

Energy System Inc.
4570 Alvarado Canyon Road
San Diego, CA 92120
Telephone 714/280-6660

Enviropane Inc.
350 North Marshall Street
Lancaster, PA 17602
Telephone 717/299-3737

ERA Del Sol
5960 Mandarin Avenue
Goleta, CA 93107
Telephone 805/967-2116

Evans Precision Inc.
3145 Lancaster-Chillicothe Road
P/O Box 366
Lancaster, OH 43130
Telephone 614/654-2196

Fafco Inc.
235 Constitution Drive
Menlo Park, CA 94025
Telephone 408/321-3650

Fedders Division Climatrol Corporation
Woodbridge Avenue
Edison, NJ 08817
Telephone 201/549-7200

Federal Energy Corporation
5505 East Evans
Denver, CO 80222
Telephone 303/753-0565

Flagala Corporation
9700 West Highway 98
Panama City, FL 32407
Telephone 904/234-6559

Florida Solar Power Inc.
P/O Box 5846
Tallahassee, FL 32301
Telephone 904/224-8270

General Energy Devices Inc.
7501 124th Avenue N.
Largo, FL 33540
Telephone 813/536-6502

Grumman Energy Systems Inc.
4175 Veterans Memorial Highway
Ronkonkoma, NY 11779
Telephone 516/575-7291

Gulf Thermal Corporation
629 17th Avenue West
Bradenton, FL 33505
Telephone 813/748-3433

Halstead & Mitchell
P/O Box 1110
Scottsboro, AL 35768
Telephone 205/259-1212

Hansberger Refrigeration Electric Company
2450 West 8th Street
Yuma, AZ 85364
Telephone 602/783-3331

Heremann Electric
127 Mountainview Road
Warren, NJ 07060
Telephone 201/752-6060

Helio Dynamics
518 South Van Ness Avenue
Los Angeles, CA 90020
Telephone 213/384-9853

Heliodyne Inc.
770 South 16th Street
Richmond, CA 94804
Telephone 415/237-9614

Helios Corporation
2120 Angus Road
Charlottesville, VA 22901
Telephone 804/977-3719

Heliosystems Inc.
3407 Ross Avenue
Dallas, TX 75206
Telephone 214/824-5971

Heliotherm Inc.
West Lenni Road
Lenni, PA 19052
Telephone 215/459-9030

Horizon Enterprises Inc.
1011 N.W. 6th Street
P/O Box V
Homestead, FL 33030
Telephone 305/245-5145

Hyperion
7209 Valtec Court
Boulder, CO 80301
Telephone 303/449-9544

Ilse Engineering Inc.
7177 Arrowhead Road
Duluth, MN 55811
Telephone 218/729-6858

Independent Living Inc.
2300 Peachford Road, Suite 2200
Atlanta, GA 30341
Telephone 404/455-0927

International Environment Corporation
83 South Water Street
Greenwich, CT 06830
Telephone 203/531-4490

Inter-Technology 1 Solar Corporation
276 Broadview Avenue
Warrenton, VA 22186
Telephone 703/347-9500

ISLC
7010 Convoy Court
San Diego, CA 92111
Telephone 714/560-9173

J.C. Solar
P/O Box 18
Pinedale, CA 93650
Telephone 209/439-3024

Kastek Corporation
P/O Box 8881
Portland, OR 97208
Telephone 503/289-0538

Lab Sciences, Divison of National Plastics, Inc.
604 Park Drive
Boca Raton, FL 33431
Telephone 305/994-1833
Largo Solar Systems Inc.
991 South 40th Avenue
Plantation, FL 33317
Telephone 305/583-8090
Lennox Industries Inc.
200 South 12th Avenue
P/O Box 280
Marshalltown, IA 50158
Telephone 515/754-4011
Libbey-Owens-Ford Company
1701 E. Broadway
Toledo, OH 43605
Telephone 419/247-4355

McKim Solar Energy Systems Inc.
1142 East 64th Street
Tulsa, OK 74136
Telephone 918/749-8896
Mann-Russell Electronics Inc.
1401 Thorne Road
Tacoma, WA 98421
Telephone 206/383-1591
MNK Enterprises Inc.
10 South 1st East
P/O Box 87
Bancroft, ID 83217
Telephone 208/648-7668

National Energy Systems Corporation
P/O Box 1176
Birmingham, AL 35201
Telephone 205/252-7726
National Solar Corporation
Novelty Lane
Essex, CT 06426
Telephone 203/767-1644
National Solar Supply
2331 Adams Drive, N.W.
Atlanta, GA 30318
Telephone 404/352-3478
National Energy Corporation
1001 Connecticut Avenue, N.W., Suite 530
Washington, D.C. 20036
Telephone 202/296-7070
National Heating Systems
2417 Front Street
West Sacramento, CA 95691
Telephone 916/372-2993

Northeastern Solar Energy Corporation
107 Northern Boulevard
Great Neck, NY 11021
Telephone 516/829-5373
Northrup Inc.
302 Nichols Drive
Hutchins, TX 75141
Telephone 214/225-4291
NRG Ltd.
901 Second Avenue East
Coralville, IA 52241
Telephone 319/354-2033

OEM Products Inc.
2701 Adamo Drive
Tampa, FL 33605
Telephone 813/247-5947
O.S. Solar Energy Inc.
P/O Box 221
Milford, OH 45150
Telephone 513/831-4879
Overly Manufacturing Company
574 West Otterman Street
Greensburg, PA 15601
Telephone 412/834-7300
Ozark Solar Energy Systems
406 Summit
Carl Junction, MO 64834
Telephone 417/649-7985

Pacific Solar Systems Inc.
711 Bangs Avenue
P/O Box 6301
Modesto, CA 95355
Telephone 209/521-6400
Pacific Solar Tool
182 McLellan Avenue
San Mateo, CA 94403
Telephone 415/345-6721
PAC Solar Collector, Division of People/Space Company
49 Garden Street
Boston, MA 02114
Telephone 617/742-8652
Paul Mueller Company
P/O Box 828
Springfield, MO 65801
Telephone 417/865-2831
Payne Inc.
1910 Forest Drive
Annapolis, MD 21401
Telephone 301/268-6150

P.C.A.
11031 Wye Drive
San Antonio, TX 78217
Telephone 512/656-9338

Permaloy Corporation
P/O Box 1559
Ogden, UT 84402
Telephone 801/731-4303

Pioneer Energy Products
Route 1, Box 189
Forest, VA 24551
Telephone 804/239-2661

Pleiad Industries Inc.
Springdale Road
West Branch, IA 52358
Telephone 319/356-2735

Polynesian Pools
1145 Washington Avenue
Holland, MI 49423
Telephone 616/392-7861

Powell Brothers Inc.
5903 Firestone Boulevard
Southgate, CA 90280
Telephone 213/869-3307

PPG Industries Inc.
One Gateway Center
Pittsburgh, PA 15222
Telephone 412/434-3555

Precision Industries, Ltd.
928 Kaamahu Place
Honolulu, HA 96817
Telephone 808/847-3902

Prima Industries Inc.
P/O Box 141
Deer Park, NY 11729
Telephone 516/242-6347

Product Development Company
3901 Red Rock Canyon Road
Rapid City, SD 57701
Telephone 605/342-6518

Radco Products Inc.
2877 Industrial Parkway
Santa Maria, CA 93454
Telephone 805/925-8748

RA Energy Systems
8630 Production Avenue, Suite A
San Diego, CA 92121
Telephone 714/578-2260

Ra-Los Inc.
559 Union Avenue
Campbell, CA 95008
Telephone 408/371-1734

RD Enterprises
Route 3, Box 258
Cartage, TX 75633
Telephone 214/693-5281

Raypak Inc.
31111 Agoura Road
West Lake Village, CA 91360
Telephone 213/889-1500

RD Herbert and Sons Company
601 Harrison Street
Nashville, TN 37219
Telephone 615/242-3501

Refrigeration Research
Solar Research Division
525 N. Fifth Street
Brighton, MI 48116
Telephone 313/227-1151

Research Engineering Manufacturing Company
3838 East Van Buren
Phoenix, AZ 85008
Telephone 602/273-4300

Revere Solar and Architectual Products Inc.
Box 151
Rome, NY 13440
Telephone 315/338-2595

Reynolds Metals Company
6601 West Broad Street
P/O Box 27003
Richmond, VA 23261
Telephone 804/281-4730

R-M Products
5010 Cook
Denver, CO 80216
Telephone 303/825-0203

Robert Mitchell Solar Systems Design
RD 3, Box 147
Selkirk, NY 12158
Telephone 518/767-3100

Sea-lect Products Inc.
807 S. Third
Kent, WA 98031
Telephone 206/852-9700

Semco Corporation
1054 N.E. 43rd Street
Ft. Lauderdale, FL 33334
Telephone 305/565-2516

Setsco, (Solar Energy Thermal Systems)
1037B Shary Circle
Concord, GA 94518
Telephone 415/676-5392

Shape Symmetry & Sun
Biddeford Industrial Park
Biddeford, ME 04005
Telephone 207/282-6155

Silves Ltd.
7 West 14th Street
New York, NY 10011
Telephone 212/691-4632

Simons Solar Environmental Systems Inc.
24 Carlisle Pike
Mechanicsburg, PA 17055
Telephone 717/697-2778

Sola Heat
1200 E. First Street
Los Angeles, CA 90033
Telephone 213/263-5823

Solar Aire
82 South Third Street
San Jose, CA 95113
Telephone 408/295-2528

Solar Alternative Inc.
30 Clark Street
Brattleboro, VT 05301
Telephone 802/254-8221

Solar America Inc.
9001 Arbor Street
Omaha, NE 68124
Telephone 402/397-2421

Solar Application Inc.
7926 Convoy Court
San Diego, CA 92111
Telephone 714/292-1857

Solarator Inc.
P/O Box 277
Madison Heights, MI 48071
Telephone 313/642-9377

Sola Ray Inc.
P/O Box 590
Old Saybrook, CT 06475
Telephone 203/299-7112

Solar Central
7213 Ridge Road
Mechanisburg, OH 43044
Telephone 513/828-1350

Solarcoa Inc.
2115 East Spring Street
Long Beach, CA 90806
Telephone 213/426-7655

Solar Collector of Santa Cruz
2902 Glen Canyon Road
Santa Cruz, CA 95060
Telephone 408/438-1770

Solar Comfort Systems, Division of Solar Systems Inc.
4853 Cordell Avenue, Suite 606
Bethesda, MD 20014
Telephone 301/951-0095 or 652-8941

Solar Concepts Inc.
818 Charcot Avenue
San Jose, CA 95131
Telephone 408/263-8110

Solar Development Inc.
4180 Westroads Drive
West Palm Beach, FL 33407
Telephone 305/842-8935

Solar Dynamics Corporation
550 Frontage Road
Northfield, IL 60093
Telephone 312/446-5242

Solar Dynamics Inc.
1320 S. Lipan Street
Denver, CO 80223
Telephone 303/777-3666

Solar Dynamics Inc.
4527 E. 11th Avenue
Hialeah, FL 33013
Telephone 305/688-4393

Solar Dynamics of Arizona
Box 647, 1100 N. Lake Havasu Drive, Suite H
Lake Havasu City, AZ 86403
Telephone 602/855-7555

Solar Electric Inc.
403 South Maple
West Branch, IA 52358
Telephone 319/643-2598

Solar Energy Applications Inc.
1102 E. Washington
Phoenix, AZ 85034
Telephone 602/244-1822

Solar Energy Components
441 Shearer Boulevard
Cocoa, FL 32922
Telephone 305/632-2888

Solar Energy Contractors
P/O Box 16425, 3156 Leon Road
Jacksonville, FL 32216
Telephone 904/641-5611

Solar Energy Inc.
12155 Magnolia Avenue, E-6
Riverside, CA 92503
Telephone 714/785-0610

Solar Energy Products Inc.
1208 N.W. 8th Avenue
Gaineville, FL 32601
Telephone 904/377-6527

Solar Energy Research Corporation
701 B South Main Street
Longmont, CO 80501
Telephone 303/772-8406

Solar Energy Resources Corporation
10639 S.W. 185 Terrace
Miami, FL 33157
Telephone 305/233-0711

Solar Energy Systems
P/O Box 625, Sentry Place
Scarsdale, NY 10583
Telephone 914/725-5570

Solar Energy Systems Inc.
2345 Santa Fe Avenue
Los Angeles, CA 90058
Telephone 213/583-5808

Solar Energy Systems Inc.
One Olney Avenue
Cherry Hill, NJ 08003
Telephone 609/424-4446

Solar Energy Systems of Gerogia
5825 Glenridge Drive, N.E. Building 2, Suite 107
Atlanta, GA 30328
Telephone 404/255-9588

Solar Engineering
P/O Box 1358
Boca Raton, FL 33432
Telephone 305/368-2456

Solar Enterprises
P/O Box 1046, 99 Wand Solar Drive
Red Bluff, CA 96080
Telephone 916/527-0551

Solar Enterprises Inc.
2800 W. Division
Arlington, TX 76012
Telephone 817/461-5571

Solar Enterprises Inc.
3770 N. Dunlop Street
St. Paul, MN 55112
Telephone 612/483-8103

Solar Equipment Corporation
P/O Box 357
Lakeside, CA 92040
Telephone 714/561-4531

Solar-Eye Products Inc.
1300 N.W. McNab Road, Buildings G&H
Fort Lauderdale, FL 33309
Telephone 305/974-2500

Solargenics Inc.
9713 Lurline Avenue
Chatsworth, CA 91311
Telephone 213/998-0806

Solargizer Corporation
220 Mulberry Street
Stillwater, MN 55082
Telephone 612/439-5734

Solar Heat
1200 E. First Street
Los Angeles, CA 90033
Telephone 213/263-5823

Solar Heat Company
P/O Box 110
Greenville, PA 16125
Telephone 412/588-5650

Solar Heat Corporation
1252 French Avenue
Lakewood, OH 44107
Telephone 216/228-2993

Solar Heat Corporation
108 Summer Street
Arlington, MA 02174
Telephone 617/646-5763

Solar Heat Manufacturing
1011 6th Avenue South
Lake Worth, FL 33460
Telephone 305/586-3839

Solar Heat of New Jersey
811 Wyretta Place
Paramus, NJ 07652
Telephone 201/652-3819

Solar Homes Inc.
2707 S. County Trail
E. Greenwich, RI 02818
Telephone 401/884-0353

Solar Home Systems Inc.
12931 West Geauga Trail
Chesterland, OH 44026
216/729-9350

Solar Industries Inc.
Route 6, P/O Box 303
Plymouth, CT 06782
Telephone 203/283-0223

Solar Innovations
412 Longfellow Boulevard
Lakeland, FL 33801
Telephone 813/688-8873

227

Solar International
5825 Glenridge Drive N.E.,
Building 2, Suite 107
Atlanta, GA 30328
Telephone 404/255-9588

Solar Kit of Florida Inc.
1102 139th Avenue
Tampa, FL 33612
Telephone 813/971-3932

Solar Life
404 Lippincott Avenue
Riverton, NJ 08077
Telephone 609/829-7022

Solarmaster
722-D West Betteravia Road
Santa Maria, CA 93454
Telephone 805/922-0205

Solarnetics Corporation
1654 Pioneer Way
El Cajon, CA 92020
Telephone 714/579-7122

Solar NRG Inc.
3202 Cooper Court
Glenwood Springs, CO 81601
Telephone 303/945-8400

Solar Products
Box 36
Spencertown, NY 12165
Telephone 518/392-5573

Solar Products Inc.
10 and 12 Hylestead Street
Providence, RI 02905
Telephone 401/467-7350

Solar Products Manufacturing Corporation
151 John Downey Drive
New Britian, CT 06051
Telephone 203/224-2164

Solar Products Sun-Tank Inc.
614 N.W. 62nd Street
Miami, FL 33150
Telephone 305/756-7609

Solar Research Systems
3001 Red Hill Avenue, 1-105
Costa Mesa, CA 92626
Telephone 714/545-4941

Solar Southwest
5700 Andrews Highway
Odessa, TX 79762
Telephone 915/362-4922

Solar Sun Inc
235 West 12th Street
Cincinnati, OH 45210
Telephone 513/241-4200

Solar Systems
26046 Eden Landing Road, Suite 41
Hayward, CA 94545
Telephone 415/785-0711

Solar Systems by Sun Dance Inc.
13939 N.W. 60th Avenue
Miami Lakes, FL 33014
Telephone 305/557-2882

Solar Systems Inc.
507 West Elm Street
Tqler, TX 75701
Telephone 214/595-4431

Solar Systems International
6065 N.W. 82nd Avenue
Miami, FL 33166
Telephone 800/327-7066

Solartec Corporation
8210 Engineer Road
San Diego, CA 92111
Telephone 714/560-8434

Solar Technology Inc.
927 Oakcliff Industrial Court
Atlanta, GA 30340
Telephone 404/449-0900

Solar Technology Int. Inc.
119 N. Center Street
Statesville, NC 28677
Telephone 704/873-7959

Solartech Systems Corporation
2216 Avenue E.
Lubbock, TX 79404
Telephone 806/765-7761

Solarter Inc.
250 Pennsylvania Avenue
Salem, OH 44460
Telephone 216/332-9100

Solar-Therm
780 Main Street
West Barnstable, MA 02668
Telephone 617/362-6471

Solar Therm
Box 426
Meadville, PA 16335
Telephone 814/724-4258

Solar Therm
203 Point Royal Drive
Rockwall, TX 75087
Telephone 214/475-2201

Solar Therm of Maryland
5105 72nd Avenue
Hyattsville, MD 20784
Telephone 301/459-6022

Solar II Enterprises
19675 Skyline Boulevard
Los Gatos, CA 95030
Telephone 408/354-3353

Solar Unlimited Inc.
4310 Governors Drive West
Huntsville, AL 35803
Telephone 205/837-7340

Solar Water Heaters of New Port Richey, Inc.
1214 U.S. Highway 19 North
New Port Richey, FL 33552
Telephone 813/848-2324

Solarway
P/O Box 217
Redwood Valley, CA 95470
Telephone 707/485-7616

Solar West Inc.
Box 892
Fresno, CA 93714
Telephone 209/222-3455

Sol-Ray Division, Unit Electric Control
130 Atlantic Drive
Maitland, FL 32751
Telephone 305/831-1900

Sol-Ray Inc.
204-B Carleton
Orange, CA 92667
Telephone 714/997-9431

Sol Tex Corporation
9101 Lipan, P/O Box 55703
Houston, TX 77055
Telephone 713/780-1733

Solar Inc.
9630 Clarewood, B-7
Houston, TX 77036
Telephone 713/772-6416

Southeastern Solar Systems Inc.
2812 New Spring Road, Suite 150
Atlanta, GA 30339
Telephone 404/434-4447

Southern Lighting Manufacturing Company
501 Elwell Avenue
Orlando, FL 32803
Telephone 305/894-8851

Southwest Ever-Tech Inc.
3030 South Valley View Boulevard
Las Vegas, NV 89102
Telephone 701/873-1975

Southwest Standard, Division of Southwest Sheet Metal Works, Inc.
P/O Box 10094
El Paso, TX 79991
Telephone 915/533-6291

Spectra Energy Systems Inc.
P/O Box 6036
Santa Barbara, CA 93111
Telephone 805/967-1053

Sunburst Solar Energy Inc.
P/O Box 2799
Menlo Park, CA 94025
Telephone 415/327-8022

Sun Century Systems
Box 2036
Florence, AL 35630
Telephone 205/764-0795

Sundu Company
3319 Keys Lane
Anaheim, CA 92804
Telephone 714/828-2873

Sunearth Solar Products Corporation
RD 1, Box 337
Green Lane, PA 18054
Telephone 215/699-7892

Sun Energy International Inc
P/O Box 6542
Concord, CA 94524
Telephone 415/676-8717

Sun Power Corporation
P/O Box 16963
Orlando, FL 32811
Telephone 305/876-2237

Sun Power Systems Ltd.
1024 West Maude Avenue, Suite 203
Sunnydale, CA 94086
Telephone 408/738-2442

Sunray Solar Heat Inc.
202 Classon Avenue
Brooklyn, NY 11205
Telephone 212/857-0193

Sunrise Energy Products Inc.
996 Mackinaw Highway
Pellston, MI 49769
Telephone 616/347-7220

Sunsav Inc.
890 East Street
Tewksbury, MA 01876
Telephone 617/851-5913

Sunshine Collection Agency Ltd.
1971 31st Street
Boulder, CO 80301
Telephone 303/449-2620

Sunshine Unlimited
900 North Jay Street
Chandler, AZ 85224
Telephone 602/963-3873

Sun Sponge
1288 Fayette Street
El Cajon, CA 92020
Telephone 714/449-6726

Sun Systems
1825 West Indian School Road
Phoenix, AZ 85015
Telephone 602/263-0699

Sun Systems Inc.
P/O Box 155
Eureka, IL 61530
Telephone 309/467-3632

Sun Top Inc.
42 East Dudley Town Road
Bloomfield, CT 06002
Telephone 203/243-1781

Sunwater Energy Products
1488 Pioneer Way, #x7
El Cajon, CA 92020
Telephone 714/579-0771

Sunworks Inc., Division of Ethone, Inc.
P/O Box 1004
New Haven, CT 06508
Telephone 203/934-6301

Systems Technology Inc.
P/O Box 337
Shalimar, FL 32579
Telephone 904/863-9213

Technitreck Corporation
1999 Pike Avenue
San Leandro, CA 94577
Telephone 415/352-0535

The Original Power Equipment Company
2617 National Drive
Garland, TX 75041
Telephone 214/271-0910

The Solaray Corporation
345 North Nimitz Highway
Honolulu, HI
Telephone 808/533-6464

The Solar Broken
1523 Valley Parkway, Suite 219
Escondido, CA 92027

The Solarshingles Company
14532 Vanowen Street
Van Nuys, CA 91605
Telephone 213/782-2828

The Stolle Corporation
1501 Michigan Street
Sidney, OH 45365
Telephone 513/492-1111

Travco Inc.
4013 Woodville Highway
Tallahassee, FL 32301
Telephone 904/878-4111

United States Solar Systems Inc.
P/O Box 48695
Los Angeles, CA 90048
Telephone 213/654-1926

Virginia Solar Components Inc.
Highway 29 South
Rustburg, VA 24588
Telephone 804/239-9523

Vulcan Solar Industries Inc.
200 Conant Street
Pawtucket, RI 02860
Telephone 401/725-6061

Wallace Company
831 Dorsey Street
P/O Box 511
Gainsville, GA 30501
Telephone 404/534-5971

Weather-Made Systems Inc.
Route 7, Box 300 D
Springfield, MO 65802
Telephone 417/865-0684

Werner Industries Inc.
978 Aurora Road
P/O Box 1466
Melbourne, FL 32935
Telephone 305/254-7611

Western Energy Inc.
454 Forest Avenue
Palo Alto, CA 94302
Telephone 415/327-3371

Western Solar Development Inc.
1236 Callen Street
Vacaville, CA 95688
Telephone 707/446-3547

Wilcox Manufacturing Corporation
P/O Box 455, 13375 U.S. 19 North
Pinellas Park, FL 33565
Telephone 813/531-7741

W.R. Robbins & Son
1401 N.W. 20th Street
Miami, FL 33142
Telephone 305/325-0880

Ying Manufacturing Corporation
1957 West 144th Street
Gardena, CA 90249
Telephone 213/770-1756

American Solarize Corporation
P.O. Box 15
Martinsville, NJ 08836
Telephone 201/356-3141

Astro Solar Corporation
457 Santa Anna Drive
Palm Springs, FL 33461
Telephone 305/965-0606

Bryant Air Conditioning
7310 West Morris Street
Indianapolis, IN 46231
Telephone 317/243-0851

Carolina Solar Equipment Company
P.O. Box 2068
Salisbury, NC 28144
Telephone 704/637-1243

Carolina Thermal Company
Iron Work Road, Route 2, Box 39
Reidsville, NC 27320
Telephone 919/342-0352

Champion Home Builder Company
5573 North Street
Dryden, MI 48428
Telephone 313/796-2211

Contemporary Systems Inc.
68 Charlonne Street
Jaffrey, NH 03452
Telephone 603/532-7972

Custom Solar Heating Systems
P.O. Box 375
Albany, NY 12201
Telephone 518/438-7358

DIY-SOL, Inc.
P.O. Box 614
Marlboro, MA 01752
Telephone 617/481-0359

Dura Plex Industries
720 E. Herrin Street
Herrin, IL 62948
Telephone 618/942-7302

E.C.M. Associates
1928 6th Street
Boulder, CO 80302
Telephone 303/443-7970

Energy Control Systems
3324 Octavia Street
Raleigh, NC 27606
Telephone 919/851-2310

Energy King
Box 248
Creston, IA 50801
Telephone 515/782-8566

Enviropane Inc.
350 N. Marshall Street
Lancaster, PA 17602
Telephone 717/288-3737

Faom Products Inc.
Gay Street
York Haven, PA 17370
Telephone 717/266-3671

Future Systems Inc.
12500 W. Cedar Drive
Lakewood, CO 80228
Telephone 303/989-0444

Gem Manufacturing Corporation
390 East Tiffin Street
Bascom, OH 44809
Telephone 419/937-2225

General Solar Corporation
3900 Magnolia Street
Denver CO 80207
Telephone 303/795-6670

Herlemann Electric
127 Mountainview Road
Warren, NJ 07060
Telephone 201/752-6060

Hudson Valley Solar
Box 388, Route 9
Valatie, NY 12184
Telephone 518/758-6535

Hyperion
7209 Valtec Court
Boulder, CO 80301
Telephone 303/449-9544

Illinois Solar Corporation
P.O. Box 841
Peoria, IL 61652
Telephone 309/673-0458

IMPAC Corporation
312 Blondeau Street
Keokuk, IA 52632
Telephone 319/524-3304

J.G. Johnston Manufacturing Company
33458 Angeles Forest Highway
Pamdale, CA 93550
Telephone 805/947-3791

Kaelin Industries Inc.
2210 N. Grand Avenue
Evansville, IN 47711
Telephone 812/423-7200

McKim Solar Energy Systems Inc
1142 East 64th Street
Tulsa, OK 74136
Telephone 918/749-8896
Mid-Western Solar Systems
2235 Irvin Cobb Drive
Paducah, KY 42001
Telephone 501/443-6295

National Energy Corporation
21716 Kendrick Avenue
Lakeville, MN 55044
Telephone 612/469-3401
Northwest Solar Systems Inc.
7700 12th Street, N.E.
Seattle, WA 98115
Telephone 206/523-3951
NRG LTD.
901 Second Avenue East
Coralville, IA 52241
Telephone 319/354-2033
NRG Manufacturing
P.O. Box 53
Napolean, OH 43545
Telephone 419/599-3618

Ohio Valley Solar
4141 Airport Road
Cincinnati, OH 45226
Telephone 513/871-1961
Ozark Solar Energy Systems
406 Summit
Carl Junction, MO 64834
Telephone 417/649-7985

Park Energy Company
Star Route 9
Jackson, WY 83001
Telephone 307/733-4950
Permaloy Corporation
P.O. Box 1559
Ogden, UT 84402
Telephone 801/731-4303

RADI-TROL
14826 7th Street
P.O. Box 1217
Victorville, CA 92392
Telephone 714/245-5368
R-M Products
5010 Cook
Denver, CO 802x6
Telephone 303/825-0203
Ryniker Steel Products
P.O. Box 1932, N.P. Industrial Site
Billings, MT 59103
Telephone 406/252-3836

Sol-Aire Energy Systems
2750 South Shoshone Street
Englewood, CO 80110
Telephone 303/426-8411
Solar American Inc.
9001 Arbor Street
Omaha, NE 68124
Telephone 402/397-2421
Solar Central
7213 Ridge Road
Mechanicsburg, OH 43044
Telephone 513/828-1350
Solar Climate Inc.
101-21 Dupont Street
Plainview, LI., NY 11803
Telephone 516/931-3218
**Solar Comfort Systems,
Division of Solar Systems Inc.**
4853 Cordell Avenue, Suite 606
Bethesda, MD 20014
Telephone 301/951-0095 or 652-8941
Solar Electric of Oklahoma
3611 E. 11th Street
Tulsa, OK 74112
Telephone 918/836-7507
Solar Energy Contractors
P.O. Box 16425, 3156 Leon Road
Jacksonville, FL 32216
Telephone 904/641-5611
Solar Energy Products Company
121 Miller Road
Avon Lake, OH 44012
Telephone 216/933-5000
Solar Energy Research Corporation
701 B South Main Street
Longmont, CO 80501
Telephone 303/772-8406

Solar Engineering and Equipment Company
3305 Metairie Road
Metairie, LA 70001
Telephone 504/837-7313

Solar-eye Products, Inc.
1300 N.W. McNab Road,
Buildings G and H
Fort Lauderdale, FL 33309
Telephone 305/974-2500

Solar Farm Industries Inc.
P.O. Box 242
Stockton, KS 67669
Telephone 913/425-6726

Solar Heat Company
P.O. Box 110
Greenville, PA 16125
Telephone 412/588-5650

Solar Homes, Inc.,
2702 S. County Trail
E. Greenwich, RI 02818
Telephone 401/884-0353

Solar Marketing Inc.
P.O. Box 1776
Omaha, NE 68102
Telephone 402/341-9080

Solar NRG Inc.
3202 Cooper Court
Glenwood Springs, CO 81601
Telephone 303/945-8400

Solaron Corporation
300 Galleria Tower
720 S. Colorado Boulevard
Denver, CO 80222
Telephone 303/759-0101

Solar I, Division of Steller Industries Inc.
7265 Commerce Drive
Mentor, OH 44060
Telephone 216/951-6363

Solar Seven Industries Inc.
3323 Moline Street
Aurora, CO 80010
Telephone 303/364-7277

Solar Shelter Engineering Inc.
Box 179, 35 South Maple Street
Kutztown, PA 19530
Telephone 215/683-6769

Solar Systems International
6065 N.W. 82nd Avenue
Miami, FL 33166
Telephone 800/327-7066

Solartech Limited
207 Queens Quay West, Toronto

Ontario, Canada M5J1A7
Telephone 416/853-0525

Solar Technology Corporation
2160 Clay Street
Denver, CO 80211
Telephone 303/455-3309

Solartec Inc.
250 Pennsylvania Avenue
Salem, OH 44460
Telephone 216/332-9100

Solar Thermics Enterprises LTD.
406 E. Taylor Street
Creston, IA 50801
Telephone 515/782-8566

Solarway
P.O. Box 217
Redwood Valley, CA 95470
Telephone 707/485-7616

S.T.A. Corporation
348 Hazard Avenue
Enfield, CT 06082
Telephone 203/749-7054

**Sun Company,
Solar Utilities Industries**
922 Lake Street, P.O. Box 387
Gothenburg, NE 69138
Telephone 308/537-7377

**Suncraft Solar, Division
of Nichols Nebraska, Inc.**
5001 East 59th
Kansas City, MO 64130
Telephone 816/333-2100

Sunpower Industries Inc.
10837 S.E. 200th Street
Kent, WA 98031
Telephone 206/854-0670

Sunrise Energy Products Inc.
996 Mackinaw Highway
Pellston, MI 49769
Telephone 616/347-7220

Sunsaver Corporation
P.O. Box 276
North Liberty, IA 52317
Telephone 319/626-2343

Sun Spot Research
1070 S. Leyden
Denver, CO 80224
Telephone 303/321-7323

Sun Stone Energy Equipment
P.O. Box 941
Sheboygan, WI 53081
Telephone 414/452-8194

Sun Systems Inc.
1825 West Indian School Road
Phoenix, AZ 85015
Telephone 602/263-0699

Sun Systems, Inc.
P.O. Box 155
Eurkea, IL 61530
Telephone 309/467-3632

Sun-Time Solar Corporation
3443-45 Prospect Avenue
Kansas City, MO 64128
Telephone 816/923-1291

Sun Unlimited Research Corporation
P.O. Box 941
Sheboygan, WI 53081
Telephone 414/452-8194

Sun Wall Inc.
P.O. Box 9723
Pittsburgh, PA 15229
Telephone 412/364-5349 or 771-4747

Sun Works, Division of Enthone Inc.
P.O. Box 1004
New Haven, CT 06508
Telephone 203/934-6301

Southwest Energy Options
Route 8, Box 30-H
Silver City, NM 88061
Telephone 505/538-9598

The Solar Store Corporation
Box 841
Peoria, IL 61652
Telephone 309/673-0458

Tubal-Cain Manufacturing Company Inc.
549 Hall Road
Elyria, OH 44035
Telephone 216/323-6098

Universal Solar Systems Inc.
Box 101
House Springs, MO 63051
Telephone 314/375-5402

Valley Industries Inc.
6 East 4th Street
Cincinnati, OH 45202
Telephone 513/241-2877

Ying Manufacturing Corporation
1957 West 144th Street
Gardena, CA 90249
Telephone 213/770-1756

FOCUSING COLLECTORS

AA1 Corporation
Box 6767
Baltimore, MD 21204
Telephone 301/666-1400

Acurex Corporation
485 Clyde Ave.
Mountain View, CA 94042
Telephone 415/964-3200

American Solar Systems
415 E. Branch Street
Arroyo Grande, CA 93420
Telephone 805/481-1010

Albuquerque Western Solar System Inc.
720 Rankin Rd., N.E.
Albuquerque, NM 87107
Telephone 505/344-7738

Alpha Solarco
Suite 2230, Kroger Building
Cincinnati, OH 45202
Telephone 513/621-1243

Bean Engineering Inc.
732 North Pastoria Avenue
Sunnydale, CA 94086
Telephone 408/738-4573

Brown Manufacturing Company
P.O. Box 14546
Oklahoma City, OK 73114
Telephone 405/751-1e23

Del Manufacturing Company
905 Monterey Pass Road
Monterey Park, CA 91754
Telephone 213/264-0860

Energy Design Corporation
P.O. Box 34294
Memphis, TN 38134
Telephone 901/382-2000

Entropy Limited
5735 Arapahoe Avenue
Boulder, CO 80303
Telephone 303/443-5103

Enviropane Inc.
350 N. Marshall Street
Lancaster, PA 17602
Telephone 717/299-3737

Falbel Energy System Corporation
P.O. Box 6
Greenwich, CT 06830
Telephone 203/357-0626

General Atomic Company
P.O. Box 81608
San Diego, CA 92138
Telephone 714/455-2090

General Electric Company,
Advanced Energy Programs
P.O. Box 13601
Philadelphia, PA 19101
Telephone 215/962-2112

General Solar Systems, Division
General Extrusions, Inc.
4040 Lake Park Road
Youngstown, OH 44507
Telephone 216/783-0270

Great Natural Structure
Boston, MA
Telephone 617/442-100

Heliopticon Corporation
P.O. Drawer 330
Plymouth, NH 03264
Telephone 603/536-2550

Hexcel Corporation
11711 Dublin Boulevard
Dublin, CA 94566
Telephone 415/828-4200

Hot line Solar Inc.
1811 Hillcress Drive
P.O. Box 546
Bellevue, NE 68005
Telephone 402/291-3888

KTA Solar Corporation
12300 Washington Avenue
Rockville, MD 20852
Telephone 301/468-2066

Mann-Russell Electronics Inc.
1401 Thorne Road Tacoma, WA 98421
Telephone 206/383-1591

McDonnell Douglas Astronautics Company
5301 Bolsa Avenue
Huntington Beach, CA 92647
Telephone 714/896-4323

Northrup Inc.
302 Nichols Drive
Hutchins, TX 75141
Telephone 214/225-4291

Owen Enterprises Inc.
436 N. Fries Avenue
Wilmington, CA 90744
Telephone 213/835-7436

Owen-Illinois-Inc.
P.O. Box 1035
Toledo, OH 43666
Telehpone 213/835-7436

Phase Z Solar Corporation
620 12th Street
Modesto, CA 95354
Telephone 209/526-2214

Rox International Inc.
2604 Hidden Lake Drive
Sarasota, FL 33577
Telephone 813/366-6053

Scientific Atlanta Inc.
3845 Pleasantdale Road
Atlanta, GA 30340
Telephone 404/449-2000

Solarcell Corporation
1455 N.E. 57th Street
Ft. Lauderdale, FL 3334
Telephone 305/462-2215

Solar Dynamics Inc.
4527 E. 11th Avenue
Hialeah, FL 33013
Telephone 305/688-4393

Solar Engineering
P.O. Box 1358
Boca Raton, FL 33432
Telephone 305/368-2456

Solar Equipment Corporation
P.O. Box 357
Lakeside, CA 92040
Telephone 714/561-4531

Solar Industries Inc.
Route 6, P.O. Box 303
Plymouth, CT 06782
Telephone 203/283-0223

Solar Industries of Florida Inc.
3221 Trout River Boulevard, P.O. Box 9013
Jacksonville, FL 32208
Telephone 904/768-4323

Solar Kinetics Corporation
P.O. Box 17308
West Hartford, CT 06117
Telephone 203/233-4461

Solar Kinetics Inc.
147 Parkhouse Street
Dallas, TX 75207
Telephone 214/747-6519

Solar Sun Inc.
235 West 12th Street
Cincinnati, OH 45210
Telephone 513/241-4200

Solartec Corporation
8210 Engineer Road
San Diego, CA 92111
Telephone 714/560-8434

Solenergy Inc.
70 Zoe Street
San Francisco, CA 94107
Telephone 415/495-4303

S. W. Energy Options
Route 8, Box 30-H
Silver City, NM 88061
Telephone 505/538-9598

Spectra Energy Systems Inc.
P.O. Box 6036
Santa Barbara, CA 93111
Telephone 805/963-1053

S. P. S. Inc.
8801 Biscayne Boulevard
Miami, FL 33138
Telephone 305/754-7766

Sun Heat Inc.
2624 South Zuni
Englewood, CO 80110
Telephone 303/922-6179

Sunmaster Corporation
12 Spruce Street
Corning, NY 14830
Telephone 607/937-5441

Sunpower Systems Corporation
510 South 52nd Street, Suite 101
Tempe, AZ 85281
Telephone 602/894-2331

Sunshine Manufacturing Company
4870 S.W. Main #4
Beaverton, OR 97005
Telephone 503/643-6172

Sun Tab Inc.
P.O. Box 754
Arlington Heights, IL 60006
Telephone 312/255-5654

Suntec Systems Inc.
21405 Hamburg Avenue
Lakeville, MN 55044
Telephone 612/469-3471

The Great Natural Structures Company
Boston, MA
Telephone 617/442-1000

Whiteline Inc.
1509 Northwestern Bank
Asheville, NC 28801
Telephone 704/258-8405

Wormser Scientific Corporation
88 Foxwood Road
Stamford, CT 06903
Telephone 203/329-2001

Z.Z. Corporation
10806 Kaylor Street
Los Alamitos, CA 90720
Telephone 213/598-3220

SOLAR ABSORBER PLATES OR TUBING

Alcan Aluminum Corporation
100 Erie View Plaza
Cleveland, OH 44110
Telephone 216/523-6800

Allegheny Ludlam Steel Corporation
Oliver Building
Pittsburgh, PA 15222
Telephone 412/562-4000

Allied Fabricators Inc.
1254 Thomas Avenue
San Francisco, CA 94124
Telephone 415/822-4577

Aluminum Company of America
1501 Alcoa Building
Pittsburgh, PA 15219
Telephone 412/553-3185

Automated Building Components Inc.
P.O. Box 592037 AMF
Miami, FL 33159
Telephone 800/327-3081

Kennecott Copper Corporation
128 Spring Street
Lexington, MA 02173
Telephone 617/862-8268

Largo Solar Systems Inc.
991 South 40th Avenue
Plantation, FL 33317
Telephone 305/583-8090

Midwest Technology Inc.
P.O. Box 26238
Dayton, OH 45416
Telephone 513/274-6020

Mohawk Steel Corporation
520 N. Michigan
Chicago, IL 60611
Telephone 312/828-0123

**Muller Brass Company,
Solar Products Division**
1925 Lapeer Avenue
Port Huron, MI 48060
Telephone 313/987-4000

New Jersey Aluminum, Easco Corporation
P.O. Box 73
North Brunswick, NJ 08902
Telephone 800/631-5856

Olin Brass Shamrock
East Alton, IL 62024
Telephone 618/258-2000

Panel-Air Corporation
1571 W. MacArthur Boulevard
Costa Mesa, CA 92626
Telephone 714/549-0311

Precision Industries Ltd.
928 Kaamahu Place
Honolulu, HI 96817
Telephone 808/847-3902

Shelley Radiant Ceiling Company
456 W. Frontage Road
Northfield, IL 60093
Telephone 312/446-2800

Solar Kit of Florida Inc.
1102 139th Avenue
Tampa, FL 33612
Telephone 813/971-3932

Southern Aluminum Finishing Company Inc.
1581 Huber Street, N.W.
Atlanta, GA 30318
Telephone 404/355-1560

Spiral Tubing Corporation
533 Downey Drive
New Britain, CT 06051
Telephone 203/224-2409

Surry Solar Service Inc.
249 Hickory Street
Mt. Airy, NC 27030
Telephone 919/786-2953

Teledyne Metal Foaming
1937 Sterling Avenue
Elkart, IN 46514
Telephone 219/295-5525

The Anaconda Company, Brass Division
414 Meadow Street
Waterbury, CT 06720
Telephone 203/574-8500

The Berry Group
P.O. Box 327
Edision, NJ 08817
Telephone 201/549/3800

Thermon Manufacturing Company
P.O. Box 609
San Marcos, TX 78666
Telephone 512/392-5801

Tranter Inc.
735 E. Hazel Street
Lansing, MI 48090
Telephone 517/372-8410

Western Solar Development Inc.
1236 Callen Street
Vacaville, CA 95688
Telephone 707/446-3547

SOLAR REFLECTORS

Kingston Industries Corporation
205 Lexington Avenue
New York, NY 10016
Telephone 212/889-0190

Mechanical Mirror Work Inc.
661 Edgecombe Avenue
New York, NY 10032
Telephone 212/795-2100

National Products Inc.
900 Baxter Avenue
Louisville, KY 40204
Telephone 502/583-0206

Otto Fabric Inc.
P.O. Box 18361
Wichita, KS 67218
Telephone 316/262-5183

Southern Aluminum Finishing Company Inc.
1581 Huber Street, N.W.
Atlanta, GA 30318
Telephone 404/355-1560

Talbert Reflectors
442 Alcatraz Avenue
Oakland, CA 94609
Telephone 415/848-5128

The Helio-Vector Company
9705 Owensmouth Avenue
Chatsworth, CA 91311 Telphone
213/341-4101

Celotex Corporation
P.O. Box 22602
Tampa, FL 33622
Telephone 813/871-4286

Insta-foam Midwest Inc.
8000 47th Street
Lyons, IL 60534
Telephone 312/447-9262

Owen Corning Fiberglass Corporation
Fiberglass Tower
Toledo, OH 43659
Telephone 419/248-8139

Pittsburgh Corning Corporation
800 Presque Isle Drive
Pittsburgh, PA 15239
Telephone 412/327-6100

SOLAR COVERINGS

American Acrylic Corporation
173 Marine Street
Farmingdale, NY 11735
Telephone 516/249-1129

ASE Industries Inc.
P.O. Box 929
Kingsport, TN 37662
Telephone 615/245-0211

**El DuPont de Namours,
Plastic Products and Resins Dept.**
Wilmington, DE 19898
Telephone 302/774-5804

Filon Division Vistron Corporation
12333 Van Ness Avenue
Hawthorne, CA 90250
Telephone 213/757-5141

Ford Motor Company, Glass Division
1 Parklane Boulevard, Suite 1000E
Dearborn, MI 48126
Telephone 313/322-5962

Graham Products Ltd.
Box 2000, Inglewood
Ontario, CA Lon 1 KO

**Guardian Industries,
Glass Manufacturing Division**
14600 Romine
Carleton, MI 48117
Telephone 313/962-2252

Helio Thermics Inc.
110 Laurens Road
Greenville, SC 29607
Telephone 803/235-8529

J.W. Carroll & Sons
22600 South Bonita Street
Carson, CA 90745
Telephone 213/775-6737

Lalwall Corporation
1111 Candia Road, Box 237
Manchester, NH 03105
Telephone 603/627-3861

Lectric Lites Company
2504 West Vickey Boulevard
Fort Worth, TX 76102
Telephone 817/332-7961

Martin Processing Inc., Film Division
P.O. Box 5068
Martinsville, VA 24112
Telephone 703/629-1711

Optical Sciences Group Inc.
24 Tiburon Street
San Rafael, CA 94901
Telephone 415/453-8980

Rohm and Haas Company
Independence Mall West
Philadelphia, PA 19105
Telephone 215/592-3000

Sheffield Plastics Inc.
Salisbury Road
Sheffield, MA 01257
Telephone 413/229-8711

**Solar Comfort Systems,
Division of Solar Systems Inc.**
4853 Cordell Avenue, Suite 606
Betheseda, MD 20014
Telephone 301/951-0095 or 652-8941

Sun Systems Inc.
P.O. Box 951
Gallatin, TN 37066
Telephone 615/242-9815

Swedcast Corporation
7350 Empire Drive
Florence, KY 41042
Telephone 606/283-1501

Swedlow Inc.
12122 Western Avenue
Garden Grove, CA 92645
Telephone 714/893-7531

SOLAR COLLECTORS—HOUSING AND FRAMING

Alcan Aluminum Corporation
100 Erie View Plaza
Cleveland, OH 44110
Telephone 216/523-6800

Allied Fabricator Inc.
1254 Thomas Avenue
San Francisco, CA 94124
Telephone 415/822-4577

Aluminum Company of America
1501 Alcoa Building
Pittsburgh, PA 15219
Telephone 412/553-3185

Dara-Plex Industries Inc.
Herrin, IL 62948
Telephone 618/942-7302

Natural Heating Systems
2417 Front Street
West Sacramento, CA 95691
Telephone 916/372-2993

New Jersey Aluminum, Easco Corporation
P.O. Box 73
North Brunswick, NJ 08902
Telephone 800/631-5856

Solar Energy Inc.
12155 Magnolia Avenue, E 6,
Riverside, CA. 92503
Telephone 714/785-0610

Solar Energy Products Inc.
1208 N.W. 8th Avenue
Gainesville, FL 32601
Telephone 904/377-6527

Solar Energytics Inc.
P.O. Box 532
Jasper, IN 47546
Telephone 812/482-1416

Southern Aluminum Finishing Company Inc.
1581 Huber Street, N.W.
Atlanta, GA 30318
Telephone 404/355-1560

Sun Systems Inc.
P.O. Box 951
Gallatin, TN 37066
Telephone 615/242-9815

Teledyne Metal Forming
1937 Sterling Avenue
Elkhart, IN 46514
Telephone 219/295-5525

SOLAR COATINGS AND SURFACE TREATMENT

American Chemet Corporation
P.O. Box 165
Deerfield, IL 60015
Telephone 312/948-0800

**Bostik Finch Inc., Subsidiary
of Emhart Corporation**
20846 South Normandy Avenue
Torrance, CA 90502
Telephone 213/320-6800

Corillium Corporation
Reston International Center
Reston, VA 22091
Telephone 703/860-2100

De Soto, Inc.
1700 South Mt. Prospect Road
Des Plaines, IL 60018
Telephone 312/391-9000

Dow Corning Corporation
2200 W. Salzburg Road
Midland, MI 48640
Telephone 517/496-4000

Ferro Corporation
One Erieview Plaza
Cleveland, OH 44114
Telephone 216/641-8580

Highland Plating Company
1128 North Highland Avenue
Los Angeles, CA 90038
Telephone 213/469-2289

Mansfield Plating Company
153 East Fifth Street
Mansfield, OH 44903
Telephone 419/522-1611

Olympic Solar Plating Corporation
308 15th Street
S.W. Canton, OH 44707
Telephone 216/452-8856

Pemaloy Corporation
P.O. Box 1559
Ogden, UT 84402
Telephone 801/731-4303

The Berry Group
P.O. Box 327
Edison, NJ 08817
Telephone 201/549-3800

The Harshaw Chemical Company
1945 E. 97th Street
Cleveland, OH 44106
Telephone 216/721-8300

Pawling Rubber Corporation
157 Maple Boulevard
Pawling, NY 12564
Telephone 914/855-1000

SOLAR COLLECTORS AND ADHESIVES

**American Cyanamid,
Bloomingdale Aerospace Products**
Old Post Road
Havre de Grace, MD 21078
Telephone 301/939-1910

Chemplast Inc.
150 Dey Road
Wayne, NJ 07470
Telephone 2p1/696-4700

Diamond Patent Company
Box 893
South San Francisco, CA 94080
Telephone 415/431-4091

Dow Corning Corporation
2200 W. Salzburg Road
Midland, MI 48640
Telephone 517/496-4000

General Sealants Corporation
15248 East Proctor Avenue
City of Industry, CA 91744
Telephone 213/330-3118

Jamak Inc.
1401 North Bowie Drive
Weatherford, TX
Telephone 817/594-8771

SWIMMING POOL SYSTEMS

Advanced Energy Technology Inc.
121C Albright Way
Los Gatos, CA 93030
Telephone 408/866-7686

All Sun Power Inc.
10400 S.W. 187th Street
Miami, FL 33157
Telephone 305/233-2224

Alten Corporation
2594 Leghorn Street
Mountain View, CA 94043
Telephone 415/969-6474

Aluminum Company of America
1501 Alcoa Building
Pittsburgh, PA 75219
Telephone 412/553-3185

American Solar Power
715 Swann Avenue
Tampa, FL 33606
Telephone 813/354-4461

Aqua Blanket Inc.
1900 Old Middlefield Way
Mountain View, CA 94043
Telephone 415/969-1372

Carolina Solar Equipment Company
P.O. Box 2068
Salisbury, NC 28144
Telephone 704/637-1243

Catalina & Sons Inc.
301 Stagg Street
Brooklyn, NY 11206
Telephone 212/821-6100

**C.F. Roark Welding and
Engineering Company Inc.**
136 N. Green Street
Brownsburg, IN 46112
Telephone 317/852-3163

Chancellor Industries
13138 Poway Road
Poway, CA 92064
Telephone 714/748-8313

Colt Inc.
71590 San Jacinto
Rancho Mirage, CA 92270
Telephone 714/346-8033
Conserdyne Corporation
4437 San Fernando Road
Glendale, CA 91204
Telephone 213/246-8408

D.W. Browning Construction Company
475 Carswell Avenue
Holly Hill, FL 32017
Telephone 904/252-1528

Energex Manufacturing Corporation
4227 S. 36th Place
Phoenix, AZ 85040
Telephone 602/267-9474
Energy Design Inc.
1925 Curry Road
Schenectady, NY 12303
Telephone 518/355-3322

Fabro Inc.
235 Consititution Drive
Menlo Park, CA 94025
Telephone 408/321-3650

KEM Associates
153 East Street
New Haven, CT 06507
Telephone 203/865-0584

National Energy System Corporation
P.O. Box 1176
Birmingham, AL 35201
Telephone 205/252-7726
National Solar Supply
2331 Adams Drive, N.W.
Atlanta, GA 30318
Telephone 404/352-3478
National Heating Systems
2417 Front Street
West Sacramento, CA 95691
Telephone 916/372-2993
Northwest Solar Systems Inc.
7700 12th Street, N.E.
Seattle, WA 98115
Telephone 206/523-3951
NRG Manufacturing
P.O. Box 53
Napoleon, OH 43545
Telephone 419/599-3618

Pacific Solar Systems Inc.
711 Bangs Avenue
P.O. Box 6301
Modesto, CA 95355
Telephone 209/521-6400
Pleiad Industries Inc.
Springfield Road
West Branch, IA 52358
Telephone 319/356-2735
Powell Brother Inc.
5903 Firestone Boulevard
Southgate, CA 90280
Telephone 213/869-3307

RA Energy Systems
8630 Production Avenue, Suite A
San Diego, CA 92121
Telephone 714/578-2260
Raypak Inc.
31111 Agoura Road
Westlake Village, CA 91360
Telephone 213/889-1500

Sola Heat
1200 E. First Street
Los Angeles, CA 90033
Telephone 213/263-5823
Solar-Aire
82 South Third Street
San Jose, CA 95113
Telephone 408/295-2528
Solar Applications Inc.
7926 Convoy Court
San Diego, CA 92111
Telephone 714/292-1857
Solarator Inc.
P.O. Box 277
Madison Heights, MI 48071
Telephone 313/642-9377
Solar Central
7213 Ridge Road
Mechanicsburg, OH 43044
Telephone 513/828-1350
Solarcoa Inc.
2115 East Spring Street
Long Beach, CA 90806
Telephone 213/426-7655
Solar Development Inc.
4180 Westroads Drive
West Palm Beach, FL 33407
Telephone 305/842-8935

Solar Dynamics Corporation
550 Frontage Road
Northfield, IL 60093
Telephone 312/446-5242

Solar Energy Applications Inc.
1102 E. Washington
Phoenix, AZ 85034
Telephone 602/344-1822

Solar Energy Componet
441 Shearer Boulevard
Cocoa, FL 32922
Telephone 305/632-2888

Solar Energy Contractors
P.O. Box 16425, 3156 Leon Road
Jacksonville, FL 32216
Telephone 904/641-5611

Solar Energy Research Corporation
701 B South Main Street
Longmont, CO 80501
Telephone 303/772-8406

Solar Energy Resources Corporation
10639 S.W. 185 Terrace
Miami, FL 33157
Telephone 305/233-0711

Solar Energy Systems Inc.
2345 Santa Fe Avenue
Los Angeles, CA 90058
Telephone 213/583-5808

Solar Energy Systems of Georgia
5825 Glenridge Drive, N.E., Building 2,
Suite 107
Atlanta, GA 30328
Telephone 404/255-9588

Solar Engineering
P.O. Box 1358
Boca Raton, FL 33432
Telephone 305/368-2456

Solargenics Inc.
9713 Lurline Avenue
Chatsworth, CA 91311
Telephone 213/998-0806

Solargizer Corporation
220 Mulberry Street
Stillwater, MN 55082
Telephone 612/439-5734

Solar Heat
1200 E. First Street
Los Angeles, CA 90033
Telephone 213/263-5823

Solar Heat Company
P.O. Box 110
Greenville, PA 16125
Telephone 412/588-5650

Solar Homes Inc.
2707 S. County Trail
E. Greenwich, RI 02818
Telephone 401/884-0353

Solar Industries Inc.
Route 6, P.O. Box 303
Plymouth, CT 06782
Telephone 203/283-0223

Solar Industries of Florida Inc.
3221 Trout River Boulevard
P.O. Box 9013
Jacksonville, FL 32208
Telephone 904/768-4323

Solar Kinetics Corporation
P.O. Box 17308
West Hartford, CT 06117
Telephone 203/233-4461

Solar 1, Division of Steller Industries, Inc.
7265 Commerce Drive
Mentor, OH 44060
Telephone 216/951-6363

Solar Products Manufacturing Corporation
151 John Downey Drive
New Britain, CT 06051
Telephone 203/224-2164

Solar Sun Inc.
235 West 12th Street
Cincinnati, OH 45210
Telephone 513/241-4200

Solar Systems
26046 Eden Landing Road, Suite 41
Hayward, CA 94545
Telephone 415/785-0711

Solar System International
6065 N.W. 82nd Avenue
Miami, FL 33166
Telephone 800/327-7066

Solartech Systems Corporation
2216 Avenue E
Lubbock, TX 79404
Telephone 806/765-7761

Solartech Inc.
250 Pennsylvania Avenue
Salem, OH 44460
Telephone 216/332-9100

Solar-term of Maryland
5105 72nd Avenue
Hyattsville, MD 20784
Telephone 301/459-6022

Sol-Ray Inc.
204-B Carleton
Orange, CA 92667
Telephone 714/997-9431

Spectra Energy Systems Inc.
P.O. Box 6036
Santa Barbara, CA 93111
Telephone 805/967-1053

Sunblazer Energy System Inc.
P.O. Box 1992
Charlotte, NC 28233
Telephone 704/333-2551

Sun Century System
Box 2036
Florence, SL 35630
Telephone 205/764-0795

Sun Energy International Inc.
P.O. Box 6542
Concord, CA 94524
Telephone 415/676-8717

Sunray Solar Heat Inc.
202 Classon Avenue
Brooklyn, NY 11205
Telephone 212/857-0193

Sunshine Unlimited
900 North Jay Street
Chandler, AZ 85224
Telephone 602/963-3878

Sunsource Pacific Inc.
832 Halekauwila Street
Honolulu, HI 96813
Telephone 808/531-0165

Sunwater Energy Products
1488 Pioneer Way, #17
El Cajon, CA 92020
Telephone 714/579-0771

The Solar Broker
1523 Valley Parkway, Suite 219
Escondido, CA 92027

The Solar Store Corporation
Box 841
Peoria, IL 61652
Telephone 309/673-0458

The Wilcon Corporation
3310 S.W. Seventh Street
Ocala, FL 32670
Telephone 904/732-2550

Universal Solar Industries Inc.
Box 101
House Springs, MO 63051
Telephone 314/375-5402

Vulcan Solar Industries Inc
200 Conant Street
Pawtucket, RI 02860
Telephone 401/725-6061

Wallace Company
831 Dorsey Street, P.O. Box 511
Gainsville, GA 30501
Telephone 404/534-5971

Wescorp
15 Stevens Street
Andover, MA 01810
Telephone 617/470-0520

HOT WATER SYSTEMS

Acorn Structurer Inc.
Box 250
Concord, MA 01720
Telephone 617/369-4111

**Advance Cooler Manufacturing Corp.,
ACM Solar Group**
Clifton Park, NY 12065
Telephone 518/371-2140

Advance Energy Technology Inc.
121C Albright Way
Los Gatos, CA 93030
Telephone 408/866-7686

All Sun Power Inc.
10400 S.W. 187th Street
Miami, FL 33157
Telephone 305/233-2224

Alter Corporation
2594 Leghorn Street
Mountain View, CA 94043
Telephone 415/969-6474

Alternative Energy Resource
1155 Larry Mahon Drive
El Paso, TX 79925
Telephone 915/593-1927

American Heliothermal Corporation
2625 S. Santa Fe Drive
Denver, CO 80223
Telephone 303/778-0650

American Home Solar Energy Systems
868 Catalina
Laguna Beach, CA 92651
Telephone 714/831-9794

American Solar Energy Corporation
55 South Colarado Boulevard
Denver, CO 80206
Telephone 303/377-6527

American Solarize Corporation
P.O. Box 15
Martinsville, NJ 08836
Telephone 201/356-3141

American Solar King Corporation
6801 New McGregor Highway
Waco, TX 76710
Telephone 817/776-3860

American Solar Manufacturing
P.O. Box 194
Byron, CA 94514
Telephone 415/634-2426

American Solar Power
715 Swann Avenue
Tampa, FL 33606
Telephone 813/254-4461

American Solar Systems
415 E. Branch Street
Arroyo Grande, Ca 93420
Telephone 805/481-1010

American Sun Industries
996 Lawrence Drive
Newbury Park, CA 91320
Telephone 805/498-9700

**American Sunpower
and Light Company, Inc.**
10005 McKalla
Austin, TX 78758
Telephone 512/837-2627

Arizona Engineering and Refrigeration
635 W. Commerce Avenue
Gilbert, AZ 85234
Telephone 602/892-9050

Beutels Solar Heater, Company
7161 N.W. 74th Street
Miami, FL 33166
Telephone 305/885-0122

Business and Technology Inc.
2800 Upton Street, N.W.
Washington, D.C. 20008
Telephone 202/362-5991

Carolina Solar Equipment Company
P.O. Box 2068
Salisbury, NC 28144
Telephone 704/637-1243

CBM Manufacturing Inc.
621 N.W. Sixth Avenue
Fort Lauderdale, FL 33311
Telephone 305/463-5810

**CF Roark Welding and Engineering
Company, Inc.**
136 N. Green Street
Brownsburg, IN 46112
Telephone 317/852-3163

Champion Home Builder Company
5573 North Street
Dryden, MI 48428
Telephone 313/796-2211

Chemical Processors Inc.
P.O. Box 10636
St. Petersburg, FL 33733
Telephone 813/822-3689

Cole Solar Systems, Inc.
440 A East Saint Elmo Road
Austin, TX 78745
Telephone 512/444-2565

Colt Inc.
71590 San Jacinto
Rancho Mirage, CA 92270
Telephone 714/346-8033

Columbia Chase Solar Energy Division
55 High Street
Holbrook, MA 02343
Telephone 617/767-0513

Conserdyne Corporation
4437 San Fernando Road
Glendale, CA 91204
Telephone 213/246-8408

Continental Solar Systems Inc.
1901 Avenue of the Stars, Suite 600,
Century City
Los Angeles, CA 90067
Telephone 213/552-0003

Custom Solar Heating Systems
P.O. Box 375
Albany, NY 12201
Telephone 518/438-7358

Dumont Industries
Box 117, Main Street
Monmouth, ME 04259
Telephone 207/933-4281

D W Browning Contracting Company
475 Carswell Avenue
Holly Hill, FL 32017
Telephone 904/252-1528

E&K Services Company
16824 74th N.E.
Bothell, WA 98011
Telephone 206/486-6660

E.C.M. Associates
1928 6th Street
Boulder, CO 80302
Telephone 303/443-7970

El Cam Inc.
5330 Debbie Lane
Santa Barbara, CA 93111

Energex Manufacturing Corporation
4227 S. 36th Place
Phoenix, AZ 85040
Telephone 602/267-9474

Energy Applications Inc.
1125 White Drive
Titusville, FL 32780
Telephone 305/269-4893

Energy Converters Inc.
2501 N. Orchard Knob Avenue
Chattanooga, TN 37406
Telephone 615/624-2608

Energy Design Inc.
1925 Curry Road
Schenectady, NY 12303
Telephone 518/355-3322

Energy Systems, Inc.
4570 Alvarado Canyon Road
San Diego, CA 92120
Telephone 714/280-6660

Fedders Division, Climatrol Corporation
Woodbridge Avenue
Edison, NJ 08817
Telephone 201/549-7200

Federal Energy Corporation
5505 E, Evans
Denver, CO 80222
Telephone 303/753-0565

Fred Rice Productions
48780 Eisenhower Drive, P.O. Box 643
La Quinta, CA 92253
Telephone 714/564-4823

Future Systems, Inc.
12500 W. Cedar Drive
Lakewood, CO 80228
Telephone 303/989-0444

General Energy Devices Inc.
7501 124th Avenue N.
Largo, FL 33540
Telephone 813/536-6502

General Solar Corporation
3900 Magnolia Street
Denver, CO 80207
Telephone 303/795-6670

Groundstar Energy Corporation
137 Rowayton Avenue
Rowayton, CT 06853
Telephone 203/838-0650

Heilemann Electric
127 Mountainview Road
Warren, NJ 07060
Telephone 201/752-6060

Heliodyne Inc.
770 South 16th Street
Richmond, CA 94804
Telephone 415/237-9614

Helios Corporation
2120 Angus Road
Charlottesville, VA 22901
Telephone 804/977-3719

Heliosystems Inc.
3407 Ross Avenue
Dallas, TX 75206
Telephone 214/824-5971

Heliotherm Inc.
West Lenni Road
Lenni, PA 19052
Telephone 215/459-9030

Hyperion
7209 Valtec Court
Boulder, CO 80301
Telephone 303/449-9544

IMEX Trading LTD.
3315 Como Lane
San Jose, CA 95118
Telephone 408/264-2591

Inter Technology 1 Solar Corporation
276 Broadview Avenue
Warrenton, VA 22186
Telephone 703/347-9500

J.C. Solar
P.O. Box 18
Pinedale, CA 93650
Telephone 209/439-3024

J.G. Johnston Manufacturing Company
33458 Angeles Forest Highway
Palmdale, CA 93550
Telephone 805/947-3791

Kem Associates
153 East Street
New Haven, CT 06507
Telephone 203/865-0584

Largo Solar Systems Inc.
991 South 40th Avenue
Plantation, FL 33317
Telephone 305/583-8090
Lennox Industries, Inc.
200 South 12th Avenue, P.O. Box 280
Marshalltown, IA 50158
Telephone 515/754-4011

McKim Solar Energy Systems Inc
1142 East 64th Street
Tulsa, OK 74136
Telephone 918/749-8896
Mid-Western Solar System
2235 Irvin Cobb Drive
Paducah, KY 42001
Telephone 501/443-6295
Mountain Mechanical Sales Inc.
5270 North Broadway Avenue
Denver, CO 80216
Telephone 303/534-3000

National Energy Corporation
21716 Kendrick Avenue
Lakeville, MN 55044
Telephone 612/469-3401
National Energy Systems Corporation
P.O. Box 1176
Birmingham, AL 35201
Telephone 205/252-7726
National Solar Supply
2331 Adams Drive, N.W.
Atlanta, GA 30318
Telephone 404/352-3478
National Energy Corporation
1001 Connecticut Avenue, N.W., Suite 530
Washington, D.C. 20036
Telephone 202/296-7070
Natural Heating Systems
2417 Front Street
West Sacramento, CA 95691
Telephone 916/372-2993
N.H. Yates & Company Inc.
117 E Church Lane
Cockeysville, MD 21030
Telephone 301/667-6300

Northup Inc.
302 Nichols Drive
Hutchins, TX 75141
Telephone 214/225-4291
Northwest Solar Systems Inc.
7700 12th Street, N.E.
Seattle, WA 98115
Telephone 206/523-3951
NRG Manufacturing
P.O. Box 53
Napoleon, OH 43545
Telephone 419/599-3618

OEM Products Inc.
2701 Adamo Drive
Tampa, FL 33605
Telephone 813/247-5947
O.S. Solar Energy Inc.
P.O. Box 221
Milford, OH 45150
Telephone 513/831-4879

Pacific Solar Systems Inc.
711 Bangs Avenue
P.O. Box 6301
Modesto, CA 95355
Telephone 209/521-6400
P.C.A.
11031 Wye Drive
San Antonio, TX 78217
Telephone 512/656-9338
Permaloy Corporation
P.O. Box 1559
Ogden, UT 84402
Telephone 801/731-4303
Piper Hydro Inc.
2895 E. La Palma
Anaheim, CA 92806
Telephone 714/630-4040
Pleiad Industries Inc.
Springdale Road
West Branch, IA 52358
Telephone 319/356-2735
Prima Industries Inc.
P.O. Box 141
Deer Park, NY 11729
Telephone 516/242-6347

Radi-Trol
14826 7th Street, P.O. Box 1217
Victorville, CA 92392
Telephone 714/245-5368

Ra Energy Systems
8630 Production Avenue, Suite A
San Diego, CA 92121
Telephone 714/578-2260

Ra-Los Inc.
559 Union Avenue
Campbell, CA 95008
Telephone 408/371-1734

Ran Solar Energy Products, Inc.
50P Brook Avenue
Deer Park, NY 11729
Telephone 516/586-5008

**Refrigeration Research,
Solar Research Division**
525 N. Fifth Street
Brighton, MI 48116
Telephone 313/227-1151

Research Products Corporation
1015 East Washington Avenue
Madison, WI 53713
Telephone 608/257-8801

**Revere Solar and
Architectural Products Inc.**
Box 151
Rome, NY 13440
Telephone 315/338-2595

**Rheem Water Heater Division,
City Investing Company**
7600 South Kedzie Avenue
Chicago, IL 60652
Telephone 312/434-7500

Shape Symmetry & Sun
Biddleford Industrial Park
Biddleford, ME 04005
Telephone 207/282-6155

Silver LTD.
7 West 14th Street
New York, NY 10011
Telephone 212/691-4632

Skytherm Processes & Engineering
2424 Wilshire Boulevard
Los Angeles, CA 90057
Telephone 213/389-2300

Solarferm LTD.
536 MacArthur Boulevard, P.O. Box M
Bourne, MA 02532
Telephone 617/563-7181

Solarhart Inc.
2333 East University
Phoenix, AZ 85034
Telephone 602/258-3671

Sola Heat
1200 E. First Street
Los Angeles, CA 90033
Telephone 213/263-5823

Sol-Aire Energy Systems
2750 South Shoshone Street
Englewood, CA 80110
Telephone 303/426-8411

Solar-Aire
82 South Third Street
San Jose, CA 95113
Telephone 408/295-2528

Solar Alternative Inc.
30 Clark Street
Brattleboro, VT 05301
Telephone 802/254-8221

Solar America Inc.
9001 Arbor Street
Omaha, NE 68124
Telephone 402/397/2421

Solar Applications Inc.
7926 Convoy Court
San Diego, CA 92111
Telephone 714/292/1857

Solarator Inc.
P.O. Box 277
Madison Heights, MI 48071
Telephone 313/642-9377

Solar Central
7213 Ridge Road
Mechanicsburg, OH 43044

Solarcoa Inc.
2115 East Spring Street
Long Beach, CA 90806
Telephone 213/426-7655

**Solar Comfort Systems, Division of
Solar Systems Inc.**
4853 Cordell Avenue, Suite 606
Bethesda, MD 20014
Telephone 301/951-0095 or 652-8941

Solar Dynamics Corporation
550 Frontage Road
Northfield, IL 60093
Telephone 312/446-5242

Solar Dynamics Inc.
1320 S. Lipan Street
Denver, CO 80223
Telephone 303/777-3666

Solar Dynamics Inc.
4527 E. 11th Avenue
Hialeah, FL 33013
Telephone 305/688-4393

Solar Energy Applications Inc.
1102 E. Washington
Phoenix, AZ 85034
Telephone 602/244-1822

Solar Energy Components
441 Shearer Boulevard
Cocoa, DL 32922
Telephone 305/632-2888

Solar Energy Contractors
P.O. Box 16425, 3156 Leon Road
Jacksonville, FL 32216
Telephone 904/641-5611

Solar Energy Products Company
121 Miller Road
Avon Lake, OH 44012
Telephone 216/933-500

Solar Energy Products Inc.
1208 N.W. 8th Avenue
Gainesville, FL 32601
Telephone 904/377-6527

Solar Energy Research Corporation
701B South Main Street
Lonmont, CO 80501
Telephone 303/772-8406

Solar Energy Resources Corporation
10639 S.W. 185 Terrace
Miami, FL 33157
Telephone 305/233-0711

Solar Energy Systems
P.O. Box 625, Sentry Place
Scarsdale, NY 10583
Telephone 914/725-5570

Solar Energy Systems Inc.
2345 Santa Fe Avenue
Los Angeles, CA 90058
Telephone 213/583-5808

Solar Energy Systems of Georgia
5825 Glenridge Drive, N.E., Building 2,
Suite 107
Atlanta, GA 30328
Telephone 404/255-9588

Solar Engineering
P.O. Box 1358
Boca Raton, FL 33432
Telephone 305/368-2456

Solar Farm Industries Inc.
P.O. Box 242
Stockton, KS 67669
Telephone 913/425-6726

Solargenics Inc.
9713 Lurline Avenue
Chatsworth, CA 91311

Solargizer Corporation
220 Mulberry Street
Stillwater, MN 55082

Solar Heat Corporation
1200 E. First Street
Los Angeles, CA 90033
Telephone 213/263-5823

Solar Heat Company
P.O. Box 110
Greenville, PA 16125
Telephone 412/588-5650

Solar Heating of New Jersey
811 Wyretta Place
Paramus, NJ 07652
Telephone 201/652-3819

Solar Homes Inc.
2707 S. County Trail, E.
Greenwich, RI 02818
Telephone 401/884-0353

Solar Industries Inc.
Route 6, Box 303
Plymouth, CT 06782
Telephone 203/283-0223

Solar Industries of Florida Inc.
3221 Trout River Boulevard, P.O. Box 9013
Jacksonville, FL 32208
Telephone 904/768-4323

Solar Marketing Corporation
P.O. Box 1776
Omaha, NE 68102
Telephone 402/341-9080

Solarnetics Corporation
1654 Pioneer Way
El Cajon, CA 92020
Telephone 714/579-7122

Solaron Corporation
300 Galleria Tower, 720
S. Colorado Boulevard
Denver, CO 80222
Telephone 303/759-0101

Solar 1, Division of Steller Industries Inc.
7265 Commerce Drive
Mentor, OH 44060
Telephone 216/951-6363

Solar Products Manufacturing
151 John Downey Drive
New Britain, CT 06051
Telephone 203/224-2164

Solar Products Sun Tank Inc.
614 N.W. 62nd Street
Miami, FL 33150
Telephone 305/756-7609

Solar Seven Industries Inc.
3323 Moline Street
Aurora, CO 80010
Telephone 303/364-7277

Solar Star Inc.
#1 Solar Lane
Parker, SD 57053
Telephone 605/297-3470

Solar Sun Inc.
235 West 12th Street
Cincinnati, OH 45210
Telephone 513/241-4200

Solar Systems
26046 Eden Landing Road, Suite 41
Hayward, CA 94545
Telephone 415/785-0711

Solar Systems International
6065 N.W. 82nd Avenue
Miami, FL 33166
Telephone 800/327-7066

Solartec Corporation
8210 Engineer Road
San Diego, CA 92111
Telephone 714/560-8434

Solartech Limited
207 Queens Quay West, Toronto
Ontario, Canada M5J1A7
Telephone 416/853-0525

Solar Technology Inc.
3927 Oakcliff Industrial Court
Atlanta, GA 30340
Telephone 404/449-0900

Solartec Systems Corporation
2216 Avenue E
Lubbock, TX 79404
Telephone 806/765-7761

Solartec Inc.
250 Pennsylvania Avenue
Salem, OH 44460
Telephone 216/332-9100

Solar-Therm of Maryland
5105 72nd Avenue
Hyattsville, MD 20784
Telephone 301/459-6022

Solar Unlimited Inc.
4310 Governors Drive West
Huntsville, AL 35805
Telephone 205/837-7340

Sol-Ray Inc.
204-B Carleton
Orange, CA 92667
Telephone 714/997-9431

Soltex Corporation
9101 Lipan, P.O. Box 55703
Houston, TX 77055
Telephone 713/780-1733

Solus Inc.
9630 Clarewood, B-7
Houston, TX 77036
Telephone 713/772-6416

Sonsolar Inc.
800 West Panorama Road
Tucson, AZ 85704
Telephone 602/297-3556

Southeastern Solar System Inc.
2812 New Spring Road, Suite 150
Atlanta, GA 30339

Southwest Ener-Tech Inc.
3030 South Valley View Boulevard
Las Vegas, NV 89102
Telephone 701/873-1975

Spectra Energy System Inc.
P.O. Box 6036
Santa Barbara, CA 93111
Telephone 805/967-1053

State Industries Inc.
Cumberland Street
Ashland City, TN 37015
Telephone 800/251-8170

Sunblazer Energy Systems Inc.
P.O. Box 1992
Charlotte, NC 28233
Telephone 704/333-2551

Sun Century Systems
Box 2036
Florence, AL 35630
Telephone 205/764-0795

Sun Company, Solar Utilities Nebraska, Inc.
922 Lake Street, P.O. Box 387
Gothenburg, NE 69138
Telephone 308/537-7377

Suncraft Solar, Division of Nichols Industries
5001 East 59th
Kansas City, MO 64130
Telephone 816/333-2100

Sunearth Solar Products Corporation
RD 1, Box 337
Green Lane, PA 18054
Telephone 215/699-7892

Sun Energy International Inc.
P.O. Box 6542
Concord, CA 94524
Telephone 415/676-8717

Sun Heat Inc.
2624 South Zuni
Englewood, CO 80110
Telephone 303/922-6179

Sun Master Corporation
12 Spruce Street
Corning, NY 14830
Telephone 607/937-5441

Sun Power Corporation
P.O. Box 16963
Orlando, FL 32811
Telephone 305/876-2237

Sunpower Systems Corporation
510 South 52nd Street, Suite 101
Tempe, AZ 85281
Telephone 602/894-2331

Sunrise Energy Products Inc.
996 Mackinaw Highway
Pellston, MI 49769
Telephone 616/347-7220

Sunray Solar Heat Inc.
202 Classon Avenue
Brooklyn, NY 11205
Telephone 212/857-0193

Sunrise Solar
7359 Reseda Boulevard
Reseda, CA 91335
Telephone 213/881-0703

Sunsav Inc.
890 East Street
Tewksbury, MA 01876
Telephone 617/851-5913

Sunshine Unlimited
900 North Jay Street
Chandler, AZ 85224
Telephone 602/963-3878

Sunsource Pacific Inc.
832 Halekauwila Street
Honolulu, HI 96813
Telephone 808/531-0165

Sun Sponge
1288 Fayette Street
El Cajon, CA 92020
Telephone 714/449-6726

Sun Stone Solar Energy Equipment
P.O. Box 941
Sheboygan, WI 53081
Telephone 414/452-8194

Sun Systems
1825 West Indian School Road
Phoenix, AZ 85015
Telephone 602/263-0699

Sun Systems Inc.
P.O. Box 155
Eureka, IL 61530
Telephone 309/467-3632

Suntap Inc.
42 East Dudley Town Road
Bloomfield, CT 06002
Telephone 203/243-1781

Sun Unlimited Research Corporation
P.O. Box 941
Sheboygan, WI 53081
Telephone 414/452-8194

Sun Wall Inc.
P.O. Box 9723
Pittsburgh, PA 15229
Telephone 412/364-5349 or 771-4747

Sunwater Energy Products
1488 Pioneer Way, #17
El Cajon, CA 92020
Telephone 714/579-0771

Sunworks, Division of Enthone, Inc.
P.O. Box 1004
New Haven, CT 06508
Telephone 203/934-6301

System Technology Inc.
P.O. Box 337
Shalimar, FL 32579
Telephone 904/863-9213

Temp-O-Matic Cooling Company
87 Luquer Street
Brooklyn, NY 11231
Telephone 212/624-5600

The Solaray Corporation
345 North Nimitz Highway
Honolulu, HI Telephone 808/533-6464

The Solar Broker
1523 Valley Parkway, Suite 219
Escondido, CA 92027

The Solar Store Corporation
Box 841
Peoria, IL 61652
Telephone 309/673-0458

The Wilcon Corporation
3310 S.W. Seventh Street
Ocala, FL 32670
Telephone 904/732-2550

The United Materials Inc.
814 West 14th Avenue
Denver, CO 80204
Telephone 303/623-4166

Universal Solar Systems Inc.
Box 101
House Springs, MÒ 63051
Telephone 314/375-5402

Vulcan Solar Industries Inc.
200 Conant Street
Pawtucket, RI 02860
Telephone 401/725-6061

Wallace Company
831 Dorsey Street, P.O. Box 511
Gainsville, GA 30501
Telephone 404/534-5971

Wescorp
15 Stevens Street
Andover, MA 01810
Telephone 617/470-0520

Whipple Corporation
10100 Santa Monica Boulevard, Suite 940
Los Angeles, CA 90067
Telephone 213/879-3552

Wilcox Manufacturing Corporation
P.O. Box 455, 13375 U.S. 19 North
Pinellas Park, FL 33565
Telephone 813/531-7741

W.L. Jackson Manufacturing Corporation Inc.
P.O. Box 11168
Chattanooga, TN 37401
Telephone 615/867-4700

SPACE HEATING SYSTEMS

Acorn Structures Inc.
Box 250
Concord, MA 01720
Telephone 617/369-4111

Advance Cooler Manufacturing Corporation, ACM Solar Group
Clifton Park, NY 12065
Telephone 518/371-2140

Advanced Energy Technology Inc.
121-C Albright Way
Los Gatos, CA 93030
Telephone 408/866-7686

Air Temp Corporation
Woodbridge Avenue
Edison, NJ 08817
Telephone 201/549-7200

Alternative Energy Resources
1155 Larry Mahon Drive
El Paso, TX 79925
Telephone 915/593-1927

American Heliothermal Corporation
2625 S. Santa Fe Drive
Denver, CO 80223
Telephone 303/778-0650

American Home Solar Energy Systems
868 Catalina
Laguna Beach, CA 92651
Telephone 714/831-9794

American Solarize Corporation
P.O. Box 15
Martinsville, NJ 08836
Telephone 201/356-3141

American Solar King Corporation
6801 New McGregor Highway
Waco, TX 76710
Telephone 817/776-3860

American Solar Manufacturing
P.O. Box 194
Byron, CA 94514
Telephone 415/634-2424

American Solar Systems
415 E. Branch Street
Arroyo Grande, CA 93420
Telephone 805/481-1010

Arizona Engineering and Refrigeration
635 W. Commerce Avenue
Gilbert, AZ 85234
Telephone 602/892-9050

Business and Technology Inc.
2800 Upton Street N.W.
Washington, D.C. 20008
Telephone 202/362-5991

Carolina Solar Equipment Company
P.O. Box 2068
Salisbury, NC 28144
Telephone 704/637-1243

Carolina Thermal Company
Iron Works Road, Route 2, Box 39
Reidsville, NC 27320
Telephone 919/342-0352

CBM Manufacturing Inc.
621 N.W. Sixth Avenue
Fort Lauderdale, FL 33311
Telephone 305/463-5810

Champion Home Builders Company
5573 North Street
Dryden, MI 48428
Telephone 313/796-2211

Cole Solar Systems Inc.
440A East Saint Elmo Road
Austin, TX 78745
Telephone 512/444-2565

Colt Inc.
71590 San Jacinto
Rancho Mirage, CA 92270
Telephone 714/346-8033

Columbia Chase Solar Energy Division
55 High Street
Holbrook, MA 02343
Telephone 617/767-0513

Conserdyne Corporation
4437 San Fernando Road
Glendale, CA 91204
Telephone 213/246-8408

Contemporary Systems Inc.
68 Charlonne Street
Jaffrey, NH 03452
Telephone 603/532-7972

Continental Solar Systems Inc.
1901 Avenue of the Stars, Suite 600,
Century City
Los Angeles, CA 90067
Telephone 213/552-0003

Custom Solar Heating Systems Inc.
P.O. Box 375
Albany, NY 12201
Telephone 518/438-7358

Dixon Energy Systems
47 East Street
Hadley, MA 01035
Telephone 413/584-8831

E.C.M. Associates
1928 6th Street
Boulder, CO 80302
Telephone 303/443-7970

El Cam Inc.
5330 Debbie Lane
Santa Barbara, CA 93111
Telephone 805/964-8676

Energex Manufacturing Corporation
4227 S. 36th Place
Phoenix, AZ 85040
Telephone 602/267-9474

Energy Converters Inc.
2501 N. Orchard Knob Avenue
Chattanooga, TN 37406
Telephone 615/624-2608

Energy Design Inc.
1925 Curry Road
Schenectady, NY 12303
Telephone 518/355-3322

Energy King
Box 248
Creston, IA 50801
Telephone 515/782-8566

Energy Systems Inc.
4570 Alvarado Canyon Road
San Diego, CA 92120
Telephone 714/280-6660

Federal Energy Corporation
5505 E. Evans
Denver, CO 80222
Telephone 303/753-0565

Future Systems Inc.
12500 W. Cedar Drive
Lakewood, CO 80228
Telephone 303/989-0444

General Energy Devices, Inc.
7501 124th Avenue N.
Largo, FL 33540
Telephone 813/536-6502

Groundstar Energy Corporation
137 Rowayton Avenue
Rowayton, CT 06853
Telephone 203/838-0650

Heilmann Electric
127 Mountainview Road
Warren, NJ 07060
Telephone 201/752-6060

Helios Corporation
2120 Angus Road
Charlottesville, VA 22901
Telephone 804/977-3719

Heliosystems Inc.
3407 Ross Avenue
Dallas, TX 75206
Telephone 214/824-5971

Hyperion
7209 Valtec Court
Boulder, CO 80301
Telephone 303/449-9544

Inter Technology Solar Corporation
276 Broadview Avenue
Warrenton, VA 22186
Telephone 703/347-9500

J.G. Johnston Manufacturing Company
33458 Angeles Forest Highway
Palmdale, CA 93550
Telephone 805/947-3791

KEM Associates
153 East Street
New Haven, CT 06507
Telephone 203/865-0584

Mid-Western Solar Systems
2235 Irvin Cobb Drive
Paducah, KY 42001
Telephone 501/443-6295

National Energy Systems Corporation
P.O. Box 1176
Birmingham, AL 35201
Telephone 205/252-7726

National Solar Supply
2331 Adams Drive, N.W.
Atlanta, GA 30318
Telephone 404/352-3478

National Energy Corporation
1001 Connecticut Avenue, N.W., Suite 530
Washington, D.C. 20036
Telephone 202/296-7070

National Heating Systems
2417 Front Street
West Sacramento, CA 95691
Telephone 916/372-2993

N.H. Yates & Company
117E Church Lane
Cockeysville, MD 21030
Telephone 301/667-6300

Northrup Inc.
302 Nichols Drive
Hutchins, TX 75141
Telephone 214/225-4291

Northwest Solar Systems Inc.
7700 12th Street, N.E.
Seattle, WA 98115
Telephone 206/523-3951

NRG Manufacturing
P.O. Box 53
Napoleon, OH 43545
Telephone 419/599-3618

OEM Products Inc.
2701 Adamo Drive
Tampa, FL 33605
Telephone 813/247-5947

Ohio Valley Solar Inc.
4141 Airport Road
Cincinnati, OH 45226
Telephone 513/871-1961

One Design Inc.
Mountain Falls Route
Winchester, VA 22601
Telephone 703/662-4898

O.S. Solar Energy Inc.
P.O. Box 221
Milford, OH 45150
Telephone 513/831-4879

Pacific Solar Systems Inc.
711 Bangs Avenue, P.O. Box 6301
Modesto, CA 95355
Telephone 209/521-6400

P.C.A.
11031 Wye Drive
San Antonio, TX 78217
Telephone 512/656-9338

Permaloy Corporation
P.O. Box 1559
Ogden, UT 84402
Telephone 801/731-4303

Piper Hydro Inc.
2895 E. La Palma
Anaheim, CA 92806
Telephone 714/630-4040

Radi-Trol
14826 7th Street, P.O. Box 1217
Victorville, CA 92392
Telephone 714/245-5368

Ra-Los Inc.
559 Union Avenue
Campbell, CA 95008
Telephone 408/371-1734

Research Products Corporation
1015 East Washington Avenue
Madison, WI 53713
Telephone 608/257-8801

Skytherm Processes & Engineering
2424 Wilshire Boulevard
Los Angeles, CA 90057
Telephone 213/389-2300

Solarfern LTD.
536 MacArthur Boulevard, P.O. Box M
Bourne, MA 02532
Telephone 617/563-7181

Solar Aire
82 South Third Street
San Jose, CA 95113
Telephone 408/295-2528

Solar Alternative Inc.
30 Clark Street
Brattleboro, VT 05301
Telephone 802/254-8221

Solar America Inc.
2620 San Mateo, N.E.
Albuquerque, NM 87110
Telephone 505/294-6522

Solar America Inc.
9001 Arbor Street
Omaha, NE 68124
Telephone 402/397-2421

Solarator Inc.
P.O. Box 277
Madison Heights, MI 48071
Telephone 313/642-9377

Solar Central
7213 Ridge Road
Mechanicsburg, OH 43044
Telephone 513/828-1350

Solarcoa Inc.
2115 East Spring Street
Long Beach, CA 90806
Telephone 213/426-7655

**Solar Comfort System,
Division of Solar Systems Inc.**
4853 Cordell Avenue, Suite 606
Bethesda, MD 20014
Telephone 301/951-0095 or 652-8941

Solar Development Inc.
4180 Westroads Drive
West Palm Beach, FL 33407
Telephone 305/842-8935

Solar Dynamics Corporation
550 Frontage Road
Northfield, IL 60093
Telephone 312/446-5242

Solar Dynamics Inc.
1320 S. Lipan Street
Denver, CO 80223
Telephone 303/777-3666

Solar Dynamics Inc.
4527 E. 11th Avenue
Hialeah, FL 33013
Telephone 305/688-4393

Solar Energy Components
441 Shearer Boulevard
Cocoa, FL 32922
Telephone 305/632-2888

Solar Energy Contractors
P.O. Box 16425, 3156 Leon Road
Jacksonville, FL 32216
Telephone 904/641-5611

Solar Energy Products Company
121 Miller Road
Avonlake, OH 44012
Telephone 216/933-5000

Solar Energy Research Corporation
701 B South Main Street
Longmont, CO 80501
Telephone 303/772-8406

Solar Energy Research Corporation
10639 S.W. 185 Terrace
Miami, FL 33157
Telephone 305/233-0711

Solar Energy Systems
P.O. Box 625, Sentry Place
Scarsdale, NY 10583
Telephone 914/725-5570

Solar Energy Systems of Georgia
5825 Glenridge Drive, N.E., Building 2,
Suite 107
Atlanta, GA 30328
Telephone 404/255-9588

Solar Enlineering
P.O. Box 1358
Boca Raton, FL 33432
Telephone 305/368-2456

Solar Enterprises Inc.
2800 W. Division
Arlington, TX 76012
Telephone 817/461-5571

Solar Farm Industries Inc.
P.O. Box 242
Stockton, KS 67669
Telephone 913/425-6726

Solargencies Inc.
9713 Lurline Avenue
Chatsworth, CA 91311
Telephone 213/998-0806

Solar Heat Company
P.O. Box 110
Greenville, PA 16125
Telephone 412/588-5650

Solar Heat Corporation
1252 French Avenue
Lakewood, OH 44107
Telephone 216/228-2993

Solar Homes Inc.
2707 S. County Trail
E. Greenwich, RI 02818
Telephone 401/884-0353

Solar Industries Inc.
Route 6, P.O. Box 303
Plymouth, CT 06782
Telephone 203/283-0223

Solar Industries Inc.
Monmouth Airport Industrial Park
Farmingdale, NJ 07727
Telephone 201/938-7000

Solar Marketing Corporation
P.O. Box 1776
Omaha, NE 68102
Telephone 402/341-9080

Solarnetics Corporation
1654 Pioneer Way
El Cajon, CA 92020
Telephone 714/579-7122

Solar I, Division of Steller Industries Inc.
7265 Commerce Drive
Mentor, OH 44060
Telephone 216/951-6363

Solar Products Manufacturing Corporation
151 John Downey Drive
New Britain, CT 06051
Telephone 203/224-2164

Solar Products Sun-Tank Inc.
614 N.W. 62nd Street
Miami, FL 33150
Telephone 305/756-7609

Solar Seven Industries Inc.
3323 Moline Street
Aurora, CO 80010
Telephone 303/364-7277

Solar Sun Inc.
235 West 12th Street
Cincinnati, OH 45210
Telephone 513/241-4200

Solar Systems
26046 Eden Landing Road, Suite 41
Hayward, CA 94545
Telephone 415/785-0711

Solar Systems International
6065 N.W. 82nd Avenue
Miami, FL 33166
Telephone 800/327-7066

Solartec Corporation
8210 Engineer Road
San Diego, CA 92111
Telephone 714/560-8434

Solar Technology Inc.
3927 Oakcliff Industrial Court
Atlanta, GA 30340
Telephone 404/449-0900

Solartech Systems Corporation
2216 Avenue E
Lubbock, TX 79404
Telephone 806/765-7761

Solartech Inc.
250 Pennsylvania Avenue
Salem, OH 44460
Telephone 216/332-9100

Solar Thermics Enterprises LTD.
406 E. Taylor Street
Creston, IA 50801
Telephone 515/782-8566

Solar-Therm of Maryland
5105 72nd Avenue
Hyattasville, MD 20784
Telephone 301/459-6022

Solar Unlimited Inc.
4310 Governors Drive West
Huntsville, AL 35805
Telephone 205/837-7340

SOLARD Corporation
7801 E. Bellview Avenue
Englewood, CO 80110
Telephone 303/773-3269

Sol-Ray Inc.
204-B Carleton
Orange, CA 92667
Telephone 714/997-9431

Southeastern Solar Yystems Inc.
2812 New Spring Road, Suite 150
Atlanta, GA 30339
Telephone 404/434-4447

Southwest Ener-tech Inc.
3030 South Valley View Boulevard
Las Vegas, NV 89102
Telephone 701/873-1975

Spectra Energy Systems Inc.
P.O. Box 6036
Santa Barbara, CA 93111
Telephone 805/967-1053

S.T.A. Corporation
348 Hazard Avenue
Enfield, CT 06082
Telephone 203/749-7054

Sunblazer Energy Systems Inc.
P.O. Box 1992
Charlotte, NC 28233
Telephone 704/333-2551

Sun Century Systems
Box 2036
Florence, AL 35630
Telephone 205/764-0795

SUN Company, Solar Utilities Nebraska Inc.
922 Lake Street, P.O. Box 387
Gothenburg, NE 69138
Telephone 308/537-7377

Sunearth Solar Products Corporation
RD 1, Box 337
Green Lane, PA 18054
Telephone 215/699-7892

Sun Heet Inc.
2624 South Zuni
Englewood, CO 80110
Telephone 303/922-6179

Sun Master Corporation
12 Spruce Street
Corning, NY 14830
Telephone 607/937-5441

Sunpower Systems Corporation
510 South 52nd Street, Suite 101
Tempe, AZ 85281
Telephone 602/894-2331

Sunrise Energy Products Inc.
996 Mackinaw Highway
Pellston, MI 49769
Telephone 616/347-7220

Sunray Solar Heat Inc.
202 Classon Avenue
Brooklyn, NY 11205
Telephone 212/857-0193

SunSaver Corporation
P.O. Box 276
North Liberty, IA 52317

Sunsav Inc.
890 East Street
Tewksbury, MA 01876
Telephone 617/851-5913

Sun Stone Solar Energy Equipment
P.O. Box 941
Sheboygan, WI 53081
Telephone 414/452-8194

Sun Systems
1825 West Indian School Road
Phoenix, AZ 85015
Telephone 602/263-0699

Sun Systems Inc.
P.O. Box 155
Eureka, IL 61530
Telephone 309/467-3632

Suntap Inc.
42 East Dudley Town Road
Bloomfield, CT 06002
Telephone 203/243-1781

Sun-Time Solar Corporation
3443-45 Prospect Avenue
Kansas City, MO 64128
Telephone 816/923-1291

Sun Unlimited Research Corporation
P.O. Box 941
Sheboygan, WI 53081
Telephone 414/452-8194

Sunwall Inc.
P.O. Box 9723
Pittsburgh, PA 15229
Telephone 412/364-5349 or 771-4747

Sunwater Energy Products
1488 Pioneer Way, #17
El Cajon, CA 92020
Telephone 714/579-0771

Systems Technology Inc.
P.O. Box 337
Shalimar, FL 32579
Telephone 904/863-9213

The Solar Broker
1523 Valley Parkway, Suite 219
Escondido, CA 92027

The Solar Room
Box 1377
Taos, NM 87571
Telephone 505/758-9344

The Solar Store Corporation
Box 841
Peoria, IL 61652
Telephone 309/673-0458

United Materials Inc.
814 West 14th Avenue
Denver, CO 80204
Telephone 303/623-4166

Universal Solar System Inc.
Box 101
House Springs, MO 63051
Telephone 314/375-5402

Vulcan Solar Industries Inc.
200 Conant Street
Pawtucket, TI 02860
Telephone 401/725-6061

Wallace Company
831 Dorsey Street, P.O. Box 511
Gainsville, GA 30501
Telephone 404/534-5971

Wescorp
15 Stevens Street
Andover, MA 01810
Telephone 617/470-0520

Wilcox Manufacturing Corporation
P.O. Box 455, 13375 U.S. 19 North
Pinellas Park, FL 33565
Telephone 813/531-7741

Wormser Scientific Corporation
88 Foxwood Road
Stamford, CT 06903
Telephone 203/329-2001

COOLING SYSTEMS

Advance Coller Manufacturing Corporation, ACM Solar Group
Clifton Park, NY 12065
Telephone 518/371-2140

Alternative Energy Resources
1155 Larry Mahon Drive
El Paso, TX 79925
Telephone 915/593-1927

American Heliothermal Corporation
2625 S. Santa Fe Drive
Denver, CO 80223
Telephone 303/778-0650

American Solarize Corporation
P.O. Box 15
Martinsville, NJ 08836
Telephone 201/356-3141

American Solar King Corporation
6801 New McGregor Highway
Waco, TX 76710
Telephone 817/776-3860

Continental Solar Systems Inc.
1901 Avenue of the Stars, Suite 600,
Century City
Los Angeles, CA 90067
Telephone 213/552/0003

Helios Corporation
2120 Angus Road
Charlottesville, VA 22901
Telephone 804/977-3719

Largo Solar Systems Inc.
991 South 40th Avenue
Plantation, FL 33317
Telephone 305/583-8090

Mid-Western Solar Systems
2235 Irvin Cobb Drive
Paducah, KY 42001
Telephone 501/443-6295
Telephone 617/851-5913

Systems Technology Inc.
Box 337
Shalimar, FL 32579
Telephone 904/863-9213

Solar Genies Inc.
9713 Lurline Avenue
Chatsworth, CA 91311
Telephone 213/998-0806

Sun Heet Inc.
2624 South Zuni
Englewood, CO 80110
Telephone 303/922-6179

Sunmaster Corporation
12 Spruce Street
Corning, NY 14830
Telephone 607/937-5441

Sunpower Systems Corporation
510 South 52nd Street, Suite 101
Tempe, AZ 85281
Telephone 602/894-2331

Sunsav Inc.
890 East Street

Wescorp
15 Stevens Street
Andover, MA 01810
Telephone 617/470-0520

DISTILLATION UNITS

Aquarian Research
P.O. Box 378
Bedford, VA 24523

Pacific Solar Tool
182 McLellan Avenue
San Mateo, CA 94403
Telephone 415/345-6721

Solar Dynamics Inc.
1320 S. Lipan Street
Denver, CO 80223
Telephone 303/777-3666

Solar Pure Water Inc.
1523 E. Valley Parkway, Suite 219
Escondido, CA 92027
Telephone 714/747-4322

Skytherm Processes & Engineering
2424 Wilshire Boulevard
Los Angeles, CA 90057
Telephone 213/389-2300

PUMPS

Armstrong Pumps Inc.
93 East Avenue
North Tonawanda, NY 14120
Telephone 716/852-4410

Ebadisco Manufacturing Canada Ltd.
1048 Fleury Street, Regina
Saskatchewan, Canada S4N 4W8

General Ener-tech
7895 Convoy Court, Suite 18
San Diego, CA 92111
Telephone 714/292-5682

Grundfos Pumps Corporation
2555 Clovis Avenue
Clovis, CA 93612
Telephone 209/299-9741

Gusmer Corporation
P.O. Box 164
Old Bridge, NJ 08857

Hartell, Division Milton Roy Company
70 Industrial Drive
Ivyland, PA 18974
Telephone 215/322-0730

Hi-tech Inc.
3204 16th Street
Zion, IL 60099
Telephone 312/746-2447

ITT Fluid Handling Division
4711 Golf Road
Skokie, IL 60076
Telephone 312/677-4030

Lombart Industries
960 Alabama Avenue
Brooklyn, NY 11207
Telephone 800/221-0446

**Memphis Pump and
Manufacturing Company Inc.**
4000 Winchester Road
Memphis, TN 38118
Telephone 901/365-6330

Micropump Corporation
1015 Shary Court
Concord, CA 94518
Telephone 415/687-0101

Paragon Division, Micropump Corporation
P.O. Box 4001
Concord, CA 94524
Telephone 415/689-6000

Premier Pump and Pool Products Inc.
4601 Alger Street
Los Angeles, CA 90039
Telephone 213/240-4900

Richdel Inc.
P.O. Drawer A
Carson City, NV 89701
Telephone 702/882-6786

Shaw Pump Inc.
9660 East Rush Street, P.O. Box 3336
South El Monte, CA 91733
Telephone 213/443-1784

Solar Innovations
412 Longfellow Boulevard
Lakeland, FL 33801
Telephone 813/688-8873

Taco Inc.
1160 Cranston Street
Cranston, RI 02920
Telephone 401/942-8000

March Manufacturing Company Inc.
1819 Pickwick Avenue
Glenview, IL 60025
Telephone 312/729-5300

CONCRETE STORAGE TANKS

M.C. Nottingham Company of California
890 S. Arroyo Parkway
Pasadena, CA 91109
Telephone 213/792-1168

Smith Pre-Cast Inc.
2410 West Broadway
Phoenix, AZ 85339
Telephone 602/268-0228

SOLAR ROCK OR BRICK STORAGE BINS

Park Energy Company
Star Route 9
Jackson, WY 83001
Telephone 307/733-4950

Permaloy Corporation
P.O. Box 1559
Ogden, UT 84402
Telephone 801/731-4303

Sol-Aire Energy Systems
2750 South Shoshone Street
Englewood, CO 80110
Telephone 303/426-8411
Solaray Inc.
324 S. Kidd Street
Whitewater, WI 53190
Telephone 414/473-2525

Solar-therm of Maryland
5105 72nd Avenue
Hyattsville, MD 20784
Telephone 301/459-6022
Sunblazer Energy Systems Inc.
P.O. Box 1992
Charlotte, NC 28233
Telephone 704/333-2551

STEEL TANKS

Alternative Energy Resources
1155 Larry Mahon Drive
El Paso, TX 79925
Telephone 915/593-1927

Independent Living Inc.
2300 Peachford Road, Suite 2200
Atlanta, GA 30341
Telephone 404/455-0927

Megatherm, Vapor Division
803 Taunton Avenue
E. Providence, RI 02914
Telephone 401/438-3800

Paul Mueller Company
P.O. Box 828
Springfield, MO 65801
Telephone 417/865-2831

R.D. Herbert and Sons Company
601 Harrison Street
Nashville, TN 37219
Telephone 615/242-3501

Solar Energy Systems Inc.
2345 Santa Fe Avenue
Los Angeles, CA 90058
Telephone 213/583-5808

Solargizer Corporation
220 Mulberry Street
Stillwater, MN 55082
Telephone 612/439-5734
Solar Heating of New Jersey
811 Wyretta Place
Paramus, NJ 07652
Telephone 201/652-3819
Solar Products Manufacturing Corporation
151 John Downey Drive
New Britain, CT 06051
Telephone 203/224-2164
Solartech Systems Corporation
2216 Avenue E
Lubbock, TX 79404
Telephone 806/765-7761
State Industries Inc.
Cumberland Street
Ashland City, TN 37015
Telephone 800/251-8170
Sunsource Pacific Inc.
832 Halekauwila Street
Honolulu, HI 96813
Telephone 808/531-0165
Sun Sponge
1288 Fayette Street
El Cajon, CA 92020
Telephone 714/449-6726

Solar Energy Systems of Georgia
5825 Glenridge Drive, N.E., Building 2,
Suite 107
Atlanta, GA 30328
Telephone 404/255-9588

PLASTIC OR FIBERGLASS TANKS

Acorn Structures, Inc.
Box 250
Concord, MA 01720
Telephone 617/369-4111
American Solar Systems
415 E. Branch Street
Arroyo Grande, CA 93420
Telephone 805/481-1010

Energy Engineering Inc.
P/O Box 1156
Tuscaloosa, AL 35401
Telephone 205/339-5598
Fiber-Rite Products, Inc.
P/O Box 9295
Cleveland, OH 44138
Telephone 216/228-2921

Flagala Corporation
9700 West Highway 98
Panama City, FL 32407
Telephone 904/234-6559

G S E Products Company
3106 Blue Bonnet
Grand Prairie, TX 75051
Telephone 214/225-2765

Kalwall Corporation
1111 Candia Road, Box 237
Manchester, NH 03105
Telephone 603/627-3861

MNK Enterprises Inc.
10 South 1st East, P/O Box 87
Bancroft, ID 83217
Telephone 208/648-7668

Owens Corning Fiberglass Corporation
Fiberglass Tower
Toledo, OH 43659
Telephone 419/248-8139

Professional Fiberglass Products Inc.
Ada Industrial Park
Ada, OK 74820
Telephone 405/436-0223

Smith Pre-cast Inc.
2410 West Broadway
Phoenix, AZ 85339
Telephone 602/268-0228

Solar Central
7213 Ridge Road
Mechanicsburg, OH 43044
Telephone 513/828-1350

Solar Systems
26046 Eden Landing Road, Suite 41
Hayward, CA 94545
Telephone 415/785-0711

Solar Unlimited Inc.
4310 Governors Drive West
Huntsville, AL 35805
Telephone 205/837-7340

Tri-Corr-A-Glass Inc.
946 Garner Street
Colorado Springs, CO 80905
Telephone 303/635-1616

Weather-Made Systems Inc.
Route 7, Box 300 D
Springfield, MO 65802
Telephone 417/865-0684

Ying Manufacturing Corporation
1957 West 144th Street
Gardena, CA 90249
Telephone 213/770-1756

TANK INSULATION AND COATINGS

Devcon Corporation
Endicott Street
Danvers, MA 01923
Telephone 617/777-1100

Foam Products, Inc.
Gay Street
York Haven, PA 17370
Telephone 717/266-3671

Insta-Foam Midwest Inc.
8000 47th Street
Lyons, IL 60534
Telephone 312/447-9262

Martin Marietta Areospace
P.O. Box 179
Denver, CO 80201
Telephone 303/794-5211

Megatherm, Vapor Division
803 Taunton Avenue
E. Providence, RI 02914
Telephone 401/438-3800

Owens Corning Fiberglass Corporation
Fiberglass Tower
Toledo, OH 43659
Telephone 419/248-8139

Pittsburgh Corning Corporation
800 Presque Isle Drive
Pittsburgh, PA 15239
Telephone 412/327-6100

Solar Sun Still Inc.
Setauket, NY 11733
Telephone 516/941-4078

Teledyne Monothane
1460 Industrial Parkway
Akron, OH 44310
Telephone 216/633-6100

Urethane Moldine Inc.
R.F.D. 3, Route 11
Laconia, NH 03246

SOLAR PIPING LOOP

A/C Fabricating Corporation
P/O Box 774
Goshen, IN 46526
Telephone 219/534-1415

Alco Controls Division, Emerson Electric
P/O Box 12700
St. Louis, MO 63141
Telephone 314/432-6300

Amtrol, Inc.
1400 Division Road
West Warrick, RI 02893
Telephone 401/884-6300

Aqueduct Inc.
1934 Cotner Avenue
Los Angeles, CA 90025
Telephone 213/477-2496

Automation Industries, Inc.,
Flexible Tubing Division
Box 5698, Station B
Greenville, SC 29606
Telephone 803/288-7175

Chase-Walton Elastomers, Inc.
27-S Apsley Street
Hudson, MA 01749
Telephone 617/485-5600

Erie Manufacturing Company
4000 S. 13th Street
Milwaukee, WI 53221
Telephone 414/483-7780

Flair Manufacturing Corporation
600 Old Willetts
Hauppauge, NY
Telephone 516/234-3600

Flo Control Inc.
3210 Winona Avenue
Burbank, CA 91510
Telephone 213/845-8741

Gusmer Corporation
P/O Box 164
Old Bridge, NJ 08857
Telephone 201/360-9000

H&H Precision Products, Division of Emerson
25 Canfield Road
Cedar Grove, NJ 07009
Telephone 201/239-1331

Mueller Brass Company,
Solar Products Division Electric Company
1925 Lapeer Avenue
Port Huron, MI 48060
Telephone 313/987-4000

Penn Division, Johnson Controls, Inc.
2221 Camden Court
Oak Brook, IL 60521
Telephone 312/654-4900

Phelps Dodge Brass
6100 South Garfield Avenue
Los Angeles, CA 90022
Telephone 213/726-1000

R&G Sloane Company Inc.
7606 N. Clybourn Avenue
Sun Valley, CA 91352
Telephone 213/767-4726

Refrigeration Research,
Solar Research Division
525 N. Fifth Street
Brighton, MI 48116
Telephone 313/227-1151

Research Engineering
Manufacturing Company
3838 E. Van Buren
Phoenix, AZ 85008
Telephone 602/273-4300

Robert Shaw Controls Company
100 W. Victoria Street
Long Beach, CA 90805
Telephone 213/638-6111

Rush Manufacturing Corporation
383 Huguenot Street
New Rochelle, NY 10801
Telephone 914/636-2700

Semco Corporation
1054 N.E. 43rd Street
Ft. Lauderdale, FL 3334
Telephone 305/565-2516

Teledyne Monothane
1460 Industrial Parkway
Akron, OH 44310
Telephone 216/633-6100

The Anaconda Company, Brass Division
414 Meadow Street
Waterbury, CT 06720
Telephone 203/574-8500

The Metraflex Company
2323 West Hubbard Street
Chicago, IL 60612
Telephone 312/738-3800

Thrush Products Inc.
P/O Box 228
Peru, IN 46970
Telephone 317/472-3351

Worchester Controls
25 Hartell Street
West Boylston, MA 01583
Telephone 617/835-6041

Union Carbide, Inc.
Tarryton Techincal Center
Tarrytown, NY 10591
Telephone 914/345-2000

SOLAR CHEMICALS: SYSTEM ADDITIVES

Bray Oil Company
1925 North Marianna Avenue
Los Angeles, CA 90032
Telephone 213/268-6171

Culligan Corporation
One Culligan Parkway
Northbrook, IL 60062
Telephone 312/498-2000

Dow Chemical Company
2020 Dow Center
Midland, MI 48640
Telephone 517/636-0391

Monsanto Plastics and Resins Company
800 N. Lindberg Boulevard
St. Louis, MO 63166
Telephone 314/694-1000

Nuclear Technology Corporation
P.O. Box 1
Amston, CT 06231
Telephone 203/537-2387

Resource Technology Corporation
151 John Downey Drive
New Britain, CT 06051
Telephone 203/224-8155

SOLAR PREHEAT DOMESTIC WATER HEATERS

**American Appliance
Manufacturing Corporation**
2341 Michigan Ave.,
Santa Monica, CA 90404.
Telephone 213/829-1755

A. O. Smith Corporation,
Box 28
Kankakee, IL 60901.
Telephone 815/933-8241

Chronomite Labs
21011 S. Figueroa,
Carson, CA 90745
Telephone 213/320-9452

Energex Manufacturing Corporation,
4227 S. 36th Place,
Phoenix, AZ 85040
Telephone 602/267-9474

Ford Products Corporation
Ford Products Road
Valley Cottage, NY 10989
Telephone 914/358-8282

**Rheem/Ruud Divisions,
City Investing Company**
7600 South Kedzie Avenue
Chicago, IL 60652
Telephone 312/434-7500

Simons Solar Environmental Systems, Inc.,
24 Carlisle Pike
Mechanicsburg, PA 17055
Telephone 717/697-2778

Solar Energy Systems, Inc.
2345 Santa Fe Avenue
Los Angeles, CA 90058
Telephone 213/583-5808

States Industries, Inc.
Cumberland Street
Ashland City, TN 37015
Telephone 800/251-8170

The Glass-Lined Water Heater Company
13000 Athens Avenue
Cleveland, OH 44107
Telephone 216/521-1377

The Wilcon Corporation
3310 S.W. Seventh Street
Ocala, FL 32670
Telephone 904/732-2550

Vaughn Corporation
386 Elm Street
Salisbury MA 01950
Telephone 617/462-6683

W. L. Jackson Manufacturing Company, Inc.
P.O. Box 11168
Chatanooga, TN 37401
Telephone 615/867-4700

PACKAGED HEAT PUMP (AIR TO AIR)

Air Temp Corporation
Woodbridge Avenue
Edison, NJ 08817
Telephone 201/549-7200

American Air Filter Company
215 Central Avenue
Louisville, KY 40277
Telephone 502/637-0325

Bard Manufacturing Company
P.O. Box 607
Bryan, OH 43506
Telephone 419/636-1194

Bryant Air Conditioning
7310 West Morris Street
Indianapolis, IN 46231
Telephone 317/243-0851

Climatrol Corporation
Woodbridge Avenue
Edison, NJ 08817
Telephone 201/549-7200

Dunham-Bush
101 Burgess Road
Harrisburg, VA 22801
Telephone 703/434-0711

Fedders Corporation, Climatrol Corporation,
Woodbridge Avenue
Edison, NJ 08817
Telephone 201/549-7200

Friedrich Air Conditioning and Refrigeration Company
P.O. Box 1540
San Antonio, TX 98295
Telephone 512/225-2000

General Electric Company, Advanced Energy Programs
P.O. Box 13601
Philadelphia, PA 19101
Telephone 215/962-2112

Heat Controller, Inc.,
1900 Wellworth Avenue, P.O. Box 1089
Jackson, MI 49203
Telephone 517/787-2100

Koldwave Division, Heat Exchangers Inc.
8100 North Monticello
Skokie, IL 60076
Telephone 312/267-8282

The Singer Company, Climate Control Division
62 Columbus Street
Auburn, NY 13021
Telephone 315/253-2771

The Trane Company
3600 Pammel Creek Road
La Crosse, WI 54601
Telephone 608/782-8000

Westinghouse Electric Company
5205 Leesburg Pike
Falls Church, VA 22041
Telephone 202/833-5950

York Division, Borg-Warner Corporation
P.O. Box 1592
York, PA 17405
Telephone 717/846-7890

PACKAGED HEAT PUMP (WATER TO AIR, WATER TO WATER)

American Air Filter Company
215 Central Avenue
Louisville, KY 40277
Telephone 502/637-0325

Command-Aire Corporation
3221 Speight Street, P.O. Box 7916
Waco, TX 76710

Dunham-Bush
101 Burgess Road
Harrisonburg, VA 22801
Telephone 703/434-0711

Friedrich Air Conditioning and
Refrigerator Co.
P.O. Box 1540
San Antonio, TX 98295
Telephone 512/225-2000

Heat Controller, Inc.
1900 Wellworth Avenue, P.O. Box 1089
Jackson, MI 49203
Telephone 517/787-2100

Lear Siegler, Inc, Mammoth Division
13120 B. County Road 6
Minneapolis, MN 55441
Telephone 612/559-2711

Refrigeration Systems Company, Inc.
611 State Street, Newburgh, IN 47630
Telephone 812/853-6606

The Singer Company, Climate
Control Division
62 Columbus St.
Auburn, NY 13021
Telephone 315/253-2771

Westinghouse Electric Company
5205 Leesburg Pike
Falls Church, VA 22041
Telephone 202/833-5950

York Division, Borg-Warner Corporation
P.O. Box 1592
York, PA 17405
Telephone 717/846-7890

ABSORPTION CHILLERS

Arkla Industries, Inc.
P.O. Box 534
Evansville, IN 47704
Telephone 812/424-3331

Carrier Air Conditioning, Carrier Parkway
P.O. Box 4808
Syracuse, NY 13221
Telephone 315/432-6038

The Trane Company
3600 Pammel Creek Road
La Crosse, WI 54601
Telephone 608/782-8000

York Division, Borg-Warner Corporation
P.O. Box 1592
York, PA 17405
Telephone 717/846-7890

DUCT SYSTEM

Bryant Air Conditioning
7310 West Morris Street
Indianapolis, IN 46231
Telephone 317/243-0851

Hi-Tech, Inc.
3204 16th Street
Zion, IL 60099
Telephone 312/746-2447

Johns-Manville
P.O. Box 5108
Denver, CO 80217
Telephone 303/979-1000

Mountain Mechanical Sales, Inc.
5270 North Broadway
Denver, CO 80216
Telephone 303/534-3000

Niagara Blower Company
405 Lexington Avenue
New York, NY 10017
Telephone 212/697-6151

Fiberglas Tower
Corporation, Owens Corning Fiberglas
Toledo, OH 43659
Telephone 419/248-8139

R-M Products
5010 Cook
Denver, CO 80216
Telephone 303/825-0203

Solar Control Corporation
5595 Arapahoe Road
Boulder, CO 80302
Telephone 303/449-9180

Solaron Corporation
300 Galleria Tower
720 S. Colorado Boulevard
Denver, CO 80222
Telephone 303/759-0101

264

Solar Shelter Engineering, Inc.
Box 179, 35 South Maple Street
Kutztown, PA 19530
Telephone 215/683-6769

Sunpower Industries, Inc.
10837 S.E. 200th Street
Kent, WA 98031
Telephone 206/854-0670

Sun Stone Solar Energy Equipment
P.O. Box 941
Sheboygan, WI 53081
Telephone 414/452-8194

SOLAR CHEMICALS: STORAGE

Artech Corporation
2816 Fallfax Drive
Falls Church, VA, 22042
Telephone 703/560-3292

Croton Chemical Company
10 Harmich Road
South Plainfield, NJ 07080
Telephone 201/754-2900

Solar Marketing Corporation
P.O. Box 1776
Omaha, NE, 68102
Telephone 402/341-9080

Solar Shelter Engineering, INC.
Box 179, 35 Maple Street
Kutztown, PA, 19530
Telephone 215/683-6769

SOLAR CONTROL PACKAGES

Air Temp Corporation
Woodbridge Avenue
Edison, NJ 08817
Telephone 201/549-7200

Bajka Engineering Enterprises
333 Fairchild Drive
Mountain View, CA 94043
Telephone 415/964-2201

Barber Colman Company
1300 Rock St.
Rockford, IL 61101
Telephone 815/877-0241

Bryant Air Conditioning
7310 West Morris Street
Indianapolis, IN 46231
Telephone 317/243-0851

Climatrol Corporation
Woodbridge Avenue
Edison, NJ 08817
Telephone 201/549-7200

DIY-SOL, Inc.
P.O. Box 614
Marlboro, MA 01752
Telephone 617/481-0359

Energy Control Systems
3324 Octavia Street
Raleigh, NC 27606
Telephone 919/851-2310

Fedders Division, Climatrol Corp.
Woodbridge Avenue
Edison, NJ 08817
Telephone 201/549-7200

FloScan Instrument Company, Inc.
3016 N.E. Blakely Street
Seattle, WA 98105
Telephone 206/524-6625

Hawthorne Industries, Inc.
1501 South Dixie Highway
West Palm Beach, FL 33401
Telephone 305/659-5400 (in Florida);
800/327-3388

Helios Corporation
2120 Angus Road
Charlottesville, VA 22901
Telephone 804/977-3719

Helio Thermics, Inc.
110 Laurens Road
Greenville, SC 29607
Telephone 803/235-8529

Heliotrope General
3733 Kenora Drive
Spring Valley, CA 92077
Telephone 714/460-3930

Honeywell, Inc.
Honeywell Plaza
Minneapolis, MN 55408
Telephone 612/332-5200

Rho Sigma
11922 Valerio Street
N. Hollywood, CA 91065
Telephone 213/982-6800

Richdel, Inc.
P.O. Drawer A
Carson City, NV 89701
Telephone 702/882-6786

Robert Shaw Controls Company
100 W. Victoria Street
Long Beach, CA 90805
Telephone 213/638-6111

Solar Control Corporation
5595 Arapahoe Road
Boulder, CO 80302
Telephone 303/449-9180

Solar Environmental Engineering Company, Inc.
P.O. Box 1914
Fort Collins, CO 80522
Telephone 303/221-4370

Solar Innovations
412 Longfellow Boulevard
Lakeland, FL 33801
Telephone 813/688-8873

Solar International
5825 Glenridge Drive N.E.
Building 2, Suite 107
Atlanta, GA 30328
Telephone 404/255-9588

Solaron Corporation
300 Galleria Tower
720 S. Colorado Boulevard
Denver, CO 80222
Telephone 303/759-0101

Solar Shelter Engineering, Inc.
Box 179, 35 South Maple Street
Kutztown, PA 19530
Telephone 215/683-6769

Solar Supply, Inc.
9163 Chesapeake
San Diego, CA 92123
Telephone 714/292-7811

Solar World, Inc.
4449 North 12th Street, Suite 7
Phoenix, AZ 85014
Telephone 602/266-5686

Solid State Solar Controls
123 Independence Drive
Menlo Park, CA 94025
Telephone 415/324-1980

Southern Lighting Manufacturing Company
501 Elwell Avenue
Orlando, FL 32803
Telephone 305/894-8851

Sunpower Systems Corporation
P.O. Box 16963
Orlando, FL 32811
Telephone 305/876-2237

Taco, Inc.
1160 Cranston Street
Cranston, RI 02920
Telephone 401/942-8000

Troger Enterprises
2024 A De La Vina
Santa Barbara, CA 93105
Telephone 805/687-6522

Trol-A-Temp
725 Federal Avenue
Kenilworth, NJ 07033
Telephone 201/245-3190

Virginia Solar Components, Inc
Highway 29 South
Rust, VA 24588
Telephone 804/239-9523

Weather-Made Systems, Inc.
Route 7, Box 300 D
Springfield, MO 65802
Telephone 417/865-0684

White-Rodgers, Division Emerson Electric
9797 Reavis Road
St. Louis, MO 63123
Telephone 314/577-1300

SUN TRACKING DEVICES

DeLavan Electronics
14605 N. 73rd Street
Scottsdale, AZ 85260
Telephone 602/948-6350

Energy Applications, Inc
1125 White Drive
Titusville, FL 32780
Telephone 305/269-4893

General Atomic Company
P.O. Box 81608
San Diego, CA 92138
Telephone 714/455-2090

MicroControl Systems, Inc.
6101-C N. Teutonia Avenue
Milwaukee, WI 53209
Telephone 414/466-7510

Sunpower Systems Corporation
510 South 52nd Street, Suite 101
Tempe, AZ 85281
Telephone 602/894-2331

SOLAR DIFFERENTIAL THERMOSTATS

American Solar Heat Corporation
7 National Place
Danbury, CT 06810
Telephone 203/792-0077

Anabil Enterprises, Inc.
525 South Aqua Clear Drive
Mustang, OK 73064
Telephone 405/376-3324

Aquarian Research
P.O. Box 378
Bedford, VA 24523

Aztec Solar Co.
P.O. Box 272
Maitland, FL 32751
Telephone 305/628-5004

C & M Systems, Inc.
P.O. Box 475
Old Saybrook, CT 06475
Telephone 203/388-3429

Deko-Labs
RT. 4, Box 256
Gainesville, FL 32601
Telephone 904/372-6009

Del Sol Control Corporation
11914 U. S. 1,
Juno, FL 33408
Telephone 305/626-6116

Ecotronics, Inc
8502 E. Cactus Wren
Scottsdale, AZ 85253
Telephone 602/948-8003

Hawthorne Industries, Inc.
1501 South Dixie Highway
West Palm Beach, FL 33401
Telephone 305/659-5400 (in Florida)
800/327-3388

Heliotrope General
3733 Kenora Drive
Spring Valley, CA 92077
Telephone 714/460-3930

Honeywell, Inc.
Honeywell Plaza
Minneapolis, MN 55408
Telephone 612/332-5200

Independent Energy, Inc.
P.O. Box 363
Kingston, RI 02881
Telephone 401/295-1762

MicroControl Systems, Inc.
6101-C N. Teutonia Avenue
Milwaukee, WI 53209
Telephone 414/466-7510

Natural Power, Inc.
Box S. E.
New Boston, NH 03070
Telephone 603/487-5512

Pak-Tronics, Inc.
4044 N. Rockwell
Chicago, IL 60618
Telephone 312/478-8585

Peabody Engineering Corporation
13 Highland Avenue
New Rochelle, NY 10801
Telephone 914/636-5044

Penn Division, Johnson Controls, Inc.
2221 Camden Court
Oak Brook, IL 60521
Telephone 312/654-4900

Ranco Controls Division
601 West Fifth Avenue
Columbus, OH 43201
Telephone 614/294-3511

Rho Sigma
11922 Valerio Street
N. Hollywood, CA 91065
Telephone 213/982-6800

Richdel, Inc.
P.O. Drawer A
Carson City, NV 89701
Telephone 702/882-6786

Robert Shaw Controls Company
100 W. Victoria Street
Long Beach, CA 90805
Telephone 213/638-6111

Simons Solar Environmental Systems, Inc.
24 Carlisle Pike
Mechanicsburg, PA 17055
Telephone 717/697-2778

Solaray, Inc.
P.O. Box 590
Old Saybrook, CT 06475
Telephone 203/399-7112

Solar Central
7213 Ridge Road
Mechanicsburg, OH 43044
Telephone 513/828-1350

Solar Energy Components
441 shearer Boulevard
Cocoa, FL 32922
Telephone 305/632-2888

Solar Control Corporation
5595 Arapahoe Road
Boulder, CO 80302
Telephone 303/449-9180

Solar Energy Products Company
121 Miller Road
Avon Lake, OH 44012
Telephone 216/933-5000

Solarics·Energy Control Systems, Inc.
P.O. Box 15183
Plantation, FL 33318
Telephone 305/971-0391

Solar-Eye Products, Inc.
1300 N. W. McNab Road, Buildings G&H
Fort Lauderdale, FL 33309
Telephone 305/974-2500

Solar Heating of New Jersey
811 Wyretta Place
Paramus, NJ 07652
Telephone 201/652-3819

Solar Industries, Inc.
Route 6, P.O. Box 303
Plymouth, CT 06782
Telephone 203/283-0223

Solar Research Systems
3001 Red Hill Avenue, 1-105
Costa Mesa, CA 92626
Telephone 714/545-4941

Solar World, Inc.
4449 North 12th Street, Suite 7
Phoenix, AZ 85014
Telephone 602/266-5686

Sunpower Systems Corporation
510 South 52nd Street, Suite 101
Tempe, AZ 85281
Telephone 602/894-2331

White-Rodgers, Division Emerson Electric
9797 Reavis Road
St. Louis, MO 63123
Telephone 314/577-1300

SUN TRACKING DEVICES

DeLavan Electronics
14605 N. 73rd Street
Scottsdale, AZ 85260
Telephone 602/948-6350

Energy Applications, Inc.
1125 White Drive
Tiutsville, FL 32780
Telephone 305/269-4893

General Atomic Company
P.O. Box 81608
San Diego, CA 92138
Telephone 714/455-2090

MicroControl Systems, Inc.
6101-C N. Teutonia Avenue
Milwaukee, WI 53209
Telephone 414/466-7510

Sunpower Systems Corporation
510 South 52nd Street, Suite 101
Tempe, AZ 85281
Telephone 602/894-2331

SOLAR DEVICES AND SENSORS VALVE CONTROLS, THERMO COUPLES, THERMISTORS, THERMOPILES, RELAYS, SWITCHES, TIMERS

Durakool, Inc.
1010 North Main Street
Elkhart, IN 46514
Telephone 219/264-1116

Elmwood Sensors, Inc.
1655 Elmwood Avenue
Cranton, RI 02907
Telephone 401/781-6500

Pak-Tronics, Inc.
4044 N. Rockwell
Chicago, IL 60618
Telephone 312/478-8585

Peabody Engineering Corporation
13 Highland Avenue
New Rochelle, NY 10801
Telephone 914/636-5044

Penn Division, Johson Controls, Inc.
2221 Camden Court
Oak Brook, IL 60521
Telephone 312/654-4900

Pyco, Inc.
600 E. Lincoln Highway
Penndel, PA 19047
Telephone 215/757-3704

Solar Energy Conponents
441 Shearer Boulevard
Cocoa, FL 32922
Telephone 305/632-2888

Solar Sensor Systems
4220 Berritt Street
Fairfax, VA 22030
Telephone 703/273-2683

Spectran Instruments
P.O. Box 891
La Habra, CA 90631
Telephone 213/694-3995

Sun of Man Solar Systems
Drawer W
Bethel Island, CA 94511
Telephone 415/684-3362

Superior Controls Company, Inc.
427 West Palmer Avenue
Glendale, CA 91204
Telephone 213/246-2434

Thordarson Meissner, Inc.
Electronic Center
Mt. Carmel, IL 62863
Telephone 618/262-5121

WIND MEASUREMENT INSTRUMENTS

Belfort Instrument Company
1600 South Clinton Street
Baltimore, MD 21224
Telephone 301/342-2626

Meteorology Research, Inc.
464 West Woodbury Road
Altadena, CA 91001
Telephone 213/791-1901

**Mt. Washington Weather
Instrument Company, Inc.**
RFD 1
Berlin, NH 03570
Telephone 603/449-3464

Natural Power, Inc.
Box S.E.
New Boston, NH 03070
Telephone 603/487-5512

Texas Electronics, Inc.
5529 Redfield Street
Dallas, TX 75209
Telephone 214/631-2490

SOLAR PASSIVE SYSTEMS

Midwest Solar Corporation
2359 Grissom Drive
St. Louis, MO 63141
Telephone 314/569-3110

Solar Building Systems, Inc.
610 West Broadway, Suite 209
Tempe, AZ 85282
Telephone 602/966-3995

Telluride Solar Works
P.O. Box 700
Telluride, CO 81435
Telephone 303/728-3303

Zomeworks Corporation
P.O. Box 712
Albuquerque, NM 87103
Telephone 505/242-5354

GLAZING PLASTICS

Ark-Tic-Seal Systems Inc.
P.O. Box 428
Butler, WI 53007
Telephone 414/276-0711

Coating Laboratories
9741 E. 56th Street North.
Owasso, OK 74055
Telephone 918/272-1911

Fabco
809 E. 18th Street
Los Angeles, CA 90021
Telephone 213/749-5244

Gila River Products
510 S. 52nd Street, #107
Tempe, AZ 85281
Telephone 602/968-8709

Kalwall Corporation
111 Candia Road, Box 237
Manchester, NH 03105
Telephone 603/627-3861

Kool Shade Corporation
722 Genevieve Street
Solana Beach, CA 92075
Telephone 714/755-5126

Madico
64 Industrial Parkway
Woburn, MA 01801
Telephone 617/935-7850

Martin Processing Inc., Film Division
P.O. Box 5068
Martinsville, VA 24112
Telephone 703/629-1711

Metallized Products
2647 24th Street North
St. Petersburg, FL 33713
Telephone 813/822-9621

Reflect-O-Screen
7717 E. Greenway Road
Scottsdale, AZ 85260
Telephone 602/991-3270

Rohm Haas Company
Independence Mall West
Philadelphia, PA 19105
Telephone 215/592-3000

Solar Cool Products
4650 N. 12th Street
Phoenix, AZ 85014
Telephone 602/266-7170

Solar Energy Construction Company
P.O. Box 718
Valley Forge, PA 19481
Telephone 215/783-7735

Solar-X Corporation
25 Needham Street
Newton, MA 02161
Telephone 617/244-8686

Stewart Company Inc.
3645 San Fernando Road
Glendale, CA 91204
Telephone 213/243-4254

Transparent Glass-Coatings Company Inc.
1959 S. La Cienega Boulevard,
Los Angeles, CA 90034
Telephone 213/870-4777

SOLAR GREENHOUSES

Colorado Sunworks
P.O. Box 455
Boulder, CO 80306
Telephone 303/443-9199

Dalen Products, Inc.
201 Sherlake Drive
Knoxville, TN 37922
Telephone 615/584-3663

Egge Research
Box 394B, RFD 6
Kingston, NY 12401
Telephone 914/336-5597

Fabrico Manufacturing Corporation
1300 West Exchange Avenue
Chicago, IL 60609
Telephone 312/254-4211

Greenhouse Systems Corporation
Box 31407
Dallas, TX 75231
Telephone 214/352-6174

Monsanto Plastics and Resins Company
800 N. Lindberg Boulevard
St. Louis, MO 63166
Telephone 314/694-1000

Solar Technology Corporation
2160 Clay Street
Denver, CO 80211
Telephone 303/455-3309

Sunshine Greenhouses
109 Cooper Street, Suite 5
Santa Cruz, CA 95060
Telephone 408/425-1451

The Energy Factory
5622 East Westover, Suite 105
Fresno, CA 93727
Telephone 209/292-6622

The Solar Room Company
Box 1377
Taos, NM 87571
Telephone 505/758-9344

U.S. Solar Pillow
247 28½ Road
Grand Junction, CO 81501
Telephone 505/461-2608

SWIMMING POOL COVERS

Aqua Blanket, Inc.
1900 Old Middlefied Way
Mountain View, CA 94043
Telephone 415/969-1372

Powerlift Pool Cover Corporation
4700 North Central Avenue, Suite 304
Phoenix, AZ 85012
Telephone 602/279-9105

Catel Manufacturing, Inc.
243 W. Maple Avenue
Monrovia, CA 91016
Telephone 213/359-2593

Sealed Air Corporation
2015 Saybrook Avenue
Commerce, CA 90040
Telephone 213/685-9666
Swim Chem Division,

L.M. Dearing Associates, Inc.
12324 Ventura Boulevard
Studio City, CA 91604
Telephone 213/769-2521

Hill Brothers Chemical Company
2445 N. 32nd Street
Phoenix, AZ 85008
Telephone 602/955-1650

Lof Brothers, Solar Appliances, Inc.
1615 17th Street
Denver, CO 80202
Telephone 303/573-0696

U.S. Solar Pillow
247 28½ Road
Grand Junction, CO 81501
Telephone 505/461-2608

MacBall Industries, Inc.
5765 Lowell Street
Oakland, CA 94608
Telephone 415/658-1124

Vinyl-Fab Industries
930 E. Drayton
Ferndale, MI 48220
Telephone 313/399-8745

AGRICULTURE AND BIOMASS

Biogas of Colorado, Inc.
5620 Kendall Court, Unit G
Arvada, CO 80002
Telephone 303/422-4354

Solar Aqua Systems, Inc.
P.O. Box 88
Encinitas, CA 92024
Telephone 714/753-0649

Chiacgo Solar Corporation
1773 California Street
Rolling Meadows, IL 60008
Telephone 312/358-1918

Thermal Company
Route 2, Box 39
Reidsville, NC 27320
Telephone 919/342-0352

R. L. Kuss and Company, Inc.
1331 Broad Avenue, P.O. Box 886
Findlay, OH 45840
Telephone 419/423-9040

Universal Solar Systems, Inc.
Box 101
House Springs, MO 63051
Telephone 314/375-5402

PHOTOVOLTAICS

Arco Solar
9701 Lurline Avenue
Chatsworth, CA 91311
Telephone 213/998-0667

Farwest Corrosion Control Company
17311 South Main Street
Gardena, CA 90248
Telephone 213/532-9524

Columbia Chase Solar Energy Division
55 High Street
Holbrook, MA 02343
Telephone 617/767-0513

International Rectifier
233 Kansas Street
El Segundo, CA 90245
Telephone 213/322-3331

McGraw Edison Company, Power Systems Division
P.O. Box 28
Bloomfield, NJ 07003
Telephone 201/751-3700

Motorola Semiconductor Products
5005 East McDowell Road
Phoenix, AZ 85008
Telephone 602/244-5459

M-7 International Company
210 Campus Drive
Arlington Heights, IL 60004
Telephone 312/255-7796

Opical Coating Laboratory, Inc.
2789 Giffen Avenue
Santa Rosa, CA 95402
Telephone 707/545-6440

Sensor Technology, Inc.
21012 Lassen
Chatsworth, CA 91311
Telephone 213/882-4100

SES, Incorporated
Tralee Industrial Park
Newark, DE 19711
Telephone 302/731-0990

Silicon Material, Inc.
341 Moffett Boulevard
Mountain View, CA 94043
Telephone 415/965-9890

Silicon Sensors, Inc.
Highway 18 East
Dodgeville, WI 53533
Telephone 608/935-2707

Siltec Corporation
3717 Haven Avenue
Menlo Park, CA 94025
Telephone 415/365-8600

Solarex Corporation
1335 Piccard Drive
Rockville, MD 20850
Telephone 301/948-0202

Solar Power Corporation
5 Executive Park Drive
N. Billeriea, MA 01862
Telephone 617/667-8376

Solec International Inc.
Two Century Plaza, Suite 484
2049 Century Park East
Los Angeles, CA 90067
Telephone 213/553-1845

Sollos Inc.
2231 Carmelina Avenue
Los Angeles, CA 90064
Telephone 213/820-5181

Spectrolab Inc.
12500 Gladstone Avenue
Sylmar, CA 91342
Telephone 213/365-4611

Spire Corporation
Patriots Park
Bedford, MA 01730
Telephone 617/275-6000

Sun Trac Corporation
1674 South Wolf Road
Wheeling, IL 60090
Telephone 312/541-2095

SOLAR CONTROL MANUFACTURERS THERMOSTATS, DIFFERENTIAL THERMOSTATIC CONTROLS TIME SWITCH CONTROLS, PUMP CONTROLS, FREEZE CONTROLS, ETC.

Deko Labs
P.O. Box 12841
Gainesville, FL 32604
Telephone 904/372-6009

Honeywell Inc.,
Systems and Research Center
2700 Ridgeway Parkway
Minneapolis, MN 55413
Telephone 612/331-4141

Natural Power Inc.
New Boston, NH 03070
Telephone 603/487-2456

Rho Sigma Unlimited
5108 Melvin Avenue
Tarzana, CA 91356
Telephone 213/342-4376

M. H. Rhodes, Inc.
99 Hompson Road
Avon, CT 06001
Telephone 203/673-3281

West Wind
309½ West Boyd Drive
Farmington, NM 87401

Zia Associates Inc.
P.O. Box 1466
5590 Arapahoe Road
Boulder, CO 80302
Telephone 303/449-9170

Acurex Corporation
485 Clyde Avenue
Mountain View, CA 94042
Telephone 415/964-3200

Amprobe Instrument
630 Merrick Road
Lynbrook, NY 11563
Telephone 516/593-5600

Bailey Instruments
515 Victor Street
Saddle Brook, NJ 07662
Telephone 201/845-7252

Barnes Engineering Company
30 Commerce Road
Stamford, CT 06904
Telephone 203/348-5381

California Measurements
150 East Montecito Avenue
Sierra Madre, CA 91024
Telephone 213/355-3713

Cambell Engineering
1302 Toney Drive
Huntsville, AL 35802
Telephone 205/883-9866

Carroll Solar Dynamics
1032 W. Kenosha, #91
Broken Arrow, OK 74012
Telephone 918/258-4448

Chemalloy Electronics Corporation
P.O. Box 10
Santee, CA 92071
Telephone 714/448-5715

Conkling Laboratories
5432 Merrick Road
Massapequa, NY 11758
Telephone 516/541-1323

Cushing Instruments
7911 Hershel Avenue, Suite 214
La Jolla, CA 92037
Telephone 714/459-3433

Devices and Services Company
3501-A Milton Avenue
Dallas, TX 75205
Telephone 214/368-5749

Dodge Products
Box 19781
Houston, TX 77024
Telephone 713/467-6262

Ecosol, LTD.
1710 The Plaza
2 West 59th Street
New York, NY 10019
Telephone 212/688-3434

Eltex Inc.
9208 Panama Avenue
Ypsilanti, MI 48197
Telephone 313/487-9517

Heliotrope General
3733 Kenora Drive
Spring Valley, CA 92077
Telephone 714/460-3930

Honeywell Inc.
Honeywell Plaza
Minneapolis, MN 55408
Telephone)12/332-5200

Hy-Cal Engineering
12105 Los Nietos Road
Santa Fe Springs, CA 90670
Telephone 213/698-7785

IMC Instruments Inc.
6659 N. Sidney Place
Glendale, WI 53209
Telephone 414/352-3810

Inservco Inc.
110 Commerce Drive
La Grange, OH 44050
Telephone 216/458-5102

Iowa Solar, Inc.
Box 246
North Liberty, IA 52317
Telephone 319/626-2342

Kahl Scientific Instrument Corporation
P.O. Box 1166
El Cajon, CA 92022
Telephone 714/444-2158

Kipp & Zonen
390 Central Avenue
Bohemia, NY 11716
Telephone 516/589-2885

273

Leupold & Stevens Inc.
P.O. Box 688
Beaverton, OR 97005
Telephone 503/646-9171

Lion Precision Corporation
60 Bridge Street
Newton, MA 02195
Telephone 617/969-4710

Matrix Inc.
537 South 31st Street
Mesa, AZ 85204
Telephone 602/832-1380

Metallized Products
2647 24th Street North
St. Petersburg, FL 33713
Telephone 813/822-9621

Molectron Corporation
177 North Wolfe Road
Sunnydale, CA 94086
Telephone 408/738-2661

Monitor Labs Inc.
4202 Sorrento Valley Boulevard
San Diego, CA 92121
Telephone 714/453-6260

Natural Power Inc.
Box S.E.
New Boston, NH 03070
Telephone 603/487-5512

Oriel Corporation of America
15 Market Street
Stamford, CT 06902
Telephone 203/357-1600

Pacific Sun Inc.
540 Santa Cruze Avenue
Menlo Park, CA 94025
Telephone 415/328-4588

Pyco Inc.
600 E. Lincoln Highway
Penndel, PA 19047
Telephone 215/757-3704

Rho Sigma
11922 Valerio Street
N. Hollywood, CA 91065
Telephone 213/982-6800

Sensors Inc.
P.O. Box 1383
Ann Arbor, MI 48106
Tleephone 313/973-1400

Solarex Corporation
1335 Piccard Drive
Rockville, MD 20850
Telephone 301/948-0202

Solec (Solar Energy Corporation)
553 Pretty Brook Road
Princeton, NJ 08540
Telephone 609/924-1879

Spectran Instruments
P.O. Box 891
La Harbra, CA 90631
Telephone 213/694-3995

S.P.S. Inc.
8801 Biscayne Boulevard
Miami, FL 33138
Telephone 305/754-7766

Technology Application Laboratory Inc.
1670 Highway A1A
Satellite Beach, FL 32937
Telephone 305/777-1400

Texas Electronics Inc.
5529 Redfield Street
Dallas, TX 75209
Telephone 214/631-2490

The Eppley Laboratory Inc.
12 Sheffield Avenue
Newport, RI 02840
Telephone 401/847-1020

The Wilcon Corporation
3310 S.W. Seventh Street
Ocala, FL 32670
Telephone 904/732-2550

Valley Forge Instrument Company Inc.
55 Buckwalter Road
Phoenixville, PA 19460
Telephone 215/933-1806

Weathertronics Inc.
2777 Del Monte Street
West Sacramento, CA 95691
Telephone 916/371-2660

OTHER SOLAR PRODUCTS

ASG Industries
1450 Lincoln Street
Kingsport, TN 37622
Telephone 615/245-0211 ALSO 1B Belmar Road
Cranbury, NJ 08512 (Light crystal glass for collector cover plates.)

Barber-Nichols Engineering Company
Denver, CO (Design and fabricate solar heated-rankine cycle, electric power, 3 ton air-conditioning system.)

Fred Rice Productions, Inc.
6313 Peach Avenue
Van Nuys, CA 91401
Telephone 213/786-3860 ("sav" cylindrical water heater systems. Also the "solar sonic flip top mobile home".)

General Electric Company, Space Division
P.O. Box 8661
Philadelphia, PA 19101 (Developing prototypes, manufactures double glazed metal flat plate collector.)

Grumman Aerospace
Bethpage, NY 11714
Telephone 516/575-7062 (Testing various collectors including their own design called "gull wing" possibly available. Also testing selective blacks and flat blacks.)

Heliotek, Inc.
33 Edinboro Street
Boston, MA 02109. (Produce "solar membrane" that is a transparent insulation; claim good solar transmission with good retention of long wave infrared radiation; 25-year life expectancy claimed.)

MND, Inc.
Post Office 15534
Atlanta, GA 30333 ("solarlab" teaching lab with interchangeable parts.)

Pittsburgh Plate Glass (PPG)
One Gateway Center
Pittsburgh, PA 15222
Telephone 412/434-2645 (Marketing aluminum and copper roll-bond type collectors; tube in plate; with two cover plates of tempered herculite glass. 34 3/16" (inches) × 76 3/1" (inches)

Revere Copper and Brass Inc., Research and Development Center
P.O. Box 151
Rome, NY 13440
Telephone 315/338-2022 (Have developed copper plate collector for integration into a roof; standard panel sizes are 2' × 8'.)

Sunhay Enterprises
1505 East Windsor Road
Glendale, CA 91205
Telephone 213/246-9352 (Manufacturers small portable hot water heaters.)

The Strong Electric Corporation
87 City Park Avenue
Toledo, OH 43601
Telephone 419/248-3741 (Manufacturer of Portable Solar Furnace with 14" parabolic mirror.)

Tranter, Inc.
735 East Hazel Street
Lansing, MI 48909
Telephone 517/372-8410 ("Econocoil" and "platecoil" available in carbon steel or stainless steel and in various sizes. Flat Plate Collectors.)

Western Botanical Company
710 Wilshire Boulevard
Santa Monica, CA 90401
(Selling a small "solar IV food dehydrator".)

Westinghouse Electric Corporation, Research & Development
P.O. Box 1693
Baltimore, MD 21203 (Research and development of "many" solar-energy components.)

PHOTOVOLTAIC CELLS

Energy Conversion Devices Inc.
1675 West Maple Road
Troy, MI 48084
Telephone 313/549-7300

Innotech Corporation
Norwalk, CT 06856
Telephone 203/846-2041

Optical Coating Laboratory, Inc.,
Centralab Semiconductor Division
2789 Griffen Avenue
Santa Rosa, CA 95403

Pennwalt Corporation,
Automatic Power Division
Hutchinson Street
Houston, TX 77002
Telephone 713/228-5208

Sensor Technology Inc.
21012 Lassen Street
Chatsworth, CA 91311
Telephone 203/882-4100

Solar Energy Company
810 18th Street Washington, D.C. 20006
Telephone 202/347-4568

Solar Power Corporation
186 Forbes Road
Braintree, MA 02184
Telephone 617/848-6877

Solar Systems, Inc.
8100 Central Park
Skokie, IL 60076
Telephone 312/676-2040

Solarex Corporation
1335 Piccard Drive
Rockville, MD 20850
Telephone 301/948-0202

SPECTROLAB Inc.
12484 Gladstone Avenue
Sylmar, CA 91342

Textron, Spectrolab Division
40 Westminister Street
Providence, RI 02903
Telephone 401/421-2800

Tyco Laboratories Inc.
Hickory Drive Waltham, MA 02154
Telephone 617/890-2400

Vactec Inc.
2423 Northline Ind. Blvd.
Maryland Heights, MO 63043
Telephone 314/872-8300

Zurn Industries Inc.
West Eigth Street
Erie, PA 16501
Telephone 814/455-0921

WIND GENERATION SYSTEMS AND DEVICES

Aero Power
2398 4th Street
Berkeley, CA 94710
Telephone 415/848-2710

American Energy Alternatives
P.O. Box 905
Boulder, CO, 80306
Telephone 303/447-0820

American Wind Turbine
1016 East Airport Road
Stillwater, OK 74074
Telephone 405/377-5333

Automatic Power Inc.
213 Hutcheson Street
Houston, TX 77003
Telephone 713/228-5208

Dempster Industries Inc.
Beatrice, NE, 68310
Telephone 402/223-4026

Grumman Energy Systems Inc.
4175 Veterans Memorial Highway
Ronkonkoma, NY 11779
Telephone 516/575-7291

KEDCO Inc.
9016 Aviation Boulevard
Inglewood, CA 90301
Telephone 213/776-6636

North Wind Power Company
Box 315
Warren, VT, 05674
Telephone 802/496-2955

Sencenbaugh Wind Electric
2235 Old Middlefield Way
Mountain View, CA, 94040
Telephone 415/954-1593

Wadler Manufacturing Company
Galena, KS, 66739
Telephone 316/783-1355

West Wind
Box 1465
Farmington, NM, 87401
Telephone 505/325-4949

SOLAR ENGINES

Rox International, Inc.
2604 Hidden Lake Drive
Sarasota, FL 33577
Telephone 813/366-6053

S.P.S., Inc.
8801 Biscayne Boulevard
Miami, FL 33138
Telephone 305/754-7766

SOLAR POWER GENERATION

McDonnell Douglas Astronautics Company
5301 Bolsa Avenue
Huntington Beach, CA 92647
Telephone 714/896-4323

Rocketdyne Division, Rockwell International
6633 Canoga Avenue
Canoga Park, CA 91304
Telephone 213/884-3075

FIREPLACE WATER HEATERS

Ballard Concrete Company
P.O. Box 7175, 410 S. Washington Avenue
Greenville, SC 29610
Telephone 803/295-0610

Hydroheat Division, Ridgway Steel Fabricators
P. O. Box 382
Ridgway, PA 15853
Telephone 814/776-1323

Pioneer Energy Products
Route 1, Box 189
Forest, VA 24551
Telephone 804/239-2661

Solatherm Corporation
1255 Timber Lake Drive
Lynchburg, VA 24502
Telephone 804/237-3249

Sturges Heat Recovery, Inc.
P.O. Box 397
Stone Ridge, NY 12484
Telephone 914/687-0281

Southeastern Solar Systems, Inc.
2812 New Spring Road, Suite 150
Atlanta, GA 30339
Telephone 404/434-4447

ENERGY MANAGEMENT SYSTEMS

Ave, Inc.
20089 Pierce Road
Saratoga, CA 95070
Telephone 408/867-1180

Circuit Pak
321 Breesport
San Antonio, TX 78216
Telephone 512/344-6880

Ecotronics, Inc.
8502 E. Cactus Wren
Scottsdale, AZ 85253

El Cam, Inc.
5330 Debbie Lane
Santa Barbara, CA 93111
Telephone 805/964-8676

Honeywell, Inc.
Honeywell Plaza
Minneapolis, MN 55408
Telephone 612/332-5200

National Energy Management Systems, Inc.
2601 Davie Boulevard
Ft. Lauderdale, FL 33312
Telephone 305/791-3262; 800/824-5136

Sunkeeper Control Corporation
P.O. Box 34, S.V.S.
Andover, MA 01810
Telephone 617/470-0555

Texas Controls, Inc.
P.O. Box 59469
Dallas, TX 75229
Telephone 214/241-6171

Vertex Corporation
808 106th Street, N.W.
Bellevue, WA 98004
Telephone 206/455-4718

Index